A hunger for l...
a passion for f...

Queen Elizabeth's reig... ...ing
years. The clans of Ireland—under the
leadership of the great O'Neill—had answered
the call to rebellion against England. And
driven by love for her Irish warlord husband,
Deirdre O'Hara—daughter of an English lord—
played her part to aid the Irish cause.

Meanwhile in England, Elizabeth Cecil,
a beautiful noblewoman, waged her own
war against enforced political marriage.
Her powerful attraction to the brash Rory
O'Donnell, O'Neill's spy, imperiled Rory's
mission and her own future....

It was a time of heroes, a time for brave men
and women to become giants of their age. And
amid the intrigue of Tudor England and
rebellious Ireland, both Deirdre and Elizabeth
struggled to prevent their lives from being
torn asunder.

In this tumultuous era, the O'Hara Dynasty
was born.

*   *   *

"Impressive—a compelling historical romance
with the sweep of a saga."
> Mina W. Mulvey
> Executive Editor, *Good Housekeeping*

"An epic saga that should please those, like myself,
with Irish blood in their veins, as well as those who
simply enjoy a rich, well-researched novel."
> Patricia Matthews
> author of *Tides of Love*

About the author...

An actress for fifteen years, Mary Canon has established a large following in the theater. A few years ago, she appeared on Broadway in the musical "Cyrano" with Christopher Plummer.

Miss Canon, who shares a passion for travel with her husband and fellow-author, Jack Canon, was born in Lewistown, Pennsylvania, but she spent much of her early life in Long Beach, California. The Canons now make their home in North Carolina.

Throughout the past five years she has assisted her husband in the researching and editing of his manuscripts. Finally, with Jack's encouragement, Mary Canon has applied her talents to developing a writing career of her own.

The result is *The Defiant*, Mary Canon's first novel.

THE O'HARA DYNASTY

The Defiant

MARY CANON

TORONTO•LONDON•NEW YORK•SYDNEY

TO MARY AND BERNICE
FOR RAISING DEFIANT ONES

Published October 1981
First printing April 1981
Second printing October 1981

ISBN 0-373-89001-X

Printed in U.S.A.

Cast of Characters

THE O'HARAS

SHANE O'HARA (THE O'HARA): Irish warlord intent on freedom from English rule. Chief of the O'Hara clan but subordinate to his cousin, The O'Neill. Husband to Deirdre. O'Hara's home is Ballylee Castle.

DEIRDRE HASKINS O'HARA: Wife of Shane. Daughter of an English lord, Henry Haskins. Deirdre defied the Queen and shocked the court by marrying an Irish rebel.

RORY O'HARA: Son of Shane and Deirdre.

SHANNA O'HARA: Daughter of Shane and Deirdre.

THE O'NEILLS

HUGH O'NEILL (THE O'NEILL): Earl of Tyrone, Baron of Dungannon and leader of the O'Neill clan. Raised in England, O'Neill returns to Ireland with rebellion in his heart, to become the most powerful Irish chieftain and commander of the rebel forces. His home is Dungannon Castle.

HENRY O'NEILL: Young member of the O'Neill clan. To ensure O'Neill's loyalty to the Crown, he is imprisoned with his brother, Art, in Dublin Castle by the English.

ART O'NEILL: Brother of Henry.

MABEL BAGENAL: Unwanted English wife of The O'Neill.

THE O'DONNELLS

BLACK HUGH O'DONNELL (THE O'DONNELL): Ruler of Tyrconnell (part of Ulster) and chief of the O'Donnell clan, he allies himself with O'Neill to end English rule. O'Donnell's home is Donegal Castle.

RED HUGH O'DONNELL: Eldest son and heir apparent (the "tanist") of Black Hugh. Imprisoned in Dublin Castle by the English to ensure his father's loyalty.

RORY O'DONNELL: Younger son of Black Hugh, brother of Red Hugh, Rory is a warrior and a philosopher. Through his father's alliance with The O'Neill, he becomes O'Neill's spy in London. Godfather of Rory and Shanna O'Hara.

THE CECILS

ELIZABETH CECIL (LADY HATTON): A proud and beautiful English noblewoman, she is involuntarily drawn to the Irish spy Rory O'Donnell. But to secure more influence at court for her scheming uncle, Robert Cecil, Elizabeth is forced into marriage with Sir William Hatton and, later, Sir Edward Coke.

WILLIAM CECIL (LORD BURGHLEY): English statesman, grandfather of Elizabeth and father of Robert. The aging Lord Burghley is Queen Elizabeth's principal minister.

ROBERT CECIL: Lord Burghley's ambitious son, Elizabeth Cecil's uncle. Robert Cecil is an influential member of Queen Elizabeth's court and plays a significant role in shaping England's—and Ireland's—destiny. Queen Elizabeth calls him her "pygmy fox," a comment on both his ingenious strategy and his malformed back.

* * *

JAMES BLAKE: English swordsman and assassin. Denied his noble birthright, Blake becomes a spy in Robert Cecil's employ to regain his lands and title.

NED BULL: English highwayman who joins forces with Rory O'Donnell to aid the Irish cause.

ANNIE CAREY: Ned Bull's mistress, a waif of the London streets.

CHARLES: Husband of Honor, Elizabeth Cecil's personal maid.

BRENNA COKE: Daughter of Elizabeth Cecil and, secretly, Rory O'Donnell.

SIR EDWARD COKE: Attorney General of England. Elizabeth Cecil's second husband.

ROBERT DEVEREUX: Earl of Essex. Ambitious English adventurer and Queen Elizabeth's favorite courtier. He is Robert Cecil's bitter enemy.

HENRY HASKINS: An English lord and Irish sympathizer. Father of Deirdre O'Hara. His home is Haskins House, where Rory O'Donnell stays while gathering intelligence at the English court.

SIR WILLIAM HATTON: Elizabeth Cecil's first husband.

HONOR: Elizabeth Cecil's personal maid.

FIACH MacHUGH O'BYRNE (THE O'BYRNE): Firebrand of the Wicklow Mountains. Leader of the O'Byrne clan and ally of The O'Neill.

McTEAGUE O'BYRNE: Irish traitor. Relative of Fiach.

GRACE O'MALLEY: Pirate queen of Connaught (Irish province).

QUEEN ELIZABETH I: The Tudor Queen, ruler of England from 1558 to 1603. Also referred to as Good Queen Bess and Gloriana.

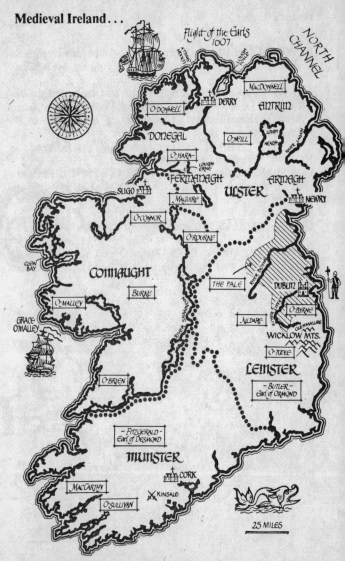

Medieval Ireland...

Flight of the Earls 1007

NORTH CHANNEL

O'DONNELL

DERRY

MacDONNELL

ANTRIM

DONEGAL

O'NEILL

LOUGH NEAGH

RIVER BANN

O'HARA

LOUGH ERNE

FERMANAGH

SLIGO

MAGUIRE

ULSTER

ARMAGH

NEWRY

O'CONNOR

O'ROURKE

CLEW BAY

CONNAUGHT

BURKE

THE PALE

RIVER BOYNE

DUBLIN

O'MALLEY

RIVER LIFFEY

KILDARE

O'BYRNE

GLENMALURE

GRACE O'MALLEY

WICKLOW MTS.

O'TOOLE

RIVER SHANNON

O'BRIEN

LEINSTER

– BUTLER – Earl of ORMOND

– FITZGERALD – Earl of DESMOND

MUNSTER

CORK

MacCARTHY

KINSALE

O'SULLIVAN

25 MILES

**...the domains of prominent Irish families
of the sixteenth century.**

Historic Ulster...

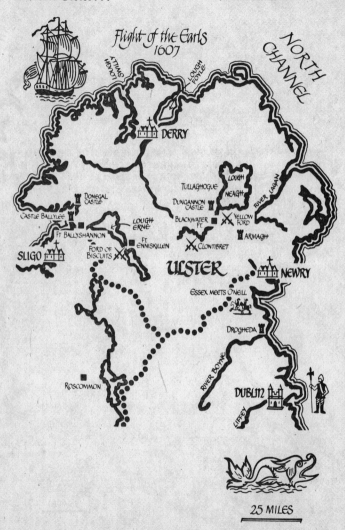

Flight of the Earls 1607

NORTH CHANNEL

LOUGH SWILLY

LOUGH FOYLE

DERRY

TULLAGHOGUE

LOUGH NEAGH

RIVER LAGAN

DUNGANNON CASTLE

DONEGAL CASTLE

CASTLE BALLYLEE

BLACKWATER FT.

YELLOW FORD

LOUGH ERNE

FT. BALLYSHANNON

FT. ENNISKILLEN

ARMAGH

CLONTIBRET

SLIGO

FORD OF BISCUITS

ULSTER

NEWRY

ESSEX MEETS O'NEILL

DROGHEDA

RIVER BOYNE

ROSCOMMON

DUBLIN

LIFFEY

25 MILES

**...locations of major battle sites,
Irish castles and English forts.**

"SURE IF A MAN BE IRISH, EVEN DENIED THE BIRTH OF THE LAND OR THE NAME, HE KNOWS IT. THERE'S SOMETHING IN THE MIND, IN THE BLOOD – AYE, IN THE VERY SOUL – THAT FORCES HIM TO ONE DAY SET EYES ON HER MISTY EMERALD SHORES. AND ONCE SEEN, THE LAND IS NEVER FORGOTTEN."

THE LAST WORDS OF AN OLD MAN
BOSTON 1970

Part I
Spring 1590

THE COACH was little more than a heavy square box suspended by leather straps from the frame that sat precariously on its four wheels. For three hours it had swayed sickeningly across the Irish countryside, with its lone white-faced occupant holding on for dear life.

Snorting with exertion the four horses strained up a hill in their creaking harness. At last the rise was reached. Trees gave way to open ground, and the coach came to a lurching halt.

"There, m'lady!"

Deirdre, daughter of Lord Haskins, breathed a deep sigh and slid across the barely padded seat. She leaned over the rim of the half door as much as her wide far-thingale skirt would allow and looked up into the grizzled bearded face of the Irish kern who had been sent to fetch her.

"There, m'lady," he said, pointing, his voice a confusing mixture of Gaelic and English. "Ballylee... home of the clan O'Hara."

Deirdre stared round-eyed across the wide heath, gold and red and bronze with summer blossoms, at her new home, the Castle Ballylee. A lump rising from her breast to her throat threatened to cut off her already unsteady breathing.

The castle rose from the pinnacle of a far hill, majestic and aloof from the world around it. Dewdrops caught the sun and shimmered like jewels on the emerald grass of the slopes. The moat was wide, and the water in it reflected bright ripples of sunlight upward onto the ominous gray and brown walls. Against the blue sky jagged parapets and soaring towers seemed to grin a leering welcome to their new mistress.

"Ballylee," she whispered.

"Aye, 'tis the most impregnable of all the clan castles in the north. Even The O'Neill's Dungannon, and Donegal, the O'Donnell fortress farther north, cannot match Ballylee. Walls twelve foot thick and too high to scale, with room in its baileys for a thousand men of foot and horse. Even the bloody English would lose a siege of Ballylee! Er, beggin' yer pardon, m'lady."

Deirdre smiled. "There's no need. For I'm only half English, and in a few days' time I'll be all O'Hara."

"Aye," the coachman growled, lifting the reins. "'Tis a new way they invade us now...with their women."

The coach lurched ahead and Deirdre was propelled against the hard board backing of the seat. But the slight jolt of pain she felt didn't show on her beautiful face. There was only serenity in the deep-set dark eyes, and a hint of a smile on her lips.

She had won the battle with her society and the battle within herself. She had spurned tradition and Queen Elizabeth's command to marry the man she loved.

The faint smile grew into an open grin of anticipation as she thought of her choice, and of the scandal it would soon cause at Whitehall.

Her only worry was the added danger and concern her marriage would cause her dear kindly father. Only a fortnight before Lord Haskins had tried one last time to dissuade her from such a rash act.

"There is a peace now in Ireland, my lovely daughter, but it's a thin peace, and likely to break with the slightest sign of rebellion."

"I know," she had replied. "But I would have the man Shane O'Hara for a husband in the wilds of Ireland before I would have an aging lord of England who'd wed me for my dowry alone." The scowl on her face turned to an impish smile. "And, besides, ye know Shane. Can ye truthfully say ye blame me?"

Lord Haskins turned to gaze out the window. It was true. As a youth of fifteen O'Hara had been brought to England to be fostered and raised in the home of an English peer. Because Lady Haskins had been Lady Rose of Ballyhara, distant cousins of the O'Haras of Ballylee, Haskins House was chosen for young Shane's fosterage.

The court assumed that the lad would be raised as a proper English gentleman, that he would convert to the Protestant religion and grow into adulthood loyal to the English crown.

They hadn't reckoned with the Irishness of Lady Haskins, nor the Irish sympathies of her husband, Lord Haskins.

Young Shane O'Hara grew up at Haskins House more Irish than ever. Charles, Deirdre's brother, was a secret Catholic, and Shane's idol. Deirdre, three years Shane's junior, fell in love with the young dark-haired Irishman the moment she met him.

When O'Hara returned to Ireland six years later he was granted his castle and lands back. At the same time he began pursuing the two things he wanted most in life: Irish freedom and the hand of Deirdre Haskins.

For three years he made clandestine excursions across the Irish Sea to woo his lady. There was never a question of doubt in Deirdre's mind, only a matter of time.

And now the time had come, brought about by several momentous events. Her mother had died suddenly of pneumonia, and her brother Charles had met a martyr's death. Shane O'Hara had been declared a rebel and could no longer sneak into England. And to Deirdre's distaste, several dandies of the court had begun to cast covetous eyes upon her, the young and beautiful Haskins's heiress.

"My only fear," Deirdre had told her father, "is for you."

Part of his reply had been a ringing laugh. "On that you must have no fear, dearest daughter, for I've played this game of politics and religion for so long it has become like another skin on this old body. I'll bow and scrape and kneel before our good Queen Bess and relate yet again how sad it is in these strange times that a parent must suffer the wayward ways and whims of rebellious children. And our good Queen will shake her head and suck her breath with pity at my plight. She will bid me spend time in the country praying that my rebel daughter should see the light and mend her ways!"

"Oh, father. . . ."

"Go with God and your heart, my daughter."

And so she had. Without servants and with meager luggage she had fled to the port of Chester and across the Irish Sea to be with the man she loved.

"Ho, there! Ho!"

Again the coach came to a halt. Deirdre's reverie was broken by the sound of a single horse's pounding hooves, and dust began filling the tiny carriage, catching in her throat and making her eyes sting.

Suddenly the coach door was wrenched open, nearly pulled from its hinges, and Deirdre was face to face with a giant whose booming voice thundered at her in Gaelic.

"So you're the English wench my cousin and good right hand has lured away to be a whore in his bed and a Queen's spy in my lands!"

Deirdre sensed frustration as well as anger in the booming voice. Leaning from the coach and shielding her eyes against the sun, she detected the same emotions in the stern features and the glaringly dark eyes under the furrowed brow.

"M'Lord O'Neill."

"Ah, ye know me!"

"Aye, and well do I know the features of the Earl of Tyrone. As a wisp of a lass I watched you plead your causes at Whitehall Court."

"Know you then The O'Neill's thoughts?" he replied, leaning forward over the neck of his prancing horse. "They be these: that the life of a clan chieftain's wife in Ireland in these days is a heavy lot. Methinks a dainty English lass can't take the hardships of Irish life, nor the heartaches brought about by warring husbands."

"And, m'lord, is it only a rumor that the great O'Neill has wifed Mabel Bagenal, daughter of Sir Nicholas, the Queen's marshal in Ireland?"

"Nay, 'tis true!" O'Neill thundered. "But I've seen the error and locked the shrew up at Dungannon Castle! And I'll not have another English bitch around me, even though I dearly love Shane O'Hara."

"As do I. I have no politics as I have no husband... yet. If m'lord does not approve of me, then I shall return to my father, Lord Haskins, and wait out my days as a nun."

"You are Catholic?"

"Before I'm English. And before I was English I was the daughter of Rose of Ballyhara."

"And now you would be Queen of Ballylee?"

"Aye, I would that."

"By the saints," O'Neill growled, backing his horse from the side of the coach, "you've the tongue for a queen. Step down and let's have a look at the daughter of Rose of Ballyhara!"

Taking a deep breath, Deirdre struggled to shift her voluminous skirt through the narrow opening. With her head held high and with all the grace she could muster, she found the single step with a booted foot and alighted onto the soil of Ireland.

O'Neill slid from the hide-covered wooden saddle and covered the space between them in three strides. Unblinking, Deirdre faced the man who ruled her future husband and who would pretend to rule all of Ireland.

It was in his eyes the moment they met hers. No words were needed between them to convey what was said in that one look. In Deirdre, O'Neill saw what he had hoped he would find in his own English wife.

Because of his youth in England, O'Neill was pulled between two cultures. Through Mabel Bagenal he had sought to blend the raw customs of Ulster Ireland with English refinements at Dungannon Castle.

Mabel Bagenal had failed miserably, and now O'Neill would be rid of her.

"You stare, m'lord."

"Aye, for I've seen such beauty in face and figure but once—in my first wife. And she died birthing my sons."

They stood, wordlessly communicating with their eyes. The tall lean man in leather jerkin and loose mantle stared down at the woman with her shoulder-wide starched ruff and huge padded leg-of-mutton sleeves.

Suddenly the long face framed by slightly graying red hair broke into a grin.

"You'll need clothes more suited to the wilds of Irish life, lass."

THE DAYS FOLLOWING DEIRDRE'S ARRIVAL at Ballylee were filled with celebrations and feasting. If the revelry was at times too loud and the drunkenness too abandoned for the tastes she had acquired in London, she never let it show on her face nor in her voice.

But neither did she crawl away from the company of her future husband's fellows, nor did she shy from their wives and concubines. With a wit like a penknife she matched their veiled barbs until the comments turned to compliments. With a learned mind and a ready tongue she argued points without arrogance or passion.

In the days leading up to her wedding she was able to charm all who came near her, until they readily agreed that Deirdre would indeed be a fit mistress of Ballylee.

There was no need to charm her future husband. His love for her was evident in every look and every gesture. The O'Hara underchiefs could hardly believe that Shane O'Hara in love was the same roistering, boistering, fierce warrior they knew and had joined on the field of battle so many times.

But Deirdre knew.

Beneath Shane O'Hara's glowering exterior there was a gentleness that only she could find. In battle men feared a blow from those short powerful arms, while in private Deirdre longed for the touch of his gentle hands.

The wedding celebration took three glorious days. It was everything Deirdre could have wanted it to be, as was the wedding night. Her new husband proved to be the lover she had always yearned for, and from the first night she began dreaming of giving him a son and heir.

The routine of married life came easy to her. The fact that she lived in savage Ireland instead of sophisticated London never bothered her at all. Deirdre knew only too well that a marriage of choice rather than of convenience for a woman of her day was a rare occurrence. She had been able to choose, and daily she thanked an understanding father and a merciful God for it.

She grew nearly as close to The O'Neill as she did to her husband through the summer and following winter. And when spring came again her prayers were rewarded; she was with child.

But her joy was short-lived.

For months she had turned a deaf ear to the talk between O'Hara, O'Neill, and the other clan chiefs—talk of new rebellion. She had pushed the thought of war from her mind, even though she knew it occupied her husband's every waking moment.

And then, on a warm summer night with light rain sifting the fog that shrouded Ballylee, Shane broke the news.

"Do ye know the fate of Red Hugh O'Donnell, lass?"

"Aye, I know the tale."

Months before their wedding the Queen's lord deputy in Ireland, Sir John Perrot, had taken a bold step to insure that the northern clans would not unite and rebel as the clan leaders in Munster had years before.

Perrot had lured The O'Donnell's eldest son, Red Hugh, as well as Art and Henry O'Neill, into a trap and had had them clamped in the Bermingham Tower of Dublin Castle as hostages.

The O'Neill's reaction had been one of violent anger, but he had bided his time, waiting for the moment to strike. And now the time had come.

"You're to Dublin!" Deirdre gasped, finally realizing what her husband was trying to tell her.

"Aye," O'Hara replied. "The time is ripe to free O'Donnell. Once done, his father, Black Hugh, will see the worth of O'Neill's words."

Deirdre couldn't hold back a choking sigh as she slipped into her husband's arms. She did manage to bite back the words, *Why you*, that threatened to shriek from her aching heart.

She knew why Shane O'Hara had been chosen. He was as faithful to O'Neill and the Irish cause as he was to Ballylee and his wife. He was fearless, and if any man had the steel in his spine needed to free O'Donnell, it was O'Hara.

"A fortnight, lass," he whispered. "Only a fortnight and I'll be back between your thighs, I swear."

Wordlessly Deirdre nodded and raised her lips to his. The kiss was brisk, hurried, but that was the way he was. She had married a warrior on that spring day a year earlier, and she had vowed to love him without trying to change him.

His heavy boots sounded hollowly on the stone of the chamber stairs, and moments later she saw him mount his horse in the courtyard below. Through the fog she watched him cross the drawbridge and the heath beyond. She watched him enter the woods and disappear. And still she watched, until the rain stopped and dawn's first light began to melt the mist from Ballylee.

She watched day and night. A fortnight passed.

A week beyond a fortnight passed.

And then The O'Neill himself rode from the oaken woods and climbed the chamber stairs.

Deirdre met him calmly.

"'Tis time you moved to Dungannon Castle, lass—for your own safety and the safety of the child."

"My Shane?"

"He lives," O'Neill replied.

"Thank God."

"The attempt failed. He sleeps this night a prisoner with O'Donnell in Bermingham Tower."

Part II
Fall 1591

THE RAIN HAD STOPPED and the English countryside was bathed in autumn hues, made dazzling and crisp by sunlit dampness. Bright sunshine highlighted the lane leading from the London road up to Wimbledon House. From the window of her corner room Elizabeth Cecil drank deeply of the fresh afternoon air and watched a lone rider materialize through the trees.

Idly she raised a hand to her rich auburn coif and curled a ringlet as the black-clad figure came close enough for recognition. It was her uncle, Robert Cecil. She nervously smoothed the light blue material of her shift over her hip as the expression on her face turned to a frown.

From the lather on her uncle's horse as he entered the courtyard, she assumed he had covered the ten miles from London to Wimbledon in great haste. Was the suit settled? And if so, how had she fared? Were the ladies at court laughing at her behind their fans? Were the wags of London gossiping of her scandal?

She could feel the skin tighten and grow flush over the fine bones of her cheek and jaw as she thought of the events of the past weeks; and then embarrassment gave way to anger as her memory went even further into the past.

It had all started a year before, barely a month past her sixteenth birthday. Over her vehement objections, Elizabeth Cecil, first daughter of Thomas and Dorothy and granddaughter of the Queen's good right hand, William Cecil, first Baron of Burghley, had been espoused, complete with handfasting and contract, to the young Earl of Southampton.

Even at first meeting, with the traditional handclasping, the ritual kiss and on through the exchange of gifts, she had thought the boy, a scant one year her senior, a dullard. Later, with the betrothal ceremony over, she had returned with her parents to Wimbledon and had made no secret of her distaste for the young earl's waggish ways, his dull pimpled face and the general barbarism of imposed wedlock. In Elizabeth's opinion, marriage was little more than a padlock, making a woman a chattel—a mere pawn to a man's insistent desire to perpetuate himself.

"My dear child," Lady Dorothy had stammered, "marriage, bearing children and keeping a home are normal desires for every woman."

"Perhaps one day, mother, that will be my desire as well. But when that day comes I would like to choose the father of my children, if I need the pain of having them."

Lady Dorothy sputtered even more and looked to her husband to dress down the child. But she got no support, not even a look. "Elizabeth, are you saying you would have no children?" she asked timidly.

The girl calmly stared at her mother, a granitelike smile on her lips. "Hasn't woman been known to procreate without man's cooperation? Wasn't such the case with the Virgin Mary?"

"Blasphemy!"

"Nay, mother. . . reasoning."

Such independence and will in a child, and a female child at that, shocked her parents into near apoplexy.

"That kind of talk comes from giving the girl too

much knowledge and learning,'' Thomas Cecil had mumbled to his wife.

But Lady Dorothy disregarded his comment and turned a cold stern eye on her recalcitrant daughter. Her words were curt and to the point, broaching no further conversation on the subject. "A marriage between Cecil and Southampton will benefit our families, ourselves and the state. Therefore there will be a match, and you will do as you are told!''

"I will not. I'll not be bartered just so Southampton can have an heir and my grandfather more influence at court. M'Lord Burghley runs England now...why must I be an added pawn?'' She didn't add that she knew her acquiescence to the match would help cement the breach between her father and grandfather—a breach that had started when the youthful Thomas had shunned his studies and politics to play the rake in France. He had dallied with Parisian ladies, drunk to excess, and gambled or otherwise squandered his allowance until he was brought home in disgrace. Now it was in Thomas's best interests to cement this match that had his father's hearty approval.

And so for months after the betrothal, while England's wars went on in Ireland, France and Brittany, Thomas Cecil's war went on at Wimbledon.

Finally, at the risk of inviting a stern rebuke from his father that he couldn't handle his own child, Thomas called upon the venerable William himself to command, demand or implore. But the grandfather fared no better than the father, and both agreed that if England were still Catholic the best solution for such a headstrong girl would have been a nunnery.

It fell upon Cecil's other son, Robert, half brother to Thomas, to show Elizabeth the merits of the match. Robert was as ambitious and wise as he was devious and clever. He alone recognized these same traits in his beautiful niece, and used them along with her strong desire for independence to show her the way to power and influence.

"We live, my sweet niece, in an age where love must play the minor part to advancement. It needs must be, because if one is to survive in our gracious Queen's court one must advance or perish."

To the Cecil family's great surprise, Robert firmly convinced Elizabeth that she should marry Southampton. He not only used his own guile in convincing her, he let her reason for herself how her own best interests could better be served were she the Countess of Southampton. Robert also made it clear to her that the more dullard the earl was, the more freedom Elizabeth could maintain in the marriage. As added fuel Robert didn't fail to elucidate the rumors of Southampton's occasional preference for the company of boys.

The overall combination appealed to the young beauty's strong-willed independence. It suddenly became not only a good but a desired match. Robert had done his job so well that by a fortnight before the marriage, Elizabeth was ready and eager for it to take place.

But then an even greater surprise greeted the Cecils, and a wealth of scandal was fed the court gossips when the young earl changed his mind. He decided that he had no desire for a wife, since he wanted to go off to war with the Earl of Essex for a life of adventure and romance.

Elizabeth was stunned, and then shamed, and then angered.

"What? *What*? That whimp, that *child*, wants adventure? He wants romance? There wouldn't be enough days in his life to satisfy a real woman for one night—and he wants *romance*?"

It was unheard of, Elizabeth's father had sputtered. It

was breach of promise and could become a judicial affair.

"I don't care what affair it could become, I'll have none of it," Elizabeth railed. "I'll wed him, if only to become his shrew. I would live with the whimp so I could crush him!"

But the boy was adamant, and he had his father's fortune and his mother's ear. His family begged the Cecils to release him from the pledge. Neither Robert nor Lord Burghley would hear of it and the bickering dragged on.

But the Queen didn't call Burghley her "fox," and Robert her "pygmy fox" for nothing. By the time the suit was settled Southampton had paid the Cecils five hundred gold crowns—a fortune to be used as a dowry to procure an even better match for the lord treasurer's granddaughter. That match had already been made secretly with Sir William Hatton, nephew and only heir to the lord chancellor and one of England's richest men, Sir Christopher Hatton.

Elizabeth met this news with tears of frustration that quickly turned into torrents of vindictive abuse and anger.

"You would let me be shamed by a whimp of a child, and then sell me to a gout-ridden, paunch-bellied old knight who has no coin to go with his title?"

Lady Dorothy tried calmly to reason her way through the storm. "But Sir William is heir to one of the vastest fortunes in England!"

"And should I wear cotton, serve myself and breed his brats in the country while he awaits wealth to overtake him? Nay, mother, a match you made to my dislike, but its wealth wooed me over. Now you chattel me to poverty with a man more than twice my age and too ill to rise from the bed, were I ever able to coax him into it. Nay, I'll not for it. First I would to the wilds of Ireland as a rebel's mistress, or to the courts of France as a slut to one of the pretenders!''

At this outburst Lady Dorothy fainted. Sir Thomas mumbled, ''One would think, daughter, that you'd spent much time at court in the company of our Queen, for you rail as well as she and use vulgar language even better.''

A crunch of gravel under boot brought Elizabeth's attention back to the present. Robert was moving along the tree-lined path beside the house toward the rear courtyard and gardens where her father awaited him.

She repressed the urge to cry out to him, to tell him that his mission was fruitless. She would never agree to the match with Sir William Hatton, and if forced into it she would cloister herself like a nun in her wedding chamber until he should die of old age before the consummation could take place.

But she remained silent and closed the louvers as he passed beneath the window lest he hear her breathing and notice her presence. Her eyes misted as she followed his figure, wishing she could appeal to him as she had in the past but knowing that it was impossible. For Robert was the chosen one; his father's need, England's plight and his own ambition had placed him beyond where she could reach him anymore.

Now they stood, the tall and short of them, with their heads wagging and their lips working in heated discussion. The frail, almost emaciated form of her dear Uncle Robert stood calmly, while her father paced and declaimed as much with his hands as with his roaring voice.

Now and then Robert would turn to follow the larger man's progress, and the unmistakable hump in his cloak would be outlined against the bubbling waters of the fountain beyond. The young girl's heart went out to her favorite relative as it always did when she saw the malformed back, a result of a childhood accident. For in her earliest memory it was always Robert who had had both a kind and a wise word for her; he alone understood the many changing moods that would never let her heart and mind work as one.

She unchecked the lattice and let the louvers slide open so the men's voices could reach her. Her father's booming bass was clear, reaching her easily, as indeed it probably reached the spire of St. Paul's, barely visible above London Town ten miles away. When he spoke, Robert's voice was as low and as calm as his brother's was booming. So much so that Elizabeth had to lean forward very near the window in order to understand his words.

Her father was ranting. "Od's blood, I've a mind to agree with Luther on women: 'Let them bear children till they die of it; that is what they are for.' And aside from all their screeches and howls in birthing, I'd say that it was easier than our job of matching them."

"You speak of Elizabeth or of all women?"

"All, and her in particular. I swear, Robert, she was a woman at five, using her wiles on all around her. A cursed man has daughters, for they're like priests and kings—they can never get enough."

"Nor we of them," Robert replied, covering the smile on his face with a kerchief.

"Hey?"

"Nothing. So she'll agree to nothing?"

"Not a whit. And if we force her, she'll off to God knows where to put further scandal on the family name." Thomas started his pacing again, his feet missing the path now and again to tread on a few flowers underfoot. "She says we've given her a rich whimp and an aging boor steeped in poverty for a choice and she'll have none of it. She says we live in an age of heroes and wealth, and that's what she'll have.''

At the window, Elizabeth nodded as Robert's chuckling laugh reached her ears. "So my niece would wed only a wealthy courtier who has returned from the wars with the people fawning at his feet?"

"Aye."

"Then perhaps we should betroth her to Essex himself. Then we would have a Cecil in the enemy camp, our Elizabeth would have a hero, and our Queen would no longer have her doting favorite at her side to ill-advise her."

Neither seeing nor hearing the humor in his younger brother's face and voice, Thomas halted his pacing and grew solemn. "How goes the family's battle with Essex and his thirsty warriors?"

Robert shrugged. "Little change. He would off to France to gain his spurs and glory at the treasury's expense."

Again Thomas railed. "Aye, it's youth...all of them! They seek glory and romance, and damn the expense! Wed Essex off and methinks his feet would regain the ground."

Robert shook his head. His half brother had inherited the family looks and athletic prowess but all wit had escaped him. Perhaps it could be attributed to their different mothers. Thomas knew little of court life. If he had, he would know that for all of Essex's petulance and irresponsibility, he was well aware of his place as the Queen's favorite. He was much too crafty to be caught bedding anyone. And as for marriage? It was the Queen's preference to surround herself with single, attractive courtiers.

But to matters at hand, Robert thought. "No matter,

Thomas. Fetch our stormy beauty down here and I'll have words with her.''

Elizabeth heard a sound behind her and quickly re-latched the window's lattice. She turned to face her mother's disapproving stare, her own face as haughty as she dared.

"Have you no shame—standing at the window thus?"

"Of course I have shame, mother." Elizabeth looked down at the shift, stretched tight across her high breasts. "But all the necessities are covered. That agrees with our good Protestant faith." She lifted her head, a slightly taunting smile on her lips. "To worry about how those necessities are outlined would be so prudish as to be Puritan—and 'tis my understanding that the Puritans are as much out of favor of late as our Catholic forebears.''

Lady Dorothy's stern face reddened. Her lips opened as if to speak, but as usual she had no reply to her daughter's ready wit. Nor did she think one necessary for such shameful talk.

Instead she spoke the message that reasoned her presence. "Your uncle would have words with you in the garden. At once."

The swish of her gown was overwhelmed by the resounding slam of the door behind her.

Elizabeth crumpled; her shoulders sagged and the face she had worn in her mother's presence transformed itself into pain and worry.

She would dearly love to go down to the garden and trade wit and repartee with her uncle at any time; but not now. Not when his talk would veer away from news of the current London fashions and the latest scandals at court to make of her an unwilling bride and a prisoner of poverty.

She pulled open the doors to her closet and surveyed her frocks. "What have I to dazzle him with, to make him realize my beauty and how it would be wasted on an old man such as Hatton?"

And then her face fell and her smile faded.

"I have nothing. Not even the best of the Queen's thousand gowns would dazzle Robert, for he sees only reality. Well, to lose is not to try."

As she selected a bodice and waistcoat, only to return them to her wardrobe and select another, a phrase kept rippling through her mind: "We live in an age of heroes." It was her own phrase and well meant when she said it. For she would have a man, not a whimp nor a corpse. There was passion in her heart and body as well as ambition in her mind. Somewhere there was a man to match both her passion and her ambition.

"Oh, God, let me put off Hatton until I find him," she cried. "For if I wait long enough in these glorious days, I know that he'll come!"

In the garden, Robert Cecil was also thinking of Elizabeth's phrase. Heroes, he mused, did serve their purpose. Drake had defeated the Armada, and now England was mistress of the seas. Raleigh had beaten the Irish and spread the empire to the Americas. Indeed, he was swiftly becoming an example for a whole generation. And that generation of dandies and gallants flocked to him in hopes that some of his fame would drift down to them.

Heroes all—tall, daring, dashing, with a flair and a taste for war. But now it was time for a new breed of hero, one more of cunning and intellect than of athletic prowess.

He chuckled, looking down at his emaciated legs barely outlined in the ballooned breeches. "Not unlike yourself, Robert Cecil; a daring statesman instead of a dashing warrior.''

He had said as much only a week before in Parliament. ''Gentlemen, we have had a decade of heroes, and they have indeed made great our land. But now is a time for change. Let us hope we can put these heroes, along with their taste for war, to rest, and get on to the business of peace and prosperity.''

He chuckled again, louder this time as he thought of the shocked faces that had greeted that speech. It had been an outright reference to the standing feud between himself and Robert Devereux, Earl of Essex and the Queen's favorite.

He knew they would admire him for it, but would they listen to it?

Essex did all in his power to fan the flames of war; war that England with a drained treasury could ill afford. He openly opposed Cecil in his bid for the position of secretary of state, wishing to have his own man, Davison, occupy that powerful seat. But common sense told Robert that with his experience and ability the Queen could not resist appointing him.

However, as in every affair of state, a little insurance was necessary. In Cecil's case it was insurance in the form of more powerful friends at court; friends like Sir William Hatton.

But, the young political genius thought, *my Elizabeth wants a young, vigorous hero. Well, we'll just have to show her the other side of the marriage.*

''And,'' he murmured aloud, glancing up at the corner window, ''with recent events only this morning transpired, that shouldn't be too difficult a task.''

CHAPTER TWO

THE WIND HOWLED mournful and ominous across the Irish bog as it sent stinging pellets of autumn rain into the riders' faces. Yet not one of the long line rode with bowed head or slitted eye. It was as if each eye in each shaggy head dared a mere storm to blur its vision or purpose.

Before them tendrils of gray mist crawled along the landscape like thick snakes. A hundred yards in front of the leader a tall figure in a heavy red mantle rose like a phoenix from the fog's shroud.

The younger of the two lead riders spoke. "Is it he?"

"Aye, 'tis The O'Neill," replied the older, larger man. "And he waves us in."

"The warm fire of a booley will feel as good as a woman after this ride, my father."

Black Hugh O'Donnell twisted his huge head in his son's direction and let his lip curl into a sneer, the only smile he knew. "Would God I could think of a woman now."

Young Rory O'Donnell watched the smile fade and his father's face return to its habitual state, a war-ravaged, aging granite mask of scars and wrinkles.

A chill passed through the younger man's heavy leather mantle and found the very core of his bones. For the son knew well the meaning of his father's words. The O'Donnell, Black Hugh, chieftain of the vast O'Donnell clan, had no passion left in his heart for anything but freedom.

And that was why they had ridden clear across Ulster through days of driving rain to meet The O'Neill; because he, too, had voiced his passion for freedom and was ready to mount a rebellion in the north to achieve it.

To father and son alike it seemed as though Ireland had been at war with itself, and with England, forever.

Indeed, since the Norman invasion generations before, the Irish clans had been raiding and killing each other with fierce regularity. But now that must end, for all the clans had a common enemy: England and her Protestant Queen.

"You have no fear of a trap, father?"

A shiver went through the great, bearlike body made even larger by the thick frieze mantle and animal-skin jerkin. "Aye, lad, the thought has passed through and rattled my brain often since his summons. He's an English wife, as has The O'Hara now. He did fosterage in the house of an English lord—raised as a proper English gentleman he was."

Rory nodded, his mind silently adding a multitude of other reasons that O'Neill might be luring the O'Donnells and the heads of lesser clans into a throat-cutting trap. In years past the two largest of the northern clans had spilled much more of each other's blood than had their common enemy, the English.

Rory pulled his horse abreast of his father's. With his eyes forward, glued to the commanding figure in the misty distance, he said, "Do you think there be any truth in the rumor that the English bitch will return his lands and title?"

The older man's coarse black beard, as long as the gray-flecked mane on his head, jiggled a shrug in answer to his son's words.

"Mayhap we'll know before the day is out. My senses tell me more than our spies that Hugh O'Neill is a crafty man who would woo Queen Elizabeth's favor with his smile, his glib tongue and his English manners, while cursing her with his Irish heart.''

The son wasn't so sure. "Nonetheless, I'd feel more at ease were this meeting at Dungannon Castle rather than a forest booley. And my back would less anticipate a blade with a full retinue of swordsmen to protect it.''

"Like our own clan, lad, the O'Neills are riddled with spies. The forest camp of an Irish farmer will draw less attention than the castle of an Irish lord. The English would dearly love to hear what will be said here this day. The thought of The O'Neill and The O'Donnell in the same wattle, sharing heather beer, would make their blood run cold.''

Rory nodded and let his eyes move from his father's stern features back to the tall figure on the distant hill. A smile creased his handsome face as he thought of the English lords spoiling their breeches and cursing their colonial governors if the clans were allowed to merge.

In his years of life the younger O'Donnell had seen nothing but war—with the English and with the other clans. It was difficult for him to comprehend that such a man as The O'Neill could emerge from the rubble that was left of Irish aristocracy to unite the clans against England.

Not that they all hadn't suffered alike under the yoke and the sword of the Tudor Queen and her father before her. Even if plantation and other means of parceling out the land among English immigrants had become reality under Queen Elizabeth, the idea had been conceived years before by her father, King Henry VIII.

Early on, Irishmen were forced to throw off their traditional dress and refrain from speaking in their Gaelic tongue, and the clan princes were forced to become anglicized as models for the lieges and serfs under them.

Rebellion against these edicts was quickly put down with brutal force. Rory, like every young Irishman of his time, had been thoroughly schooled in English treachery with stories of the pardon of Maynooth in '35 and the Munster slaughter in 1580.

In both cases the rebels had laid down their arms in unconditional surrender, only to be butchered to the last man. During the Munster slaughter the Irish turncoat general, Ormond, had marched a huge force through the province killing everyone they met, no matter what age or sex. They laid waste the land, burning fields and buildings till it was said that not a lowing calf nor a child's cry would be heard for years.

But now it was 1591, and from both the English and the Irish view, things seemed relatively under control. The English felt safe to the south, in the area around Dublin called the Pale, preferring to ignore what remained of the clans to the north. The northerners stood safe behind their natural fortresses—the lakes, mountains and deep forests that wound their way from coast to coast as if by clan design.

Above this Ulster line, Irish and Scot visited each other at will and did a brisk trade in shot, powder and heavy artillery; progressive materials of war heretofore used only by the English to keep the clans splintered.

Now The O'Neill was replacing pike and lance with musket and shot. For months bards and chroniclers had traveled the back country, whispering in feverish tones the stories of how the crafty O'Neill was building an army with modern weapons right under the English nose.

At first the stories amused the O'Donnells. Surely they could be no more than anecdotes of wishful thinking. But as the tales abounded and variations of the same tale were retold, Black Hugh O'Donnell began to listen. Eventually he sent his own spies into the woodlands, the booley, and the castle to find truth in rumor.

Slowly the information filtered back that O'Neill was indeed doing the impossible. In the guise of roofing material for Dungannon Castle he had imported great amounts of lead. The castle roof never saw repair; the lead found its way into shot and bullets.

By royal proclamation an Irish prince could maintain an army of defense made up of only limited numbers of trained men. O'Neill abided by this law, but with a variance of his own. When one set of men had been trained, he released them and hired new untrained recruits. When these betaghs were trained, they too were released, only to be replaced again in the cycle.

O'Neill missed not the slightest chance to find an Irishman who would fight. On a personal hunting trip he would come across a farmer in a field. Much to the man's amazement, the great lord would press his own musket into his hand and point out a target. If the man's eye were keen he found himself the owner of a gun and enough powder and shot to improve its keenness "for the day he would see Ireland free."

But O'Donnell, hearing the truth in all the rumors, still found it difficult to accept such a turnabout in The O'Neill. As a boy the young Baron Dungannon had been taken from Ireland to be fostered in an English home; first that of Lord Sydney and then the Earl of Leicester. It was a common practice inaugurated in the court of Elizabeth, the reasoning behind it being that it was far better to convert the youth of leading Irish clans to Protestantism and loyalty to the crown rather than kill them. Then at a certain age they could return to Ireland, to their lands and, in some cases, to their titles—to become missionaries teaching the wisdom of English rule to their subjects.

O'Neill had been such a disciple. Upon his return he had proclaimed his fealty to the crown and had outwardly run his life on Elizabeth's behalf. So much so that after only a few years he was summoned back to England and by Elizabeth's hand made Earl of Tyrone, heir to all the O'Neill lands and fortunes in Ulster.

One prerequisite of the Queen was that he would never assume the clan title of The O'Neill. He agreed, and for several more years ruled his corner of Ireland as Earl of Tyrone. But as Tyrone he had built and armed the army that would one day give him The O'Neill mantle.

Now that day had come, as it had for O'Donnell. And with it had come the cry to arms, the desire of O'Neill to merge with O'Donnell and crush the English.

Snorts from the horses brought Rory back from his reverie. His eye darted to the hill, much closer now, to see that the figure had disappeared into the mist. His nose detected the fires of the booley, carrying with them the scent of freshly cooked victuals.

"Stand!" His father's horse stopped abruptly. Rory's horse shied slightly to the side. "You've been dreaming, lad," said O'Donnell.

"That I have, father."

"Of what. . . wench or war?"

"Neither, father. Of a better tomorrow."

"A tankard on that, lad," the older man chuckled. "Come! We shall walk in from here."

CHAPTER THREE

ELIZABETH COULD HEAR the measured tread of her uncle's pacing on the garden path as she fretted over her wardrobe.

"What will dazzle and befog the mind of a man whose eyes see nothing but the results of ambition?" she intoned to herself, lightly running a finger from frock to frock.

After much deliberation she finally chose a green doublet the color of her eyes, with a high ruff that would accent the richness of her auburn hair. She had already cinched the farthingale around her, making her already tiny waist even smaller. Over this she draped a richly embroidered satin skirt sprinkled with rows of pearls down the front and around the wide hem.

She rejected the bodkin, thinking the current fad of women wearing daggers silly, and completed the ensemble with gloves and a scarf of a green velvet slightly darker than the doublet.

After applying a light touch of rouge to her already flushed cheeks she stepped back from the mirror to scan the results. She liked what she saw, but lightly cursed the current styles that hid all of a woman's figure but her breasts from the male eye. And hers were all too prominent, often bringing stares she disliked and comments she little wanted to hear.

"But all in all, dear Uncle Robert, how can you endorse giving all this to an old man who would use its worth so sparingly?"

With one last check in the mirror she turned and swept out of the room.

Robert Cecil watched his niece emerge from the

house and slowly approach him. Her skirt so filled the narrow path that she seemed to glide through the sea of blossoming roses, columbine and lilacs. He openly admired his favorite niece as she grew nearer. The little girl he had entertained as a child was now a strikingly beautiful woman, with broad shoulders, a narrow waist and jutting breasts that were more than half revealed by the fashionable low-cut bodice. Hers was a passionate face marked by flashing green eyes, high cheekbones and a strong jawline that revealed her independent nature.

She stopped and curtsied low. With her head bowed so that he could see the fine white line of her neck between ruff and curls, she spoke.

"*Sir* Robert, congratulations. I understand your knighthood will soon give you the position in the Queen's privy council that you crave."

Robert's lips pursed into a smile as he gently raised her and kissed both her cheeks. "My new title pales beside the greater beauty each time I see you, dear Elizabeth."

"Such poesy, uncle. Methinks you'd make a courtier as well as a statesman."

Chuckling, he took her arm and seated her on a nearby stone bench. "Only with you do I ever use such language. And a courtier I would never make. Indeed, I wouldn't have the time, as our young gallants do, to change my suit three times a day in order to air my wardrobe. No, at court I leave all that to Essex and the fops who surround him."

Elizabeth studied his emotionless face with its beaked nose, its small fine bones and its high intelligent forehead. What tack should she take? Should she go right to the heart of the matter? No, better to get there in a roundabout fashion through banter.

"And how goes your feud with our national hero?"

"No better. Essex would feather his fortunes with war while we Cecils try to create peace. He puts pressure on the Queen for every appointment of state that is made. He opposes me for the post of secretary of state and presses for his own man. And even while the Queen knows that I already do the work of that high office, I fear she listens to him all too well."

"All the more reason for you to stay near the court," Elizabeth said, lightly caressing the edge of her smiling lips with her fan, "instead of riding the countryside in search of wives for doddering old men."

Robert allowed just the trace of smile on his own lips. "I hasten to my father's house at Theobalds now for that very reason. The Queen holds court there awaiting m'Lord Burghley's return from Bath."

"Grandfather ails again? He takes the waters?"

"Only for a fortnight. I'm afraid that affairs of state won't allow him too much leisure in the country. He will no doubt join the Queen as she travels to the great houses throughout the provinces on her summer progress this year."

"Would that I could be a part of the court, a handmaiden to the Queen, perhaps. But, of course, only women in a single state receive that honor."

"True."

"While married women languish in the country."

"Elizabeth...."

Abruptly she plucked a blossom from the profusion of blooms beside her. "Isn't the gillyflower beautiful this year? And the plum trees have blossomed so enchantingly."

"You are the most infuriating girl...."

"Woman, Robert." Again the fan passed coyly

before her eyes and a deep breath swelled the bosom and drew his eyes. "Or haven't you noticed."

His laugh was loud and long. "Your beauty would give rise to a corpse, you wench, and you know it." And then, as only Robert could do it, his face returned to its emotionless mask and his eyes grew hard. "And the plum trees will always blossom, whether you are maid or mother."

Her tone also changed, matching the steel edge in his as her head whirled around, her eyes flashed as they met his icy stare. "Perhaps. But their fragrance would be a good deal sweeter if I, like my Queen, could choose my own destiny in matters of whom I bed."

"Wealth is not only influence, Elizabeth. It's also duty. As the wife of—"

Her light laugh was strained but it served the purpose of interrupting his speech. "Pooh on your affairs of state. Come, sit beside me!" She patted the bench and motioned with her fan for him to join her. "I would hear something of interest for a change—fashion and gossip. Tell me, dear uncle, what is the latest scandal?"

Robert sighed heavily but chuckled at her reversion to youth. As a little girl she had always pulled him away from a group so he could relate the latest scandals at Whitehall.

"Well, let me see.... Robert Compton was commanded from court for kissing Mistress Carlyle in the Queen's presence."

"No!"

"Yes. It's said they'll marry to escape the Queen's wrath. Raleigh lies afuming in the Tower. Bess Throckmorton has blossomed with child... there is little doubt whose. It has been suggested that she marry before she births. And—oh, yes—Lady Mary Howard was banished."

"With whose child?"

"No, a different reason. It seems she not only possessed but had the audacity to wear during a garden stroll a velvet suit with a powdered border of pearls finer than anything in the Queen's own wardrobe."

Elizabeth tittered, her own problem momentarily forgotten as Robert related one tidbit after another. For Robert's part, he was both amused and amazed at her rapt attention to matters so shallow, and her sudden fluctuation in moods and interests. He had always been a little awed with the many facets of his niece's character. One time she would be calculatingly hard, almost shrewish in her demands, as well as cunningly astute in her knowledge and assessment of people. Another time, such as now, she could become giddy over matters that carried no more importance than the cost of a new pair of gloves.

"Our good Bess does adore her finery, and she allows no better on another than adorns her own back. Is it true that age had finally taken its toll? Some say she has had all the mirrors removed from her chambers so she won't have to gaze upon the wrinkles!"

"I believe it's true. But even now in her dotage a courtier's good leg and impudent face are the best passports to favor and fortune under her maiden eye. And that brings me to the here and now...."

He folded her free hand in his and lightly tugged the fan down from her face until their eyes again met. A slight chill rippled across her shoulders when she met his stare.

Though she had always felt at ease with her youthful uncle, there was another side of him she often saw in his eyes. Even when she was a little girl they could rivet her, making her cease chattering to listen raptly to his every word.

For Robert Cecil's eyes were his most arresting feature. So piercing were they that he could lock them on a person or object unfamiliar to him and weeks later draw a perfect picture of what he had seen.

His voice when he spoke was senatorial with the tones he normally used in the council and courts of law. Like his burning eyes, it demanded nothing less than her complete attention.

"We live, Elizabeth, in a time where royal favor is a necessity of life. It must become a person's full passion. To garner the Queen's favor is a business, a career. To combat the petty jealousies—the intrigues, both large and small, of court life—one needs good friends and influential followers...as well as great amounts of coin."

The young girl's heavily lashed green eyes darted from her uncle's for only a second before returning to blaze an answer.

"I won't do it. I won't sacrifice my youth to an old man, even if he has the promise of a fortune! Like m'Lady Farthingale I would rather languish in the court of France as a pampered whore...or gamble on love in the Ulster wilds with an Irish rebel like Deirdre Haskins!"

To her surprise, Robert answered her verbal assault with a spate of laughter. "Spoken like a true firebrand, my sweet! If it weren't for your beautiful face and perfect body, I would wonder if you weren't the fruit of another's loins, rather than my handsome but weak half brother."

"I mean every word of it, uncle. I mean it!"

"Elizabeth, listen to me!" Now the tone was stern and the voice deep, goné suddenly hoarse with a passion she hadn't heard before. "No matter what power we Cecils possess, it would be a flighty thing if I don't replace my father before he dies. We live in a time of intrigue when men lust for power and wealth. Without those advantages we are nothing. Marriage to Sir William will give you the wealth and power I know you desire...and it will give me another voice at court.''

Tears formed like a heavy mist over Elizabeth's eyes. She grasped at straws, trying to conjure up any thought or word that would appeal to him not to force this marriage. ''Perhaps I want more than an old man who has no more than a title. Sir William waits for his uncle's death to obtain his fortune. Must I endure the wait with him? I would have better!''

''You aspire high, Elizabeth.''

''I am a Cecil.''

''True, as am I. But I am a realist. We Cecils can trace only two generations. Born high, I'm afraid we are not. You even less than I.''

This stung Elizabeth and she had to bite her lip to keep from shouting a coarse reply. But she knew Robert's words were true. Robert, and not her father Thomas, was old Burghley's favorite son.

Even now her father was dependent. Any favors from his kinsmen came through Robert. For this reason Elizabeth knew that crossing her uncle would mean cutting off any advancement through the Cecil name for herself. Love her he did, but his love for England and for power was greater.

But her heart was bleeding and her breast beat with a passion she knew no tired old man could satisfy. Why, oh, why did a woman's place in life have to be made through marriage? And since it did, why couldn't that marriage be one of desire as well as of position?

But wealth and position were for Elizabeth as much of a need as love was. So marriage became like a stratagem of war, wherein a woman can err but once.

Her heart told her that she needed love, but her mind
told her that life was a marketplace where a woman's
only commodities were beauty and gentility.

"If I still refuse?"

"Sir William is bound for a wife, for he has no
heir."

"At his age he might well not be able," she replied,
gently stabbing the moisture from her eyes.

"All the better for his wife," Robert chuckled.

"How so?"

He placed his hand gently on her cheek and lifted
her chin. "You are young and beautiful, my sweet
Elizabeth, and a blind man could sense your passion.
M'Lord William is aging and frail. Age and wedlock
bring many a man to his final nightcap."

"You are an evil man, Robert Cecil." She was once
again smiling, the tears having suddenly dried in their
ducts.

"Nay, I am a practical man. Should Sir William die
before an heir is born, the widow would have the house
and vast lands at Holdenby, the income of his southern
and his Irish property, and Hatton House in London."

"That's all well and good if his uncle precedes him.
At this point I think it's a match race as to who will
meet Charon first."

Robert leaned far forward until his face was almost
touching hers. When she looked into his eyes she saw
that the intensity that had chilled her before was gone,
replaced now by amusement.

"He already has. Sir Christopher Hatton died early
this morning, leaving all his earthly wealth to his
nephew."

The fan dropped to Elizabeth's lap. Her mouth fell
open as she sputtered, trying to speak. "Why...why
didn't you tell me before?" Green eyes, now sparkling

as brightly as emeralds, narrowed as she studied her uncle's smiling face and knew already his answer. In his own devious, almost ruthless way he had toyed with her.

He had wanted to know exactly what her sentiments and objections were concerning the match with Sir William, on the side of love or of wealth and power. And she had told him all too easily.

"So you see, mistress of Holdenby you'll be on the very day of your marriage. That should calm your fears and make the match more palatable, shouldn't it... Lady Hatton?"

Elizabeth stood up, coquettishly using her fan to cover the smile that replaced her glum demeanor. "We play intrigue in war and intrigue in peace. Oh, were I a man, uncle, I would glean your deviousness and, like you, grow to rule. But I am a woman, and gently accept the wisdom of my grandfather's choice of husbands."

"My dear Elizabeth, as long as I'll know you, I don't think you will ever gently accept anything."

CHAPTER FOUR

THE MEAL HAD BEEN PLANNED for outside, under the dark wide-leaved trees. But when the rains came and didn't stop, Deirdre, wife of The O'Hara and now acting as hostess and household head for her husband's cousin, The O'Neill, commanded that everything be moved inside the tiny wattle.

Inside the windowless thatched-roof hut the smoke mingled with the heat from the fire to bring tears to her eyes and pangs of nausea to her child-filled body. The heady aromas of food and near-naked bodies added to the closeness of the room, making everything swim before her eyes.

She reached out into the air as if to find a pillar to support herself. Instead her hand met the dampness of The O'Neill's coarse woolen mantle.

"You've come a long way down from the daughter of an English lord and the wife of an Irish prince to become a scullery maid, cousin."

Her eyes traveled up, up across the broad chest to the smiling yet solemn face. Heat in the wattle caused steam to rise from his damp mantle. It swirled around his rugged features, granting her the same eerie picture that the riders had witnessed on the hill outside; a rugged expressionless face somewhat obscured by mist.

To Deirdre the man behind the face, like the face beyond the mist, would always be a little obscure. For no one, not she nor even her husband, The O'Hara, could pierce the veneer he wore for the world.

Not since that first day, when he had ridden like a maddened bull up to her carriage and practically removed the door from its fragile hinges, had she gone deeper than the skin of his emotions or the surface of his thoughts.

O'Neill steadied her with his strong hand and admired the degree of fairness in her flushed face, in her hair black as jet and tending to unruly curls in the heat. He looked deep into her eyes, as dark and shining as her hair, and saw the sweetness and wisdom he had come to admire.

"Even with a waddling body ye're as fair an Irish wench as any I've seen."

"I'm too weary to curtsy," Deirdre replied, managing a flushed smile.

"You should rest," The O'Neill said, lightly running

a finger across her brow to remove the dampness. "You carry the next O'Hara in your belly."

"I pray there's hope for brothers and sisters," she replied, the strength of his nearness driving the nausea away.

O'Neill nodded, squeezing her shoulder more gently than he clamped his jaw in determination.

Weeks before, O'Neill had returned from London after charming Elizabeth's council and reassuring them that he, like Ormond in the south, was protector of the Queen's law in the north. He had convinced Queen and council that the accusations of treason and of conspiracy with the Spanish leveled against him were groundless.

They weren't, and Dublin Castle suspected as much. Perrot had refused O'Neill's latest offer to ransom the Irish hostages in Dublin Castle.

"If my father could see me now," Deirdre said, chuckling.

"If our good lord deputy, Sir John Perrot, could see you now," O'Neill replied. "A peer's daughter planning a booley feast for Irish rebels!"

Deirdre's smile faded to a thin line. "No longer a peer's daughter, but an Irishman's wife who sleeps in a cold bed."

The thought made O'Neill smile grimly. Perrot's treachery would this day prove to be his downfall.

"I swear I'll return The O'Hara to you, bring Art and Henry O'Neill back to the clan, and give O'Donnell back his eldest son, his heir apparent, his tanist."

Deirdre wasn't so sure. In her mind and heart she knew the duplicity of her own people. And she now knew the savagery of the Irish clans she had married into. She had grave doubts that this day's meeting would bring them together.

The bloody workings of the O'Neill succession itself had shocked her and had made her wonder if there could ever be peace in Ireland.

The old O'Neill, Conn, had fathered two sons, Sean and Matthew. Sean was ambitious, a man with great charm, great gall, even greater pride, and a streak of viciousness that would let him share power with no one.

Though Matthew, his illegitimate brother, made no motion to wear The O'Neill mantle, Sean took no chances. He murdered his brother as well as Matthew's elder son Brian, and set off for England to charm Queen Elizabeth and claim his lands. Matthew's two younger sons, Hugh and Cormac, posed no threat. But to place them even further from any claims to the O'Neill heritage, Sean readily agreed to Elizabeth's plan of fosterage. . . placing them in English homes for their education.

Sean the Proud, as he came to be called, vowed to the Queen that he would make war on all her enemies in his own land and rid Ireland of the dreaded Scots on the plains of Antrim.

Since every clan in Ireland was an enemy of the Queen, it meant that Sean would wage war on the whole populace. He did just that, and quite successfully until the English discovered that the taxes from the defeated clans never reached England. They were diverted into the coffers of Sean O'Neill.

Elizabeth sent yet another in a long line of armies to Ireland. Sean was defeated and took refuge with a rival clan, the MacDonnells, whom he had treated perhaps the worst of all his enemies. The MacDonnells promptly killed him, and the clan wars started all over again.

And now Deirdre's own adopted people, the O'Haras, had joined with the O'Neills. But for how long? And would the O'Donnells, the Maguires and the O'Briens join them for good this day?

These were the questions flowing through Deirdre Haskins-O'Hara's half-English, half-Irish mind as she stared into The O'Neill's dark brooding eyes and tried to read his thoughts. Would this wild man be able to repair the rent in the clans? Would he be able to meld enemy to enemy, Irishman to Irishman, to fight a common foe?

And if he did, would the rebellion succeed? And if it did succeed, if Ireland were free at last, would her son—if the kicking in her womb was indeed a boy child—would he be able to breed future O'Haras in peace?

Deirdre didn't know. And she found it easier to force herself not to care or think about it. Unlike most women of her age—her English sisters *and* the Irish warrior wives—she preferred love and peace to war and ambition.

But to O'Neill and her recently imprisoned husband, Shane, a free Ireland—no matter how bloody—was the reason for their lives.

And if Ireland still weren't free when the fruit of her body became a man, then he too would fight—and perhaps die—before his time.

This is what she saw in O'Neill's cold stare, and it made her shiver.

"You can't be cold...."

"No," she said, and added as an afterthought, "it's the child." She ran her hands lovingly over her belly. "He's restless today."

"He's anxious for the light of day and the smell of a free Ireland."

"And the taste of blood and war...."

Any warmth that came with the mention of the child quickly disappeared from his eyes. "'Tis the duty of every man to be free. Would you have England rule us forever?"

"I would have no man rule another." She saw a slight smile curl his full lip and knew that it foreshadowed either a discussion or an argument. She wanted neither. "I hear them," she said brusquely. "On to your duty, O'Neill, and I'll to mine. You feed the fires of rebellion and I'll feed the rebel bellies." She didn't add, as she often had in the past, "So we can all rush to our deaths much the faster."

O'Neill watched her wide hips, made even more womanly by the pregnancy, move across the room toward the other women. He bit down hard on his lip as he felt a tug at his heart. He was a man of honor and of vision, but he loved and coveted his cousin's wife.

How many nights since Shane's capture and Deirdre's move to Dungannon had he crawled from his bed and looked longingly at her window across the courtyard for a sign. For he thought she felt the same. He thought he saw an answering longing in her eyes every time she glanced his way. His skin would grow clammy and his mouth dry when he thought of covering her glorious body with his own.

But it couldn't be. His love was for Ireland and his lust was for freedom. To a driven man like O'Neill, denial was partially the measure of success.

So deny he would, no matter the torture in his heart.

CHAPTER FIVE

THE RAIN was like a glazed wall as O'Neill stepped outside through the low narrow door. Its chill and the blast of fresh air on his face cleared his mind. Through slitted eyes he watched the O'Donnells hand over their horses, and he studied both father and son as they slowly approached across the clearing.

Black Hugh O'Donnell, even in advanced years, was as huge in stature and fierce in demeanor as his reputation made him to be. His weather-darkened face was nearly obscured by the wild tangle of raven-black hair and untrimmed beard. But no amount of hair could hide the burning blue of his eyes.

The elder O'Donnell walked with a decided, painful limp. O'Neill knew it to be a product of his clan wars with Sean the Proud, O'Neill's own half uncle. It was a good sign that O'Donnell didn't stop in the center of the clearing and demand the stripping of clothes from all present, to prove the lack of hidden weapons. The fact that he moved steadily forward without this old clan precaution told O'Neill that the other man's position was almost decided already.

The son was as tall as the father, but only half so bulky. His body was almost a picture of musical grace as he lithely moved in his father's shadow. The features weren't nearly as coarse, and the eyes, beneath the heavy brows, seemed to look on the world with taunting amusement.

O'Neill cemented his assessment as the two men stopped just before him. While the father was a bull-like warrior of immense strength and courage, the son added grace and, O'Neill hoped, wit and wisdom to his inheritance.

"O'Neill."

"O'Donnell."

The two men extended their right arms, their hands falling with a dull thud on the other's shoulder. Such a blow would have felled a small horse, but neither man winced.

"My second son, Rory, heir to The O'Donnell if the English have their way and let my eldest, my tanist,

Red Hugh's bones be gnawed to dust by the rats in Dublin Castle.''

O'Neill nodded gravely and moved his gaze to the other man. He liked the way the younger O'Donnell's eyes flickered with a trace of amusement and distrust when they met his. There was no fawning in this lad over the great O'Neill, and that was as it should be.

"I've heard of your fight at Armagh. They say you were a tiger and truly your father's son."

"I thank you... but we lost."

For the first time that day O'Neill's face broke into a clean wide smile. "Today we'll find a way to rectify that, and a path to rape the English bitch. But come, a tankard and meat. As The O'Hara's good wife says, full bellies make better rebels!"

One by one they entered and took the blessing. The women brought drink at once to slake the thirst of the long ride. For comfort from the wattle's intense heat clothes were discarded, until the men, like the women who bustled about serving them, were naked beneath their gaping mantles.

Over brimming tankards of heated heather beer, talk was of crops and cattle, with only an occasional mention made of raids or battle.

Young Rory looked with approval on the full-breasted, fair-skinned O'Neill women. For they, like the O'Donnell lasses and all Irish women, were beautiful in their natural state.

Soon the meal was ready. They all sat on cushions of straw and fern leaves at the huge oblong table that was low to the ground. The inference of the simple woodland setting and the meal itself wasn't lost on the O'Donnells. O'Neill was telling them, in his own way, that a prince needed no pomp to prove his stature.

This message was carried on into the meal. The old

traditions were observed. A friar stood patiently behind The O'Neill, waiting to bless the food after the poem of welcome was recited to the guests by orator and harper.

This done, O'Neill attacked the huge slab of meat before him with his own short sword and served his guests. The women served herbs, watercress, mushrooms and shamroots, with not an English vegetable in sight.

Conversation came to a standstill as they attacked the meal with lusty appetites. The slab of meat diminished to bones, and these were thrown to the dogs anxiously waiting with drooling fangs in the darkened corners of the wattle. Tankard after tankard of milk, heated with warm stones, disappeared down thirsty gullets. One by one, plates were overturned. And only then did talk resume.

"Come, gentlemen," O'Neill said at last. "Let us squat naked by the fire like the savages the English say we are and talk of Ireland."

The two elders discarded their mantles and moved toward the fire. Rory rose, and as he removed his mantle, revealing the long hard line of his youthful but already battle-scarred body, he faced Deirdre still seated at the table's head.

"And do the English women, as well as the men, see us as savages?"

There was instant silence throughout the wattle. Heads covertly shifted toward O'Neill to see his reaction to this taunt directed at the absent O'Hara's wife. Such an affront was unheard of, but could almost be expected when clans met head-on, either in war or in talks of peace.

"Rory...." O'Donnell took a step toward his son

but found his momentum halted by O'Neill's strong grip.

Deirdre calmly surveyed the young O'Donnell's naked body gleaming in the firelight. At last her eyes came to rest on his, and a tiny smile played at the corners of her lips. "I know not of savages. I know only of handsome young men, barely bearded and already scarred by stupidity."

Instinctively Rory's hand went to the long purple scar at his side. "An English lance, m'lady. I thought him quite savage when he inflicted it. I daresay he thought me equally as savage when my sword sent him to hell without his head. But tell me. How *do* the noble English see us?"

Her smile broadened as she rolled to her hip and brought her now weighty body to her feet. "Very well, I'll tell you as I've heard it so often. The English see you as heathens, agile of body, thick of brain, and your only redeeming quality the brewing of fine whiskey fit for the gods. Would you like a glass to settle your meal?"

A faint chuckle could be heard from the direction of the fire and a slight blush crimsoned the young warrior's face.

From the set of his jaw and the instant tension rippling through his body it was evident that Rory's first impulse was anger and then retaliation. But as Deirdre's eyes and taunting smile met his, he relaxed and the amused air returned to his features.

"M'lady has a wit that matches her beauty. A glass?"

"Common among the lords and ladies of England— not much for slaking a thirst but charming to occupy the hands when lacking in wit and conversation."

The young O'Donnell threw back his head and roared with laughter. Behind him titters from the younger women joined sighs of relief from the more aged. The first volley of discord had been fired between the clans and it had fallen short.

"We call the potion *uisce beathadh*, m'lady, and yes, I'll drink. But I'll guzzle it from a tankard made of wood, for as a son of Ireland I'll have naught of English foppery."

"But you might, lad," came The O'Neill's voice, accompanied by a clap on the shoulder, "well you might. Come, sit you down between the two strong men of Erin that we may gauge your wit in war as well as my Lady Deirdre has in peace!"

O'Donnell related the latest from his spies concerning their own kinsmen and The O'Hara in Dublin Castle.

"The beatings have stopped, but they barely survive the hunger and lack of sunlight as well as the filth in which they are forced to sleep."

O'Neill nodded, keeping his eyes on the turf fire's glow rather than risk a glance at Deirdre. "And what of the priest, Offlay? I sent him to King Philip to once again plead for arms and trained men from Spain. A rumor abounds that he was caught upon his return."

The O'Donnells exchanged quick glances before Rory spoke.

"'Tis true. Hung he was and drawn and quartered before his breath was out. He abides quiet now in a hole outside Dublin's walls."

"Naught will be gained of Spain but talk and more talk," growled Black Hugh.

"Perhaps true," O'Neill sighed, "but let us hope that the priest was quiet *before* he died. He knew all. A wrong word from him and years of planning could be wasted. We have enough English spies among us—we can't bear it if our own are unable to withstand the rack.''

"Cormac, my harper, has true word of it," O'Donnell said. "He was celled for a trifle and saw and heard it all before his release. Would you hear of Offlay from his own lips?''

"Aye, I would," The O'Neill rasped, and signaled for the harper.

Cormac the harper was a slight misshapen man with a heavy step and sad downcast eyes. When given the reason for his summons, he nodded and began his tale in a singsong voice, the mark of his trade.

"As to your fears, m'lord, I think silence was the priest's only gift to the English. I know he was tortured often, for I could hear his screams. But because the torturing continued, I reasoned there was still cause for it. About five weeks after his capture—an early morning it was—I watched the guards lead him out to the castle yard. All the prisoners had a clear view of what happened. I suspect it was planned as such.''

The harper took a deep breath, then continued. "They seated the poor devil in the stocks, with his legs placed over iron bars. Then they put leather boots on him, clear to his knees and past. Inside the boots they poured oil and tallow...then built a fire under the bars. I can still hear his screams as the oil began to boil.''

"And still he said nothing?" O'Neill was staring intently at the other man now.

"Nothing. Eventually they took him back to his cell. That night they hung him on gallow's green. I couldn't swear it, but I reckoned that he was already dead, stretching his neck just making a spectacle for them.''

Silence followed the harper's story, broken only by

an occasional cough of uneasiness from the other listeners in the darkness beyond the fire.

"Thank you, you may go."

A gentle murmur accompanied the man's exit, suddenly broken by a sob.

"M'lady?" said O'Neill.

"Nothing. . . just my beads for the poor man." Deirdre paused, and there was a movement as the whiteness of her hand glided up to brush a tear from her cheek. "How can men do unto men so unjustly?"

O'Neill's head jerked up, his eyes the color of cold blue gems as he stared at her dim figure beyond the fire. "Men unto men? Only a turn of phrase, m'lady, I'm sure, for at last report we had a queen upon the throne. But I'm afraid that the milk of female kindness flows sluggishly in these, the latter days of our good Queen Bess."

Silence followed his words and the men sipped in thought, each of the two clan chiefs waiting for the other to guide the conversation down the path for which they all waited.

At last O'Neill's calm monotone broke the quiet. "My spies say the English of the Pale rob the London government as seditiously as they plunder the Irish peasantry."

"Aye, I've talked with Fitzgerald of Kildare and the other leavings of the Desmond wars. They say were an honest governor come to Dublin they might entertain in truth a suit for peace."

Without looking up O'Neill wagged his head slightly and continued. "I think those same thieving Englishmen in Dublin know not their God, be he Catholic or Protestant."

"Our cause is Catholic, yet Philip—nay, even the Pope—has given us a deaf ear." O'Donnell sipped.

Rory could hold back no longer. "By the saint's breath, why don't we come out and say it!"

Both elders turned furrowed brows at the younger O'Donnell's brashness, immediately silencing any further outburst. Again there were female titters around the wattle, bringing yet a second flush to the young man's face.

O'Neill let a slight smile curl the corners of his lips and then lifted his eyes to the father. "Methinks, O'Donnell, that we are of the same mind: much more interested in immediate freedom than ultimate salvation."

O'Neill's smile was mirrored in the elder O'Donnell's face. "Aye, O'Neill, for if the Church's powers see not enough worth in our cause as Catholic, then I say we should fight our cause as Irish."

O'Neill scooted forward on his haunches. "But as Irish, saving the Church."

"Aye, we'll do that, too," O'Donnell agreed.

One word came from Deirdre—"Blasphemy!"—but the men ignored it as O'Neill twisted on his bare buttocks to face both members of the clan.

When he spoke, his words were thoughtful and spaced for clarity. The fierceness and passion in his voice mirrored his heart and soon erased any doubts in his visitors' minds of his intent.

"With Offlay goes Ireland's last hope of aid from Philip's Spain, or from the Pope himself. England doesn't fear the clans divided for that very reason. But were they united, facing the English shoulder to shoulder, the very windows of Whitehall would rattle with the court's anguished screams. Already Elizabeth's coffers are depleted because of her French wars. And even if the Armada is a shambles, Spain is still a threat and must be held at bay.

"The northern lands of Ulster must be united with the south, including the ports and the English Pale. I have a plan to free our kin and The O'Hara from Dublin Castle. Once done, I will send The O'Hara into the south to move among the clans and respark rebellion."

"'Tis said The O'Hara has a temper longer and more unyielding than his sword. The southern clans are hostile, and they fare better under the English after the Desmond wars than we do in the north. Can he curb his temper should they at first refuse your proposal?" O'Donnell spoke, passing a wary eye toward Deirdre, who was still barely discernible in the grayness between firelight and darkness.

She sensed the look and raised her head. "My husband has calmed since his marriage. He has learned patience from me, just as he has acquired common sense from The O'Neill."

She ended the speech with a look of reassurance at O'Neill. The younger O'Donnell saw the glance and the one of thanks from O'Neill. Respect for the Lady Deirdre increased even more in Rory's mind. It was all too obvious that she didn't approve of what they planned, but in the final outing she was her husband's wife and a woman true to her clan.

O'Neill continued. "The clans of O'Neill and O'Donnell are the most powerful in the land, but the Munster clans of MacCarthy, O'Sullivan and O'Brien need to be aligned, as well as O'Connor and O'Rourke in Connaught and Maguire of Fermanagh. Unwavering allegiance must be obtained from the southern and coastal clans, and even the Scots of Antrim as well if the British are to be defeated once and for all."

Here O'Neill took a deep breath and used his eyes,

those dark orbs that saw everything and said nothing, to stare into the very souls of the men who faced him.

"I think if we make a pact here today, all Ireland will follow." His hands slammed flat to the ground between them.

They were immediately covered by O'Donnell's. "'Tis done—done, I say. Where and when do we strike first?"

"'Tis near St. John's Eve now. I think we can be ready come St. Martin's Eve, November 10, a year."

"Agreed." O'Donnell's big body shook as if the battle were only an hour hence, rather than many months.

"'Tis settled then, with only one more thing to decide." O'Neill's eyes moved from the father to bore as equally hard on the son. "We'll need information before then, firsthand from England. And when it all starts we'll need someone in England to tell us where they plan to strike in retaliation."

Rory was quick to realize the meaning in O'Neill's coldly staring eyes. "Me? A spy? And a spy in London at that? Nay, O'Neill, I'd be a fish in dry dock were I to venture outside of Ireland!"

"I think not," O'Neill replied.

"Nor do I." All three heads turned as Deirdre scooted farther into the circle of light. "Hugh's half uncle Sean charmed the Queen, the court, and all of London so that it was years before they realized how he prospered from his duplicity. Just recently the same was done again by The O'Neill sitting before you, who now claims half the privy council as his intimates!"

She flashed the same smile she had used before and directly faced the younger O'Donnell. "The Queen admires, indeed she *dotes*, on masculine youth and beauty. You have both, Rory O'Donnell. And all London bows to brash adventurers with rough ways but gentle manners. It gives them someone to talk about and breaks the boredom.''

"Rough ways I have. Gentle English manners I'm without.''

"Under my tutelage, lad, you'll have them in six months' time,'' O'Neill said. "As well as the right words to go along with your already glib tongue.''

The young O'Donnell looked to his father and saw no response.

"But I'm a soldier, not a spy!''

O'Neill's face hardened, his voice adopting the tone used on a recalcitrant child. "As I have moved us from pike and lance to cannon and musket in the field, we must progress, like the English, to win the backstairs war of stealth and intrigue.''

"Aye, lad,'' chimed in The O'Donnell, "O'Neill is right. A soldier can fight as well with his mind and tongue today as he can with sword and buckler.''

"Lord Burghley is Elizabeth's good right arm because he does far more than keep tight the strings of England's purse.'' Deirdre's voice retained its calm tone, but added to it now was an intensity of emotion that the young Rory hadn't noticed before. "His network of spies reaches far beyond England. Even now the Irish countryside is littered with their number. If you want to succeed, the clans *must* have an able ear in London!''

"M'lady's tone changes somewhat,'' Rory said, meeting her clear eyes. "She rails against rebellion on the one side but urges it on the other.''

"I would have God out of politics before governments kill more in the guise of His cause.''

Here her voice broke and O'Neill took up her words. "At last count there were thirty-two heads of so-called traitors and malcontents rotting on London Bridge; Charles Haskins, Deirdre's brother, is one of them.''

Slowly Rory leaned forward to place his widespread hands over O'Neill's. "Then I sincerely hope that the two of you tutor me well, lest my head become thirty-three.''

CHAPTER SIX

As the autumn rains turned to freezing snow and winter's whiteness stalked the land, young Rory proved to be an apt pupil.

From O'Neill he quickly learned the ways of the English court. From Deirdre he learned to soften the Gaelic in his speech until his English was nearly perfect. With both of them he delved into the English mind and gleaned what the fine lords and their ladies would like to hear from a bright Irish lad come to London seeking favor and fortune.

Because it was winter, the summer booley houses where shepherds stayed while grazing their flocks were empty. During Rory's training he was moved secretly from booley to booley in the forests around Dungannon Castle. News was circulated around the countryside that Rory and Black Hugh had fought over the O'Donnell titles, Rory claiming to be the rightful heir, the tanist, and demanding the title of earl because of Red Hugh's imprisonment and probable death, while Black Hugh staunchly defended his eldest son's birthright. The upshot was the rumor that Rory had renounced his O'Donnell claims and fled to France. Such family infighting had been a common thing in the past and would be readily believed in Whitehall now.

With English spies filling the Irish countryside like locusts, O'Neill was sure that word of the younger O'Donnell's defection would reach both Dublin and Whitehall before Rory's arrival in London. It was hoped that by then the court would accept him as one less wild Irish warlord to worry about.

And while in the north Rory was fast at work playing schoolboy to the arts of spying and diplomacy, agents of O'Neill were equally busy in the south fulfilling his vow to free The O'Hara and Red Hugh.

THE WIND HOWLED around Dublin Castle. It blew harsh gusts of blinding snow through the slit of Bermingham Tower and into the face of Shane O'Hara. He crouched, staring out at nature's wrath, oblivious to the cold and wet.

By craning his neck he could see the wall leading to the fortress gate. Beyond and beneath the wall was a wide deep trench. And beyond that again lay Dublin and farther south the Wicklow Mountains and freedom.

The sound of stone scratching stone behind him jerked his head around.

"Three years, three months and two days," came the graveled voice of Red Hugh O'Donnell. "The last mark."

"And a very Merry Christmas to ye, Hugh," O'Hara barked in a whisper.

So far all was well. From somewhere in the depths of the tower he could hear the guards already carousing with Christmas Eve cheer.

Thankfully the routine hadn't been altered because of the holiday. As usual the four of them—himself, Art and Henry O'Neill, and Red Hugh—had been taken from their respective cells an hour before and put in this larger common one. This was their hour of daily exercise before being taken to the dining hall where they were slopped for the day. Once this was done they would be led to the privy and then reshackled and returned to their cells.

But this night, be the good Lord willing and enough O'Neill coin in greedy English hands, there would be not only a change in their routine but an end to it.

With a groan Red Hugh hauled his squat body to his feet and joined The O'Hara at the slitted window.

"What think ye?"

O'Hara followed the other's gaze through the swirling mist and snow. "The Wicklows are white and the wind is freezing. It'll be a rough journey."

"Aye."

They turned at once and their eyes met. Both their heads were filled with the same thought.

If they did get into the mountains could they survive long enough to get over them?

Shane O'Hara's incarceration had been the shortest, so the mettle of his body was the least affected. Poor Henry in the last year had become addled, and they couldn't be sure his body would obey his mind. His brother, Art, was corpulent—too much so for swift travel over rough terrain. Poor food, torture and long periods confined in small dank places had also taken their toll on Red Hugh.

"Mayhap the snow will hide us," Red Hugh sighed.

"Or lose us from our rescuers as well as our pursuers," O'Hara countered, crawling deeper into his mantle as the cold, stiff wind rained white flakes across their bearded faces.

"I'll not spend another night in a cell cursing the first Norman foot that stepped on Irish soil," Red Hugh rasped. "By a week's time I'll be shouting my vengeance in Donegal with a belly full of meat and my hips splitting a hot wench's thighs or I'll be dead."

O'Hara nodded and let his thoughts turn in upon themselves. He, too, yearned to stand free again on the massive stone ramparts of the Castle Ballylee. His eyes ached for the sight of his own wild coastline with the sea foaming white a hundred feet high as it crashed against the rocks. His ears pined for the lowing of his own herds and the horn of the hunt in his own forest.

And like Red Hugh, his loins ached for a woman. But not just any woman. His Deirdre would be halfway to term now with a firm round belly and bursting breasts.

He shuffled his body into a more comfortable position as he thought of Deirdre and his first legitimate heir. True, bastards Shane O'Hara had aplenty, and as many mothers for them. But love he'd found but once and he'd known it the moment he'd laid eyes on her. Thirteen she was, and just blossoming with a mane of rich sable hair and dark eyes that flashed a challenge to every man she met.

A low growling chuckle rolled from between his cracked lips as he thought of himself, The O'Hara, married to an English heiress, the daughter of a lord. Then the smile turned downward and he nodded grimly to himself as he thought of how his Deirdre had proved her worth and mettle as an Irish wife.

Aye, he thought, his huge head nodding in the chilled darkness, *she's inherited the spirit of her Irish mother, she has. And despite my rough manner, my warring ways and my ferocious temper, I've captured a fine lady's heart, and her love.*

"As she has mine," he whispered.

"You spoke, O'Hara?"

"Nay, 'twas but the wind whistlin' through the ice on my beard."

There was a general rearrangement of bodies in the cell for comfort, and then silence again.

To the crown, the good Lord Haskins bemoaned his daughter's disobedience, but secretly he had blessed the marriage and promised to settle his lands one day on its issue. Would O'Hara ever see that issue?

Yes, damme, he thought, *I'll live to put a sword in the lad's hand and a good horse between his legs!*

There was a scraping sound in the corridor and a faint seepage of yellow light from the cracks around the heavy iron door.

"They're coming."

Red Hugh and the others were already on their feet. O'Hara joined them as the door groaned open and three guards entered the cell. Two guards took positions by the door, muskets at the ready, while the third went from man to man relieving their arms and ankles of the heavy chains and fetters.

This done, they were marched single file through the hall and down the narrow winding stair to the tower's first floor. The heat from the room's huge hearth and the kitchen fires in the adjoining rooms took but a part of the aching chill from their bones.

Other prisoners, not considered as valuable or as dangerous, cooked and served the evening meal. One of them, Seamus O'Dern, spooned a soup of watery meat into bowls and halved two loaves of dry bread for sopping.

"Sure an' it must be some saint's day," Red Hugh intoned, "for there's more than two pieces of meat in the slop."

"Aye, lads," Seamus quipped, "and that's not all

the good Queen's men have planned for your Christmas cheer.''

Art and Henry stared into their bowls. Red Hugh and Shane looked questioningly at their three guards as if they knew naught of Seamus's words.

One of the guards, a ferretlike little man whose main occupation seemed to be scratching his crotch, beamed a toothless smile at them from across the room.

"Aye, lads," he cackled, "Seamus speaks the truth. You'll get more meat than what you see in your soup tonight."

"And what may that be?" asked O'Hara.

"Ye'll see," said another of the guards, and roared with laughter. "But not before we've tested the wares."

Still laughing, the two of them exited, leaving only the ferret to act as guard.

Art fell to his soup with a will. The other three had failing bellies but forced it down. It might be a long time before anything hot passed their lips again.

Seamus managed to pass the word that the tools of their escape had been planted. The fact that the two guards were off somewhere with the doxies hired from Dublin's streets told the four that the plan was on.

When the meal was finished they were marched up to the privy room by the ferret.

"Do your job fast, lads," he said. "The whores will keep me mates busy for no more than a half hour. 'Tis then I'll discover I can't get through the door, and I'll be forced to raise the alarm."

"How much gold creases your pocket for this, little man?"

O'Hara was answered with a toothless smile and a cackle. "Not near enough, Master Prince O'Hara, but times is hard. Now be to it!"

Inside the tiny room they quickly located the loose stone near the floor between the two privy chutes. Behind it they found two long lengths of rope, a chain and a strong oaken staff.

"The ferret bastard," Red Hugh hissed. "Nary a single dagger or pistol."

O'Hara only shrugged. He had already assumed the offered weapons would be a myth. The coin provided for them was probably safely stored in the traitorous Englishman's purse. "No matter. Hurry."

O'Hara used the chain on the pulls of the two doors. When it was securely looped he blocked its uncoupling with the staff. By the time he was finished Art and Red Hugh had secured the ropes and played them out through the two privy chutes into the darkness below.

"Off with your mantles," O'Hara hissed, "there won't be room for such bulk to pass through."

"But we'll freeze out there in only linen shirts and breeches."

"Off with them...do as he says," Red Hugh barked in a voice used to being obeyed. "Freezing out there is better than rotting in here."

Off went the heavy mantles. In twos, they squeezed through the offal and accumulated stench of a thousand prisoners. Once free, they foot-walked down the stone wall with the rope burning their hands.

The ropes were short. As silently as possible they dropped through the darkness and the swirling snow into the freezing water.

"No, be ye daft, Henry?" Red Hugh hissed. "This way!"

Addled poor Henry was. He had paddled to the tower side of the ditch and was about to crawl out and back into his captors' arms when Red Hugh stopped him.

At last they gained the opposite side and crawled to the top. Just then the freezing wind hit their soaked clothing and brought a groan in unison from all four throats.

"We'll freeze," Henry gasped. "Let's go back."

"Nay," O'Hara hissed. "It's irons, oil, and the ceiling by your heels if you go back now. Hugh?"

"This way," Red Hugh whispered and led them off toward the dim lights of Dublin.

At a corner of the castle they dropped off the last low wall into the deepening snow and rolled to their feet to face a cowering creature in a crimson mantle, his head covered with a huge cowl.

Instinctively O'Hara reached out with his two loglike arms until his fingers found the man's throat. Luckily the cowl slipped aside and the man's face was illuminated before O'Hara had snapped his neck like a twig.

"Hold, O'Hara," Red Hugh O'Donnell cried out. "'Tis our guide, my father's harper, Cormac."

Sheepishly The O'Hara released the man and brought him to his feet.

"Od's blood, you've hands like talons and the strength of a bull," said the harper, hacking air back into his lungs.

"Enough to say I'm sorry," O'Hara replied, "but I've no time for it. Can you lead us out?"

The harper nodded. "The gates of the city stand open. Walk alone, but each of you keep me in sight. The weather may kill us, but we'll disappear in its shroud."

The harper's words proved true. They passed several people as they moved through the streets, but none paid them heed. Anyone out on such a blustery evening had their heads sunk deep into their own cloaks and mantles, intent on the warm shelter of their own homes.

In minutes they passed through Dublin and made for the open plain of Slieve Roe, Red Mountain. Behind them they could hear the tower bell alerting the garrison and the adjoining town of their escape.

"Do ye think they'll be sendin' a party after us?" Shane bellowed above the wind.

"Aye, but our tracks fill faster than we make 'em," Red Hugh replied. "They'll have a bloody time following us."

The harper's mantle they passed between them at intervals for some brief respite from the biting cold. Only by constantly shouting did they keep some semblance of contact. But even so, by the time they reached the border of Dublin and Wicklow Henry was missing.

"We daren't go back now," O'Hara said.

"Aye, and a search in this would be futile," added Red Hugh.

The harper stayed neutral. It was their decision to make. Art, biting his lips and holding back tears of dismay at his brother's fate, agreed.

Up and over Red Mountain they went, their pace slowed by a panting Art O'Neill. His weight and lack of exercise were sapping his strength. Red Hugh fared only a little better. As a boy he had bounded like a deer across the slopes of the Donegal Mountains, but three years in a dungeon had taken its toll and weakened his limbs.

By the time they reached the peak the cold and wet had entered their bones. Sharp rocks and piercing brambles had ruined what was left of their boots, to leave their lower legs and feet torn and bleeding.

"No more," moaned Art, sinking to the snow. "No more. . . must rest."

There was no argument. The others crashed with him, as close together as possible to share their heat.

It was dawn, but the difference of night into day was negligible.

"Yonder lies Three Rock Mountain and Glencree," Cormac said. "And beyond that the Glenmalure stronghold of Fiach MacHugh O'Byrne. It's there the English know we'll go, but it's there we'll be safe."

The rest was short. By late afternoon they had passed the worst of Three Rock, but Glencree was merely a mist somewhere below. By now Art was fatigued beyond endurance. Red Hugh's feet were frostbitten and without feeling. Shane O'Hara had stumbled into a ravine and torn a deep gash in his leg, which made walking almost impossible.

They held a council. The only one fit to continue was Cormac, the harper. He knew the way, and alone he could travel with speed. It was decided that he should proceed to Glenmalure and bring help.

They found a shallow cave among the rocks. It was little more than an overhang but it served to break some of the wind and impede part of the snow.

Together the three of them huddled under Cormac's mantle as the snow swallowed up the harper.

"Godspeed," Art muttered and was asleep.

"Well," Red Hugh sighed, "if O'Byrne doesn't find us, at least the English won't, either."

"How so?"

Red Hugh answered with a look and O'Hara followed it.

Their three bodies, under the mantle, were already covered with a three-inch layer of snow.

CHAPTER SEVEN

ONLY WHEN THE ESCAPE was accomplished did The O'Neill inform the others. Then for two weeks following it was an agony of waiting. Once free of Dublin Castle the escapees were to rendezvous with O'Byrne, the firebrand of the Wicklow Mountains. But O'Byrne had been unable to locate the men, and it was feared that January in the mountains had claimed them.

"'Tis ironic," Deirdre lamented, "that with a score of wounds from sword, pike and lance, my Shane should fall victim to the snow."

Rory was unable to offer a word to bolster her spirits. He could only gaze in reverence as she stoically sat before the fire. In the weeks and months she had been his tutor, they had grown close. Like O'Hara and O'Neill he had grown to love her gentle ways, and couldn't help but compare the gentleness of Deirdre to the harshness of Ulster wives.

He had even joked with her that, as a final prize upon his return, he would carry off an English gentlewoman to share his bed in the wars to come.

In reply Deirdre had gently stroked his fine-featured face and smiled. "If an Englishwoman, or any woman, could turn your hate and lust for battle into a desire for a tranquil hearth, I would say there was hope for peace."

It was early February when news came. The loyal harper, Cormac, had ridden through the night to bring them the tale.

"Your brother, Red Hugh is safe and even now crosses the River Liffey bound for Donegal," he told Rory. "Your husband, The O'Hara, m'lady, sends his deepest love and will join you in less than three days' time.''

The details of the search and rescue were harrowing, and already balladeers were filling the glens and mountains with the tale.

A troop of O'Byrne's best, led by the harper, had set off from Glenmalure with ample food, ale and mead. Henry O'Neill they found at once, frozen. Hours later the remaining three were found, where Cormac had left them.

At first it was feared that all three were dead. Their bodies were completely covered by snow and they were discovered only because of the mound they made in the smooth blanket of white.

Only Art had succumbed. He was buried right there in the Wicklows, and the other two were secreted to a private house deep in the forest recesses. It was there that they had been recuperating.

With the weight of widowhood lifted from Deirdre's shoulders she resumed Rory's schooling. She cut his hair, fashioning the wild Irish glib hanging across his forehead into a proper English cut, and polished his English, Latin and French.

Then The O'Hara arrived, and Rory could see at once the love he and Deirdre shared. Shane was a short powerful man, with a gruff voice bellowing from a barrel chest and gentle hands and eyes when they came to rest on his lady.

From the day of Shane's stormy arrival, already surrounded by his trusted guards, his urraghs, and gnashing for battle, Rory saw less and less of Deirdre. Her absence made him realize how strong his attachment to her had become. But like the rebel he'd been raised, he cursed such a weakness and threw himself even harder into the preparations for London.

Maps were drawn so that he could easily find his way from the landing at Holyhead via either of the main roads to London. And even the maze of London itself was made somewhat clearer to him, so that with his own ingenuity he could make his way to Haskins House without assistance.

For The O'Neill this became important, because he discovered in his new ally's son a quick temper and a willingness to go for the sword before conversation. Were he thus to arrive in London, appearing as a bumpkin traveler, the fiery young Irishman might be forced to duel his way from Cripplegate to Holborn Road, where Haskins House was situated.

"Watch and be wary, lad, for thievery and roguery are everywhere in the countryside as well as in London Town. It would do us no good to have you run through or fall to a dag's bullet even before your arrival!"

At last the evening of his departure came, and with it Black Hugh O'Donnell arrived, rising from a sickbed to wish his son Godspeed.

They stood, The O'Neill and The O'Donnell, before the young man, each warning him again of the danger he faced should the English learn his true mission. Then, as one, they clasped him to their hulking frames.

"Farewell and Godspeed, lad." The O'Neill's voice was full of fire and steel. "Bring us a free Ireland!"

"Go with God, my son." His father's eyes were strangely misted.

Rory held his gaze for a long moment, then reached for his horse's reins.

"Rory."

He turned and saw Deirdre moving toward him from the door of the wattle. She put her small slender hand on his where it rested on the saddle as he prepared to mount.

"The next year will see changes in us all, if indeed we are all here to see it." There were tears in her eyes as she spoke, and the words choked in her throat.

Her sorrow affected him more than he dared to admit. She was barely two years his senior, but there was a beauty and calmness about her, a kindness and serenity that gave her maturity beyond her years.

In that moment he realized with relief the true nature of his affection for her. For him she had played the role of a tender mother, or the wise older sister he had never known. It was with this realization that he looked beyond Deirdre to O'Hara's face.

For the first time since the two had met, The O'Hara's features softened and he nodded at the younger man in understanding.

"Know that my prayers will all be for your safe return." Deirdre spoke softly.

Rory had started to reply, to calm her fears with his usual brashness, when she silenced him with a finger to the lips.

"No, let me have my little say. You are young and wild and know only the black and white of our lives here in the north. The deceits of London and its people are more devious than you will ever know. That will be the real danger you'll find. The self-servers and the ambition-seekers are your real enemies, for wars, intrigue, deception and treachery are conceived by the few and implemented on us all."

Here she lightly kissed him on both cheeks and placed his hands on the roundness of her full belly. "Should this child be a boy, he will be called Rory. And because of what you are about to do, perhaps he will one day help rule a free Ireland as Rory, The O'Hara."

Rory returned her kisses, then with a final wave, he

vaulted into the saddle. "And may your son have his mother's beauty and kindness, m'lady, so he will not have war as his only salvation."

Days later, with his own words still ringing in his ears, he landed at Holyhead and prepared for the ride to London.

His first purchase was a horse of the best quality he could find. His second, clothes that would mark him as a country gentleman on the road to London, a traveler of some means but no wealth. For this he chose a forest jacket faced with worsted and fastened with pewter buttons. He accepted the tailor's suggestion of fashionable breeches, but insisted on heavy stockings and hose along with a woolen riding cape to combat the evening's chill.

"Od's pity, sir, a word of advice. It's best you bear the evening's cold by an inn's warm fire, for the high roads are alive with cutthroats who would as soon rob ten men as one after the sun has set."

Rory had long since grown tired of such warnings from O'Neill. To hear them also from a humble tailor wearied him. "Then, sir, I'd say it's best you affix a sturdy sash to those breeches to hold my brace of pistols. And direct me to a fair leather merchant for a more serviceable belt and scabbard for dagger and sword. For they say it's five days' ride to London, but I plan on some use of the evening's hours to make it four."

Leaving at break of dawn the following morning, he rode true to his word into the late evening hours and spent the first night in Shrewsbury. The inn there he found charming and its widowed keeper a woman of wit and warmth. So much so that after a measure of sack and a hearty meal, a goodly portion of the hard edge of hate he'd had for all Englishmen since birth rounded itself off.

The next day he passed through Shropshire, and found his pace slowing as he admired the endless fertile fields and the thick forests made green by April rains. Then he remembered the forests of Ireland, and how they had been raped by the English so that his kinsmen's raiding parties would find no security in their darkness. This spurred him on to make Redditch shortly after nightfall.

It was there, even after the long and tiring ride through the countryside, that Rory's keen senses and sharp eye returned.

It was moonlight when he rode into the torchlit courtyard of the Inn of the Golden Boar.

"See to yer horse, sir?"

The ostler was a boy, no more than fifteen, but he had a hard and empty eye that looked more at Rory's traveling bag than at his horse.

"Have at him with a good rubdown and an ample bag of feed. I'll need him long before dawn's light." Rory stepped from the horse and proffered the reins. But just as he suspected, the boy showed more interest in his capcase, snatching it from the back of the saddle and hefting it in both hands.

"Five of the clock, sir?"

"Closer to four. . . and I'll take that."

The gnarled old man who escorted Rory to his room showed an equal interest in his belongings. He found two reasons to shift them to another part of the room as Rory fished a penny from his purse.

"Help with your things, sir?"

"Won't be necessary. . . here you are."

The old man pocketed the penny with such dexterity that Rory was sure he could retrieve its mates from his purse just as easily.

"Irish, ain't ya, sir?"

"Aye. English-Irish, from the Pale."

"Served in Ireland, I did. The Irish wars of Desmond was terrible things. Lost this eye, I did, and no pension does the government give an old soldier when he comes home."

Rory was too tired to listen to the old man's grief, but something in what he said sparked curiosity. "But you volunteered to fight for Queen and country."

"Nay, volunteer I didn't. I was pressed from an alehouse at closing, so sotted I didn't know 'twas the guard that took me!"

"Are there many like you in England?"

"Aye, an' mostly beggin' for their bread and board." He paused, eyeing Rory's purse. "But as you see, sir, I've a pride. I work for me meat."

Rory passed him another penny. "Then have a sack with your meat tonight."

"Oh, thank ya, thank ya, sir!"

"Now be off. It's sleep I need if I'm on the road before light."

He slept soundly and woke refreshed with his morning call. But over a light breakfast he again thought about the old man's words, and resolved first thing to inquire from Henry Haskins how many discontented veterans of Elizabeth's wars there were in England.

When the same beady-eyed young man came to announce that his horse was waiting, Rory was also reminded of the danger signals he had sensed the night before. Before entering the courtyard he removed his pistols from his bag. By the time he mounted they rested in his sash, loaded and primed and concealed by his heavy cloak.

"London, is it, sir?"

"Aye," Rory replied, staring down into the boy's vacant eyes.

"Then you'd best take the low road over the Cotswolds. It's left at the break. They say the rains have rutted the high road badly. Your horse could lose his footing in the dark."

"That I will," Rory smiled, throwing the boy a coin and reining around. "And thanks for the word."

"Farewell, sir," the boy called after him. "An' think nothing of it, for travelers is me business."

I would bet they are, Rory thought, smiling to himself as the sound of cobblestones beneath his horse's hooves shifted to gravel and then to the packed mud of the road.

An hour's ride found him at the fork, scanning with narrowed eyes what could be seen down both tracks in the dim moonlight. For as far as he could see, both roads were the same—ruts axle-deep from carts and carriages.

He mused, his mind churning over O'Neill's words, "Be wary, lad, English rogues are everywhere," and the boy's words, "You'd best take the low road. It's left at the break."

"Damned if an Irish lord should veer from an English cutpurse!"

Sliding one of the pistols from his sash, he settled it into a pocket in the cloak's lining and reined his horse left, down the low road.

Ten minutes later he rounded a sharp bend and found his way blocked by two riders, both in buckram, with wide-brimmed hats hiding the moonlight from their faces.

"Stand and show your hands, Irishman, for we'll have your capcase and purse!" The voice, hoarse with drink and with age, came from the larger of the two men. He was slightly to Rory's left. The other man held a pistol at eye level, and steadied with both hands and pointing directly at Rory's breast.

"And if I would fight rather than deliver?"

The man's laugh was raspy, with no amusement. "There'll be no fight. It's the gallows for robbery as well as murder on the high road. They would hang us whether me mate's bullet is splitting your gullet or not. So let's have it."

The explosion took both robbers by surprise. Rory barely smelled the mingled odor of powder and burned cloth as he kicked his horse forward, directly into the larger man's mount. The first man's body had scarcely touched the ground before it was joined by his mate.

Rory reined his horse short and reared him around, his sword already in his grip. To his surprise, moonlight glinted from dagger and short sword in his enemy's hands.

"Irishman, I believe ye 'ave killed me mate." The big man's hat had fallen off, revealing a thick mat of unruly black hair clotted with splotches of gray. His face was wide, the lips curled in a leering grin, and even with the dim moonlight Rory could see the webbing of broken veins in his cheeks and nose from too much sack.

"Aye, that I have, and you'll soon join him in hell."

The horse pitched forward from the shock of Rory's heels. At the same instant his sword descended in a cleaving arc toward the black-mopped head. But its only contact was steel on steel. Below his blade, Rory could see the x of dagger and short sword. And no matter the pressure he brought to bear, the other man's was greater.

Then the rogue's strength was matched by his agility. He loosed Rory's sword and deftly sidestepped its cut-

ting swath. At the same time the balls of his feet
became springs. He leaped high above the horse's
shoulder and curved his arm in a smooth arc that sent
hilt and hand against Rory's head in a crushing blow.

The young Irishman rolled in the dirt and rocked to
his feet, shaking the blood from his eyes. "You've ample quickness as well as strength for an old man."

"Aye, lad, you can tell your children...if you live to
make 'em...that you were bested by Ned Bull. Now
I'll have your purse!"

He charged like his namesake. Rory had little time to
do more than grasp his dagger with his free hand and
meet him head-on. Again the man was stone, an unyielding wall. Rory twisted aside, letting the man's
momentum carry him, stumbling, into the ditch beside
the road. With a howl he floundered out of sight.

In seconds Rory was at the edge, ready to dive after
him. There was no need. The big man came up the side
as fast as he'd gone down it, his powerful legs churning
the mud like a waterwheel.

They met again, and for the better part of a half hour
it was a grinding grunting battle, with no quarter given
and no end in sight. Rory was sure he had scored twice,
but the big man merely shrugged and dove for him
again.

At last they paused, paces apart, their backs to trees
and their chests heaving with pain from the lack of
breath.

"By me mother's blood, lad, you don't fight nor
shoot like an Irish farmer."

Rory was amazed that the man could speak. His own
lungs felt as if they had collapsed. He managed to gasp
a few more times without revealing his weariness and
then replied, "Have you held up so many Irish farmers
that you know their mettle, Ned Bull?"

"Nay, but I fought the Queen's wars at Armagh in the north, and the like in Munster."

"Do all good English soldiers turn to roguery?"

Ned Bull heaved himself upright and steadied his legs. Again the two short swords came chest high. "All that I know have. Well, let's to it again, lad. It's near dawn and a highwayman should find his hole before the light of day."

Rory tried, but couldn't find the strength to lift his arms. He found it equally hard to give up his purse and horse. More of O'Neill's wisdom rang in his mind: "Guile, lad, guile and wit. For you must survive at any cost; your corpse in an English ditch or your head on London Bridge won't give Ireland what she needs."

He let both dagger and sword slip to the ground and eased a hand beneath his cloak. "Our war is over, Ned Bull, and I'd like to let you live."

The black hair waved as the huge body shook with laughter. "Live, is it, lad? And how would you kill me with your steel on the ground?"

He lurched forward a step and halted as Rory withdrew the pistol from his cloak and leveled it at his chest.

"Kill me then."

"Nay. Stand, Ned Bull! For there's nothing I want more than your freedom to ply your trade." Rory pushed himself from the tree and retrieved his weapons. As he lurched toward his horse, he called over his shoulder. "Rob and kill all the Englishmen you want, Ned Bull. It will save me the trouble."

"You're a rebel!"

"That I am, just like yourself." He managed to pull himself into the saddle and reined around to face the big man, who now leaned again against the tree. "Tell me who tipped you off...was it the boy or the old man?''

"The old man. He marched with me in France and Ireland. A good soldier he was, but he only has the stomach to be a stall or a tipster now.''

"And him?'' Rory gestured toward the grotesquely sprawled body in the roadway.

"My brother.''

Rory let the shock register on his face. "I'm sorry.''

"Don't be. This way's better than the stretching of a rope. More gentlemanly.''

With a nod of agreement Rory turned his horse and galloped down the road.

He shook his head, and not to clear it. "These English,'' he muttered, "there's no consistency to them. Well, now, I've met the good and the bad of the countryside...let's see what London offers!''

CHAPTER EIGHT

RORY O'DONNELL HAD BARELY DISAPPEARED into the mists of the mountains bound for England's shores when his father, Black Hugh, seemed to fade before Deirdre's and O'Neill's eyes.

They both insisted that the old warrior be slipped into Dungannon Castle and nursed there.

He would have none of it.

"Nay, I've seen the raven and heard the howling of the dog. It is my time, and I know it. I'll be shrouded in Tyrconnell by the sea with my heir, Red Hugh, standing by my grave.''

So an escort was arranged. If O'Donnell was right in predicting his death, O'Neill wouldn't dare appear as one of the mourners. At that point in their plans it would be political disaster. Deirdre's laying in was imminent, so she too would stay at Dungannon. It fell to The O'Hara to deliver the dying O'Donnell to his son, Red Hugh.

It took three days to cross the ancient O'Donnell lands, and Black Hugh faded further with each hour. At last, near sunset of the third day, the little party reached the windswept wilds above Donegal Bay where Red Hugh was in hiding.

The elder O'Donnell insisted that he bestow the clan mantle on his son.

"Know ye now, lad," rasped the weakened old voice as the sea pounded the rocks below them, "that you are now The O'Donnell and Prince of Tyrconnell. Fight, and if you must, die for this birthright, for the land is all you have to give your sons. If the land is not yours to give, then your sons, your grandsons and your great-grandsons will naught have reason to stay. And my soul will burn in misery whether it reside in heaven or hell if there comes a time with no O'Donnell in Erin."

The son, so like his father in body, leaned his powerful frame forward. He accepted the mantle, kissed the old man's forehead, and stepped back to wait.

As he was born to Irish tradition, Black Hugh died; his soul exited the body in the wee hours before dawn.

"Saint Patrick judges him now," wailed the new chief. "Shroud him like a king and begin the keening!"

So saying, he shook the morning dampness from his flaming beard and hair and moved away from the bier to join The O'Hara.

The two men stood, tankards in hand, as the women swarmed over the corpse.

"God rest his soul," intoned The O'Hara.

"There'll be no rest for his soul, nor for ours, 'til

we're lords again in our own land," growled The O'Donnell.

And miles from the sea in Tyrone, Deirdre cried out with the first pain of birth as Rory O'Hara fought his way into the world.

CHAPTER NINE

RORY O'DONNELL ENTERED London through the Cripplegate arch in the old Roman wall and rode toward the Holborn-Cheapside road. He was barely inside the city wall when the stark differences between the countryside and the town rose to meet his eyes and assault his nostrils. The din of peddlers, hawkers, orange girls and yelling footmen and drivers trying to wend their carriages through the narrow streets had a numbing effect on his ears.

He paused and rose in the stirrups in order to view the city and obtain his bearings at the same time. Squat houses and shops were jammed together, forming the streets they bordered into a twisting maze that wound with no rhyme or reason from his position to the Thames.

The river itself was a wide clear ribbon of beauty, dotted with ships and swans. To his left was Tower Hill and the massive stone walls of the Tower itself. Sweeping his gaze to the far right he saw the noble houses of the Strand and the palace and grounds of Whitehall just beyond.

With this orientation he moved on through the streets. The deeper into the town he got, the more the aroma of the open sewers and the piles of garbage assailed his senses

So different, he thought, from the rolling green hills and flower-scented fresh air of Ireland, or even of the simple English countryside he had just ridden through.

He had heard plague rumors from travelers on the road and quickly saw that they were true. On many doors he saw the red crosses, and tacked to the lintels above them bills bearing the inscription Lord Have Mercy Upon Us.

At Cheapside he turned right and took his bearing on Newgate from St. Paul's.

Sounds overcame smells and bombarded his thoughts. His horse shied, barely missing a staggering man all in black.

"Rats or mice! Ha' ye any rats, mice, polecats or weasels? Or ha' ye any sows sick of the measles? I can kill them, and I can kill moles, and I can kill vermin that creepth up and creepth down and peepth into holes."

Rory spurred his horse around the rat catcher and breathed again as he pressed under Newgate arch and into the open country of High Holborn.

Could he stand living in such a place for the length of time that would be required? Yes, he could, he mused, for the senses could never compete with the spirit. And these sights, sounds, and smells could never touch his soul.

A short ride took him past the barrister Coke's house on his left and the sprawling grounds and opulence of Hatton House on his right. Just short of Chancery Lane he found himself facing the courtyard gate of Haskins House.

One ring of the bell brought a groom and the old knight himself. When Haskins realized who Rory was he received him warmly, embracing the young Irishman as if he were a son. The groom took his horse, and after freshening himself from the ride, Rory was sat right down to a sumptuous meal.

He quickly discovered that Deirdre's description of her father and his politics was accurate. He was a kindly old man who, like his daughter, desired nothing more than peace for all. And though he was English through and through, he was foremost a Catholic, with a strong desire to see a Catholic again on the throne. For years he had been rankled by Elizabeth Tudor's claims of fealty to the old religion prior to her coronation, and her seeming lack of any religion since.

Through the meal the Irishman's curiosity was as healthy as his appetite. He tried to steer the conversation away from Queen and court and along more pertinent lines. Haskins would have none of it, and a cautious look from Rory to his housekeeper as she bustled in and out serving the food told the younger man why.

At last the meal was finished. They retired to a tiny secluded study in an upper corner of the house, and Haskins's whole demeanor changed.

"I was close to Cecil during his allegiance to Catholic Mary. I retain that closeness now, for as far as the Cecils know, my leanings...like the wind...changed with theirs."

Rory leaned back and scrutinized the old man with a wary eye. Deirdre had answered few of his questions concerning her father.

"If he wishes you to know his reasons," she had said, "he'll tell you himself."

Would he?

"M'lord?"

"Aye?"

"Your leanings? Do they still shift with the wind? Forgive me for prying, but my head rests in your hands. And it is a curiosity, don't you think—a peer of Gloriana's realm with such views?''

"Ahh, a curious youth," replied the old man, adding a multitude of wrinkles to his face with a grimace that was half smile, half frown. "My daughter has told you little."

"Practically nothing beyond the manners of the court."

Haskins nodded, studying the wine he swirled in his glass a moment before rising and pacing the tiny room. His voice started in a whisper and rose to a quiet bellow as the story rolled from his lips.

"As a Catholic, a nationalist myself and a humane man I leaned naturally toward the Irish cause. My wife, an Irishwoman, urged me to volunteer during the early uprisings. I did, and was appalled at the butchery on both sides. But I was a coward and returned to England having accomplished nothing. You remember Campion?"

Rory thought for a moment. "Edmund Campion, the Jesuit martyr?"

"Martyr indeed. More the simple victim. He was a good and just man. A man who sought nothing but tolerance for his faith. He believed as much in Queen and realm as he did in God and faith.

"Thrice racked, he was tried on a trumped-up charge of conspiracy, and sentenced to Tyburn. Had they merely hung him it wouldn't have been so bad. But they hung a sign on him, put a feather in his hat and made a clown of him all the way out Holborn."

The old man paused there, visibly shaken, but continued before Rory could speak. "I stood close to the gallows, as did my son, Charles. They hung Campion and cut him down while he was still kicking. Two men held him while a third applied the knife. Do you know what they cut?"

"I know." Rory's voice was barely a whisper.

"Even then he was still alive, still screaming, as they tied the four horses. He was quiet only when fully quartered. Campion was my friend, as were the eight others who died that day, all like common thieves."

Haskins was at the window now, his knuckles white against the glass as he gazed across Holborn to the Tower.

"They hung his head on London Bridge. On that day both Charles and myself vowed to be Catholics until the day we died. Charles's day came five years after Campion's. Mercifully he was only beheaded. But his head is still up there, rotting with Edmund's and the rest."

Rory didn't look up as Haskins regained the chair across from him.

"Do you see now why an old man with few years left anyway will hold to his views?"

"I see." Again Rory kept his voice to a whisper.

"And there are more, lad, many more. When it's safe, you'll meet 'em."

"Aye, and methinks not just the aristocracy." Rory told him of his meeting on the high road and what Ned Bull had said.

"It's true. London, as well as the countryside, abounds with rogues and scoundrels—many of them bitter after service to the Queen. And the Jesuits and Puritans grow in numbers every day."

"If all those groups could be marshaled with the hope of a better lot and England's return to the Church...what would we have?"

Haskins grinned. "My son, we would have a civil war."

Their talk went on through the setting of the sun, and the old man pleaded weariness at last. Rory rose, opting for a stroll around the town.

"Beware of the hour," Haskins cautioned. "For to be abroad too late marks a man as a vagabond or rogue unless he can prove his business to the watch."

"And perhaps a rogue I'll want to be," Rory replied, smiling. "If I were to find men of Ned Bull's persuasion, where would I look?"

Haskins mentioned a house and two taverns that catered to London's gallants as well as to men and women of shady character and background, then bid his young guest good-night.

Again, upon reaching the street, the sounds and smells of teeming London met Rory full in the face. But as he walked, there were signs everywhere that the city was winding down for the day. Apprentices were busily resetting shutters, and moving stalls and the wares they contained back inside houses.

There were fewer pedestrians now, and more carts and coaches rattling through the streets, the prosperity of the sallow-faced merchants and goldsmiths inside them obvious by the fine gold chains they wore draped over their richly furred robes.

Rory stopped for a second to gaze off into the distance at London Bridge, his eyes slitted in order to find the midway point of the twenty arches. There, he knew, was the gatehouse tower and the spires that held the heads of English traitors and victims of political executions.

But his concentration was suddenly broken by a shouted warning from behind him. "By your leave... by your leave!"

Rory whirled around and saw a trio of gallants bearing down on him, shouldering other pedestrians out of

their way. Resplendent in silks, satins and jewels, they
swaggered with such pomposity that Rory was hard put
not to laugh.

Their leader was the gaudiest. His hair was powdered
and his pursed lips were so pink that Rory thought they
might be rouged.

As Rory watched him approach he remembered
Haskins's wrath when speaking of the young wastrels
of London: "They play at being gentlemen, but they
wear their lands on their back. And each must show his
mettle by besting the other in gaudy dress. Od's blood,
to count the fashions among our foppish young
gallants would be to number the stars in the heavens
and the fish in the sea!"

Suddenly the dandy was upon him. "By your leave,
sir!" A gloved hand brushed Rory, who instinctively
stepped aside. The men were past and entering a tavern
before the affront hit Rory's senses and anger flushed
the back of his neck.

He looked up at the creaking tavern sign swinging
above his head: The Bear and Ragged Staff. It was one
of the two taverns mentioned by Haskins as a haunt of
highwaymen and their ilk. With a smile he pushed open
the heavy oaken door and entered.

The main tavern room was all bustle and confusion,
the air heavy with the smoke of pipes—so much so that
Rory's eyes immediately began to water. How could
anyone enjoy such a vile habit that stained the air and
burned the eyes, he wondered.

Men were eating and drinking in small groups, while
drawers rushed to and fro, feverishly supplying them
with tankards of wine or ale. In a far corner the trio of
dandies had joined two more of their kind. All of them
posed and preened for each other, and for the large
parlor in general.

Rory found an empty stool at a table already occupied by two boisterous men. One was relating the background of two highwaymen who had been hanged at Tyburn that morning.

When he finished the other commented, "'Tis still a better way to die than from the lack of food on your table. I dunno what it's comin' to when an honest man can no longer make an honest livin'."

Taking advantage of the ale-loosened tongues, Rory interjected into the conversation, "And what forces an honest man like yourself to take to the high road?"

"Like myself?" said the man, gulping from his tankard and knitting his brows in thought. "When the fine lords desert their lands and come to London Town, the lands go neglected. And when there's no land for the likes of us to till, we must to London, too. Some of us find a trade that's honest...others take the easier way."

"It's the likes of them there," chimed in the second man, nodding his head toward the five fops standing in the corner. "They're the sons who own the land, and they should be workin' it instead of squanderin' it struttin' their fine feathers in the streets of London. Were they where they belong we'd be workin'...and half the thieves roamin' the high road would be back on the land!"

Mentally Rory added another group, farm workers, to his growing list of malcontents. But it was the London underground he wanted to hear about. He deftly shifted the conversation back in that direction and plied his table companions with another tankard of ale apiece.

They told him of Muggleston's house in Whitechapel, where the knaves in buckram lodged like kings, flaunting their ill-gotten wealth to the poor and en-

couraging many a youngster to follow in their footsteps. They relayed tales of graft in the prisons themselves; how thieves and strumpets could get a night's
lodging in Newgate or Ludgate prisons by paying
certain gaolers. This way they could escape the
watch, which was constantly scouring the streets for
them.

Rory listened raptly and silently to all that they told
him, storing each detail in his mind for later use. At the
end of an hour he would gladly have heard more, but
the tavern was emptying.

He accompanied the two men outside, where he
thanked them for the good conversation and the evening's comradery. They were about to go their separate
ways when the door burst open. The same young man
who had brushed Rory aside before now appeared on
the step.

"By your leave, sir!" came the command, full of impudence. And, again, the gloved hand came up to
brush Rory's shoulder.

But this time the Irishman expected it. He caught the
lacy cuff at the man's wrist in a firm grip and smiled
when a look of pain creased the almost delicate
features.

"Once an evening is enough. This time it's by *your*
leave, sir." He motioned his arm in a sweeping arc. "I
believe there's room around me."

"I walk around no man, sir."

Rory released his wrist and stepped back. "Then
you'll meet me head-on." Light from the torches by the
tavern door glinted on the sword in Rory's hand.

By now Rory's two companions were long gone into
the night, and his opponent's friends filled the tavern
doorway. At the sight of Rory's sword the whole group
broke into laughter.

"A sword! And a flat-bladed sword at that!" said one, howling with laughter.

"Give him a taste of the culture we've gleaned from the French and the Italians, James!" said a second, his laughter, too, coming in peals.

"Let's hope you can laugh as well at your friend's blood," Rory hissed. "Draw your blade, peacock!"

"The term, sir, is *en garde*." His voice was suddenly an icy chill. Gone was the amusement, and the tiny lisp Rory had earlier detected. "Perhaps, bumpkin, you would prefer to flee rather than witness my blade. You see, I am James Blake."

"I don't give a damn if you're the Archbishop of Canterbury. Defend yourself."

"Very well, bumpkin, you're about to learn that your sword and dagger are old-fashioned and as nothing against a rapier."

His hand moved like lightning. There was a swish of steel through the air and Rory felt a tug at each shoulder. He looked down to find wide slashes in his jacket and blood already seeping through the material.

Before he regained his senses there was another sharp jab of pain at his left wrist, and his dagger clattered to the street.

"Your sword, bumpkin. At least attempt to defend yourself."

With a growl of anger deep in his throat Rory threw himself at his attacker. But the man wasn't there. He had leaped to the side, and his blade whipped across Rory's back, once more rending his jacket and leaving a gaping gash in his skin.

Twice more Rory tried to break through his opponent's defenses and failed. He soon realized that the lighter, quicker weapon in Blake's hand was all offense—an offense his heavier, bulkier sword had no defense against.

He was about to swallow his pride, to cut and run, when a loud tramping sound came from the end of the street.

"James, it's the watch!" called one of the men in the doorway before he broke into a run.

"You are a lucky man, bumpkin, for I've no time to finish you. Your corpse isn't worth a night in m'lord mayor's gaol."

And then he, too, was gone. Rory stood alone in the torchlight as around the corner came the watch, five strong, carrying lanterns and armed with muskets.

"Who goes there?"

Rory gave no reply. He turned and bolted toward the darkness in the opposite direction. Like James Blake, he wanted no part of a night in gaol—especially his first night in London.

Several times he tripped in the inky darkness. And each time he regained his feet he realized that the watch, aided by their lanterns, had gained on him. Here and there light gleamed through cracks in doors and shutters, but most of the houses were already steeped in darkness.

Suddenly he rounded a corner and nearly tumbled beneath the hooves and wheels of an oncoming carriage. With pain grating his shoulders and back, he managed to twist and roll under the coach's frame just as it passed.

Quickly, with more pain gripping his bleeding shoulders, he managed to secure a hold on the luggage boot and hoist himself up onto the vehicle's rear platform, where he crouched unseen.

At a warning from the watch the driver ground the cumbersome vehicle to a halt.

"Who goes there?"

"A lady passes with her worldly goods to Holborn Street, Hatton House."

"Is the lady married?" came the constable's reply.

"Nay, but naught of the streets is she. For she's highborn, a Cecil, and would wed on the morrow."

"Pass then, and good night to you and your mistress."

The words Holborn Street and Hatton House jarred Rory's memory. If his mind wasn't too befogged, he was sure that Hatton House was but a stone's throw from Haskins House. If he could hang on to the jolting, rocking coach long enough, he would have a safe ride home.

But could he hold on?

Another hundred yards told him no. Already he could feel numbness in his arms from the effects of his wounds. There was only one solution.

Holding to the boot with his left hand, he strained his right around the side of the coach and groped about until his fingers closed over the handle. With a secure hold there, he slid his left hand up to the filigree that decorated the top.

As luck would have it, the coachman made a swerving turn just as he opened the door and vaulted inside. The motion served to bring the interior of the coach out to meet him, and he found himself sprawled across the most beautiful woman he had ever seen.

Her eyes rounded and her mouth flew open. The scream was quickly cut to a gasp by his bloody hand.

"M'lady, I'm only a weary traveler and at your service. I ask nothing but the favor of your scarf and kerchief to stem the tide of these pesky wounds—along with a short ride in the direction you now travel."

In reply she managed to open her mouth and clamp

down with all the force in her jaws on the soft heel of his hand.

He yelped in pain and yanked his hand away, leaving a sheet of skin between her white teeth. She spat, sputtered, and scoured her mouth and chin with the sleeve of her dress.

"You've ruined my gown, you fool!"

"For that I am in your debt—and I'd like to be for the scarf, too."

"Here, take it!" She ripped the silk from her throat and threw it at him. "I thought your breed only plied the game on the high roads."

Rory awkwardly stuffed the scarf under his shirt and jacket. "If you imply that I'm a highwayman, m'lady, you're wrong." Here he lifted his head and flashed her a wide smile. "In truth, I'm a simple country lad come to London to learn the art of French swordsmanship."

She suddenly giggled. "I take it this was your first lesson."

His eyebrows curled into a sculptured frown, but the smile remained on his lips. "And very nearly my last." Gently he tugged the material from his left shoulder to inspect the damage.

It was worse than the right and still bleeding.

"Grief, you are wounded. You're bleeding to death!"

"Not quite," Rory chuckled, "but your kerchief would help." She placed it in his hand, but he was unable to secure it over the wound.

"Here, let me."

She slid closer to him in the already narrow coach and folded the kerchief carefully over the bleeding gash. Her face was directly below his, and the heady odor of her perfume filled his nostrils just as the sight of her full breasts rising above her bodice filled his mind with sudden desire. They rose and fell, as her breathing deepened, to remind him of how long it had been since he had lain with a woman.

"There," she said, leaning back. "But I don't know if that will get you to where you're going."

"It will have to." His eyes riveted upon her face, etching every hollow and beautiful curve into his memory. "You will be the most beautiful bride London has ever seen."

"How did you...?" Her hands rose to the dark juncture of her breasts.

"I heard your coachman tell the watch."

"I...I'm to become Lady Hatton, wife to Sir William."

"That's a pity."

Her chin came up as her eyes flashed. "How dare you? A rogue in the night—"

Again his hand silenced her words, but this time gently. "I dare anything, m'lady, because I have nothing to lose. If memory serves me right, William Hatton is aging and somewhat infirm. Your beauty and the fire in your eyes should seek a man with passion to match it."

The coach stopped. A quick glance told him they were at the gate of Hatton House. "I'll leave you now...and many thanks."

"A fig for your thanks. Just begone!"

He was at the door and turned at her words. He looked full at her face shining in the flickering light of the coach's two candles, and again her proud beauty stirred his senses.

His thoughts were echoed in her eyes. He moved closer to her and she gasped. She could no longer see his face, but the explosive tension in his body was like waves of heat radiating between them.

She could feel it seeping into the skin of her forearms. She could feel a tightness in her chest as it soaked through her bodice and prickled the skin of her breasts. Without realizing it she tilted her mouth up toward his.

The instant desire his lips aroused in her made her heart beat faster. Her body felt as a ship must feel, lurching forward when a full wind hits its sails.

And then the coachman was clamoring back to his seat and Rory was out the door.

"Wait. Who are you?"

His even teeth gleamed in the moonlight as he smiled up at her. "Your rogue of the night, m'lady, who from this day forth does your bidding."

And then he was gone.

The coach jolted ahead, and Elizabeth Cecil squeezed her arms tightly around her shuddering sides.

CHAPTER TEN

SHANE O'HARA SLID THE linen coverlet from his nude body and stifled a yawn as he eased himself from the bed. His arm reached out, found the wall, and steadied him until his legs found blood and the dizziness left his eyes.

Too many battles and too many old wounds, he thought, and soon there would be more.

On stiffened legs he tottered to the window slit and looked out. It was a gray and misty night. The meadows below the castle walls were veiled in shadows. Here and there he could see cookfires made of good Irish peat burning against the dampness.

He felt a chill and only then realized he was naked. Absently he ran his hands across his powerful body.

There was a scar from armpit to buttock on his right side from a British pike. A hollow in his left thigh from a British ball. Beneath the black and matted hair on his massive chest, four—no, five puckered lines of flesh. More than one dagger in the hand of a rival clansman had failed to find his heart.

And there were other scars, on his back, his neck, his legs. . .but he didn't count them. Instead he turned his eyes to his wife's angelic face in the bed. Even in sleep there was that tiny frown between Deirdre's wide-set eyes.

He had caused that frown when they had argued the night before, and she had carried it to bed. Was she reliving their angry words even now in her sleep?

"There will never be peace," she had raged. "Once the English are driven out and the lords of Ireland rule their own land, the clans will again turn on each other."

"It's the way."

"It's not the way. It's stupidity. You're all fools."

"Woman, if you were an Irish wife—"

"I'm your wife and sorry for it. Shane, I've accepted seeing you die, but let it be for a reason other than love of battle."

Then he had hit her and had stormed through the castle like a raging bear. In the scullery he'd spied a wench. He half carried, half dragged her to the stable. There on a thin bed of straw he fell between her quivering thighs and took her more like a beast than a man.

The wench had screamed at his entrance and then whined at his rutting. Slowly the whine turned into an urging groan, until her response was matching his attack. It went on and on, one convulsion on the heels of another, until they were both spent and gasping.

Shane was immediately sorry; for both the girl and for Deirdre.

Afterward he had sought solace in drink until the wee hours, and then he'd staggered to bed. Gently he had shaken his wife. No response. Was she mousing? Hiding sightless and soundless in her own tiny corner?

"It's sorry I am, lass, and that's the truth of it. For there is a difference between us no matter how highborn we've both been. The way you've lived has been genteel. Even now in my chill Irish castle you do it with a natural elegance. Ye try to make this pile of stone an English manor house, and I thank ye for it. But under the tapestry, the curtains and the fancy lace, me sweet love, is still the stone. And I'm afeared the man is as much made of stone as his house. Once the foundations are strongly laid, no amount of fancy trappings will change 'em.

"But for you, I'll try, I truly will. Of all the women I've lain with, I've loved only you."

But she had been sleeping. He'd been speaking as if to an empty bed.

Now, in the morning chill, Shane shook his head. He was sober again, his head clear enough to know that those tender words, made maudlin from drink, wouldn't return.

Perhaps that was good.

He covered his nakedness with a mantle and stirred the peat in the hearth until he could feel the waves of heat permeate the room. He paused by the crib and looked down at his son, Rory, the tanist O'Hara.

Again a chill rippled his skin and found the marrow in his bones. But this time it wasn t caused by the silent wind through the slitted window. O'Hara was thinking as a father. He was looking ahead to the years of tomorrows that would face the soft little bundle now sleeping so innocently in a world of change.

The tiny eyelids fluttered, then opened. The pupils, jet black and already as piercing as his sire's, took in and accepted the huge bulk looming above them. They rolled around his small, confined, safe world and closed again. The puckered pink lips twisted in a tiny smile and Rory O'Hara slept.

"Aye, she speaks the truth, little one," O'Hara hushed in a raspy whisper. "I live for war, for it's all I know. Mayhap God and yer sainted mother will school you for more."

He turned and negotiated the narrow stone steps from the upper chamber out onto the ramparts of Ballylee. It was a good if forbidding fortress, with its back to the sea and its twelve-foot-thick running wall facing the land and any attack that would come. O'Hara knew and loved every stone, every turret, every room and gate in Ballylee.

He walked along the curtain wall and climbed more narrow steps to one of the four towers that overlooked the sea. It was near daybreak and the sounds of the new day beginning wafted up from the lower bailey to vie with the roar of the crashing breakers pounding the rocks.

Roused by the stewards from their cellar pallets, servants were already lighting fires in the kitchens and the great hall. On the landward towers across the courtyard he could hear his men-at-arms clambering toward the walls to relieve the night watch.

O'Hara padded across the tower's stones on his bare feet and looked down. Both the upper and lower courtyards hummed with activity. Grooms were just finishing the stables' sweep. A few were already feeding the horses. His smith's forge was burning brighter by the second in preparation for the day's work. Other servants hurriedly emptied basins and chamberpots before they brought in fresh scented rushes for the floors. The laundress was already soaking sheets and clothes in caustic soda. Soon she and her helpers would be pounding and rinsing them before they were spread on the walls to dry in the morning sun. Smells of mutton, beef and game rose from the cook's great iron cauldron over the bailey fires to fill O'Hara's nostrils.

It was a picture of peaceful domestic serenity, and one that O'Hara had enjoyed on hundreds of mornings.

But it contrasted sharply with the thoughts that filled his mind and the images that flickered across his eyes as he raised his head. His gaze traveled over the turrets of the great tower to the hills and forests just blossoming with false dawn.

Looking through the trees and early morning mists O'Hara imagined he could see the English, pikes on their shoulders, marching six abreast toward Ballylee. He could hear the thud of their feet and the jarring rhythm of their marching drums.

And then the sound of cannon and musket filled the air, joining the screams of dying men. Bluecoats fell, dotting the green hills with English bodies.

Siege cannons suddenly appeared at the forest edge belching flame and smoke. His own warriors began toppling from Ballylee's walls. They fell, trailing limbs and blood behind them, into the moat below.

And then it was over and the bluecoats were retreating into the trees.

O'Hara blinked, and a second assault started. Only this time the advancing soldiers weren't English. They were Irish, come to siege Ballylee.

A shuffling sound behind him shattered the image.

He blinked again and there was only mist among the trees.

But the thought remained, the doubt.

Was she right? If he, The O'Neill, wild Red Hugh, the Maguires, the O'Byrnes, and all the others beat the English, what then? Would they all turn against each other? Would the clan wars start all over again?

He didn't turn. He knew who stood behind him. The fresh sea breeze had carried her sweet scent until it filled the air around his head.

"We've an hour before rising time, husband."

He paid no attention.

"I've a stone in my heart," he said, his voice barely a whisper above the wind.

"How so? And why?" She moved to his side, and her scent became powerful enough to dizzy his head.

"Ye speak the truth and I'm sad that I can do nothing for it. I've taken ye out of yer world and made you accept mine. And ye've done it fine. Much more than were it the other way, for The O'Hara would be a misfit in yers."

She moved under his arm and then through the break in his mantle. Gently but firmly she pressed her naked body against his until he could feel her warmth through the thin chemise. "I know, my husband, but it's the choice I made and the one I want. Know that the harsh words I've said this night were out of love, and out of fear for that love."

"I do." He nodded until his beard grazed her neck and his face found the thick richness of her dark hair. "And know you that for all my faults, all my wild nature and all my thirst for the sound of battle, I live 'til the day I die to love but one woman."

She turned, and in so doing her chemise parted until he could feel the soft silk of her skin. Her heavy breasts spread across his chest and her hips came forward to meet his.

"We have an hour before rising, my love," she said, gently tugging his shaggy head down until their lips met.

The kiss sent a shudder through both their bodies. She moved against him, the softness between her thighs caressing him with a plea and then a demand. O'Hara's reaction was instantaneous. He tried but he couldn't will it away. She was smiling when he lifted his face from hers.

"But. . ." he sputtered, "'tis too soon. Yerself said—"

Her lips silenced his with another kiss. And then she came up on her toes. Her body moved over his knowingly, womanly. Her lips slid from his across his cheek to his ear.

"Come bed me, husband, there are other ways."

CHAPTER ELEVEN

"I, ELIZABETH, TAKE THEE, William, to be my wedded husband, to have and to hold from this day forward, for better or for worse, for richer or for poorer, in sickness and in health; to be. . .to be. . . ."

"Yes, my child. . .go on!"

Elizabeth Cecil cast a furtive glance to her right, toward the man she was taking as her husband. At one time Sir William Hatton had probably been a fine figure of a man. Now there were heavy streaks of gray in his spiked beard and veined lines caused by drink in his nose and flushed cheeks. He was already short, but added weight made him now slump shorter until the top of his head was but an inch or two above hers.

"My child. . .to be. . . ."

Four, perhaps five seconds passed. For Elizabeth it seemed an eternity before she could get on with the next, the hardest part, of the speech. The part that was most galling for her to say and mean.

Her knees had been water when she had stepped from the carriage less than a half hour before: so much so that her father and her Uncle Robert had been forced to assist her into the procession.

Then she was moving forward, beautiful, she knew, in flowing white that was richly embroidered with silver. The murmured sighs of approval had bolstered her by the time her twelve maids of honor had gathered the train of her wedding smock. With a deep breath she was able to shake the thick mane of her waist-length auburn hair into place and follow the minstrels and vase bearer up the steps to her waiting groom.

It was the voice of an unseen wag whispering to his companion halfway to the church door that made ice of the water in her knees and momentarily brought her up short.

"Sir William will have a task with that piece. Methinks it's an honest man who marries early, but a wise one who marries not at all."

The flush in her cheeks reddened and she was about to whirl toward them when the second wag's retort stilled her movement. "Aye, but methinks marriages these days are rather made for fornication than for constancy, don't you agree? Not so much in hope of issue as for gain of money."

The reply came with a low leering chuckle. "More for lucre than for love!"

Damn them, damn them all, Elizabeth had thought,

barely restraining an impulse to turn and shout at the two speakers as well as the crowd, "What else is a woman to do? It is the contract, not the marriage, that the man makes important. What else can the woman do but follow? A sad plight it is that only *man's* two lusts, power and loins, be satisfied by the marriage ceremony!"

But she remained silent, gathered her wits around her and found resolve. Away went the fears and doubts that had been filling her mind like a spring-fed well. She moved forward again, chin high, putting as much flash and arrogance in her eyes as she could muster.

But now she must say the words in front of God and man, and she found them choking in her throat.

At her shoulder the groom's brow had become exceedingly damp, and he was coughing into his kerchief. The assemblage was tittering and the bishop was scowling as he spoke. "The words, my child, are—"

"I remember." Elizabeth was slightly surprised at the strength in her voice. "To be bonnie and buxom, in bed and at board, till death do us depart, if Holy Church it will ordain; and thereto I plight thee my troth."

Elizabeth was sure that the audible sigh to her left came from Robert Cecil.

She heard little of the ring ceremony, and didn't realize it was over until she looked down and saw the tiny gold hands around her finger clasping a heart-shaped diamond.

The bishop's final words came with a rush, "May you be blessed by the Lord who made the universe out of nothing," and Elizabeth Cecil realized that she was now Lady Hatton.

But before the full impact of her new title became

clear, she found herself being whisked through the crowd to a waiting carriage.

The procession along the Strand back to Hatton House for the traditional feasting and dancing passed like a haze before her eyes. She and her new husband were joined in the carriage by her mother, beaming proudly, her father, frowning slightly, and her Uncle Robert.

Her grandfather, Lord Burghley, had declined to attend, pleading gout and other vestiges of ill health. Elizabeth shrewdly guessed that the elder Cecil had remained in the background for an alternate reason. His absence would give Robert room to politic among the wedding's powerful guests.

Already her uncle was at work on Sir William, aligning Hatton with the Cecils against Essex in the upcoming Parliament.

"Henry of France, m'lord, would bankrupt us with his wars," Robert was saying. "And as for the Irish, they remain in disarray, hardly taking time from their slaughter of each other to threaten the throne. Even now a brother to the rebel O'Donnell, one called Rory, is in London to pledge allegiance in return for safe harbor against his brother, Red Hugh."

Sir William's voice was a rasping reply, already partially slurred with wine. "I've but lately come to the house, Robert. What would you have me do in Lords?"

"Bow to the Queen for monies she must have," Robert replied, "but waylay Essex's insistence of future wars. I will do the same in Commons to his new toady, our cousin, Bacon."

"I fear for these days," Hatton moaned, fighting his own lethargy. "Our lady the Queen does and has always wanted from her Parliaments pounds without palaver. Her early Parliaments yielded gracefully, her middle Parliaments yielded angrily, and her Parliaments now are near revolt. Methinks I would to Bath for the waters during their sessions and be well out of it.''

Vaguely Elizabeth had heard their words, particularly the last spoken by her husband. They stirred her. *Verily,* she thought, *spoken by a true coward.*

Then her eyes met Robert's, and between them passed the true meaning of her marriage. Silently her uncle was telling her that it was her duty as a Cecil to change her husband's mind.

Her reply was vocal and as vehemently intense as his stare. ''A fig on this, uncle,'' she sputtered. ''Save talk of your wars, both foreign and private, for another day. For I would enjoy the feasting, the masquers, the dancing and all the customs of bride ale without the cares of government spoiling my day.''

Elizabeth didn't add that the longer the feasting and drinking lasted, the further away lay the time to be bedded by her new groom.

''As you wish, m'lady,'' Robert replied, handing his niece from the carriage and moving off into the milling opulence of the guests.

Befitting the Hatton wealth and the Cecil status, the wedding feast was a sumptuous occasion. Unlike Robert, the wedding guests inside the walls and gates of Hatton House viewed the event as a brief respite from the cares of government. Laughing chattering ladies, splendidly gowned in azure blues and soft purples, their throats, fingers and hair resplendent with glittering gems, flirted coquettishly with equally well-attired gallants.

And outside, the poor lined the gates, knowing that in honor of the occasion they would be fed with the leavings when the lords' and ladies' appetites were finally sated.

And leavings there were bound to be, for the grounds were littered with tables piled shoulder high with boiled pike, capon, and turkey chicks. Great silver platters of wild duck, swan and venison required three servants to carry them. Above a pit two whole kids turned with pudding in their bellies.

To wash down the food and to temper the rich sauces of musk, saffron and ambergris, there were equally great amounts of drink. A hand never had to reach far to quench a thirsty throat with beer, ale, or a variety of wines that included sack, alicant, claret, Rhenish, muscadine and charneco.

While the men drank and gorged, the women entered the great hall of Hatton House to gossip and to admire the bride's gifts.

And there was much to admire. A set of dainty spurs set with diamonds; a perfume bottle made of one entire agate emblazoned with rich quartz. Silver and gold plate dazzled the eye, and rich velvets and satins for future gowns titillated the touch. Pieces of furniture and vanity accoutrements had been assembled for the bride's boudoir.

The Queen, though not in attendance, had sent silver dishes curiously enameled with Spanish characters. The ladies, upon touching these pieces, nodded to themselves at the less than extravagant value but said nothing. It was accepted that the Queen reckoned her smile and blessing far more valuable than any gift that would deplete her coffers.

On the last table, before the spoked and arched doorway leading into the depths of the house, lay the gift of gifts, Sir William's bridal present to the new Lady Hatton.

Gleaming white, with many hues where it rested against a cloth of deep red velvet, was a neck-to-bosom chain of sparkling diamonds. As its complement were two very rich pendant diamonds for her ears, as well as a tiara also set with diamonds and mounted with two huge and perfect pearls.

Standing there alone for a moment, Elizabeth allowed herself to gasp and tremble at the gift's great worth. Slowly a smile creased her crimson lips as the enormity of her new title and station came fully home to her at last.

She let her eyes drift up to the high ceiling and paneled walls, then into the hall beyond, where the recently remodeled staircase curved in sweeping grandeur to the upper three floors. It was all a monument to Sir Christopher's good taste, his great wealth, and an unknown woodcarver's artistry.

She couldn't help but realize that the jewels before her, and Hatton House around her, were only a part of her husband's wealth. There were also the vast gardens and acres surrounding the palatial estate at Holdenby in Northamptonshire. The farmlands in the south of England brought in thousands of pounds a year. And who could fathom how much revenue would be gained from the recently acquired twelve thousand acres of Munster land in Ireland once the Irish question was settled?

Suddenly nothing else mattered. In her heart of hearts, Elizabeth knew that she was consciously allowing herself to be dictated to by her love of magnificent and expensive things.

As if to confirm the fact, her hands reached out to caress the diamonds while her mind played with one phrase over and over: "And now it's mine. It's all mine."

IN THE GARDENS Robert Cecil moved deftly from one gathering to another, testing the temper and leanings of each group and individual.

To some, such as the brothers Anthony and Francis Bacon, he was courteous and civil but not overly friendly. It had become all too obvious in recent days that both brothers were seeking a furtherance of their fortunes by moving into the Essex camp.

"What say you, Francis?"

"Rob—Rob—Robert, I—must, uh, speak to you on a matter of grave importance."

Robert Cecil knew which matter all too well. Bacon sought the office of the solicitor general, as a stepping stone to further influence at court. As did his father, Robert thought Bacon too young and too inexperienced for the post.

And as for a place at court, the young barrister lacked the dash as well as the well-turned leg of a courtier. His viperish eyes had a darting quality, and he was too eager, with a tendency to stutter.

No, Robert thought, gently making his excuses and moving away, if there had been any hope for Bacon, he had lost it with what he thought to be his secret overtures to Essex.

To allow Bacon a clear understanding of his position, Robert moved directly to the side of Edward Coke, Francis's rival for office.

To Coke, Robert was warm and friendly, even though the man was a bit too garrulous and miserly for Robert's taste. The younger Cecil knew that Coke's appointment as solicitor general was imminent for many reasons. Besides his overtures of loyalty to the Cecils, his expertise in the law was legend. As for his financial acumen in such high office, Coke had proved himself able by taking his inheritance—coupled with the dowry of thirty thousand pounds from his wife Bridget—and improving it many times over.

Edward Coke was well on his way to becoming a rich man, which in such strenuous times was indeed no mean feat.

When Coke, through verbal parry and thrust, had satisfied himself that an elevated position would soon be his, he reverted to his boorish side.

"A waste this, Robert, a sad waste of coin."

"What is this you speak of?"

"Such extravagant weddings, of course," growled the prematurely wrinkled face. "The vast amounts expended on weddings, sack and clothing are but frippery. I sometimes think I should drop the law in lieu of dyeing feathers for fops and gallants, like the Puritans in the Blackfriars mall. Look! Look you there at that popinjay!"

Robert halfheartedly followed Coke's pointing finger through the revelers. "That's a young gallant only recently put in my father's employ, one James Blake by name."

Robert didn't add that for all of Blake's foppish ways and bawdy reputation, he was also one of the cleverest spies in Lord Burghley's vast network.

"A popinjay," the barrister groused. "Why, the ruff at his neck alone would cost four pounds!"

Robert couldn't suppress a smile. "It is rather large, isn't it?"

"Large? Bah, I should pay so much to make my head look as though it were on a platter!"

"I pray you, Edward, don't let our gracious Queen hear you rail so, for if she has her way in the style of ruffs, our young courtiers will take to the air in days of high wind!"

After a short interval of listening to dull theories on

law, Robert excused himself to Coke and moved across the lawn toward the source of the barrister's wrath. One of the men Robert wanted most to talk to this day was James Blake.

ELIZABETH'S HEAD WAS SPINNING as she exited from the great hall, down the wide stone steps to the lawns. She was sure that nothing could spoil her day now, that no one could mar her sudden resolve to accept and enjoy her lot.

She was wrong.

Her slippered foot had barely touched the soft grass when she came face to face with the smiling, handsome man she had come to call her "rogue of the night."

"Congratulations, m'lady," he said, making her an awkward knee and brushing his lips across her hand. "As a bride you are even more beautiful. But then the wedding day has yet to turn into night."

Impudence, she bridled, but with a raw charm that stabbed at her breast and threatened to take her breath away. In the bright sunlight, away from the carriage's dark shadows, he was even more handsome than she remembered. His dark, almost olive face was beardless, with only a suggestion of mustache following the insolent curve of his upper lip.

Abruptly she found her tongue. "I didn't know the gates had been thrown open to the rabble."

The full lips pulled even further from his even white teeth and, oddly, the wide smile added impact to the already strong jaw. "Aye, m'lady, rabble I am in the company of so much wealth." His keen eye roamed quickly over the guests and returned to meet hers. "And beauty."

Again Elizabeth flushed as his bold eye seemed to

peel the wedding gown from her flesh and leave her
body naked to his gaze.

"I find you a puzzle, sir," she said, reading all too
well the desire in his dark eyes. "From whence do you
come? I detect an accent in your speech."

"Ireland. From Ulster," he replied, "to plead my
case of a faithless father and a rebel brother to the
Queen. I am Rory, exiled son of Black Hugh O'Donnell."

Elizabeth took a step backward, a sudden intake of
breath causing her breasts to rise above her bodice. Her
hands came up as if to disguise the swell. The flustered
movement brought a flicker of amusement to his eyes.

"Alas, m'lady, I can see that you subscribe to the
tale that all Irishmen are savages."

Again he took her hand, and this time his lips
lingered much longer than necessary. Over his broad
shoulders Elizabeth could see other women casting
glances their way and tittering behind their fans.

Or were they just looking at him?

As he released her hand and came back to his full
height, Elizabeth found herself making comparisons.
Rory O'Donnell, in tight-fitting breeches that hugged
his lean muscular legs and a fitted waistcoat that ac-
cented his broad shoulders and chest, cut a fine figure,
one that few of her fellow Englishmen present could
match.

"Oh, bumpkin, I see you've found yourself a tailor!
His cut is slightly out of style, but presentable."

They both whirled around. Elizabeth didn't know
the gaudily dressed, angular young man who had approached them, but O'Donnell obviously did.

"Ah, my 'by your leave' opponent. Good day, sir."
Rory attempted an awkward bow. "Rory O'Donnell."

"James Blake, at your service." Blake's bow was

smoothly effected, taking in Elizabeth as well as Rory.
"'Tis a pity you're unarmed; we could resume our
frolic."

Rory chuckled and turned to Elizabeth. "The gentleman has lately become my fencing master," he
quipped, and returned his attention to the young dandy. "I look forward to my next lesson, but at a later
time. 'Twould be a pity to mar the lady's wedding with
the sight of English blood."

Blake got the inference and laughed himself. "For a
bumpkin you have wit. Another day it will be.
M'lady."

With another perfectly executed leg to Elizabeth,
Blake moved away through the small circle that had accumulated around them in hopes of excitement.

"I take it that Master Blake was the cause of your
flight last evening."

"That he was," Rory replied, all humor gone from
his face as he watched the retreating figure. His eyes
were cold, with a vacant quality that chilled Elizabeth
when he looked again into hers. And his voice when he
spoke had an edge of steel in its tone. "Odd it is, but I
have a strange foreboding that one day I will indeed
have to kill that man."

A second chill rippled up Elizabeth's spine, and a
slight dizziness attacked her brain. She had never seen
James Blake prior to this day, but she had heard of
him. His prowess with a rapier was legend, and it was
said the victims of its sharp point couldn't be counted
on the fingers of two hands.

Suddenly the thought of this wild young Irishman's handsome face contorted in death, his broad
breast impaled by James Blake's skill, made her want
to cry out.

"Beware," she said. "James Blake has the reputation of being a cunning and devious man, and his skill as a swordsman knows no match.''

Again the humor flashed in his eyes and the lips curved into a sardonic smile. "I take heart at m'lady's fears for my safety." Here his voice lowered to a scant whisper that found only her ears. "But still your fears, for your rogue of the night plans on a long life of service to his lady."

The reference to himself with her own phrase shocked her. It brought her downcast eyes up in a flash of surprise. But before she could reply, Elizabeth found herself surrounded by chattering handmaidens.

There was no mistaking their intent. It was time to bed the bride and groom. Elizabeth shuddered at the thought. Only minutes before she had reconciled herself to being Lady Hatton, bolstered by the wealth and power her new station would give her in London and at court.

But that was before she had again come into contact with her dashing young rogue of the night.

As she was led back up the stairs and into the house, she cast a quick glance over her shoulder at the man she now knew as Rory O'Donnell.

Their eyes met, and Elizabeth felt her spirits lift. She was sure that in his gaze she detected sadness. She could only hope that his sadness stemmed from her situation, that she was off to another man.

And then she knew it for a fact. Just before she was whisked completely out of sight, his lips moved, forming the words, "Someday."

And several paces away, Robert Cecil didn't fail to detect the mood exchanged between his newlywed niece and the Irishman. But instead of a frown, it brought a slight smile to his taciturn face.

Keeping track of O'Donnell and his activities in London might be an easy matter after all.

"Sir Robert."

He didn't turn. He recognized the voice of James Blake at his shoulder. "Aye?"

"He's well baited and, I should think, primed."

Robert nodded and the smile spread. The meaning of Blake's words had already been discussed between them. Unknown to Rory O'Donnell, his presence in London had been known long before Lord Haskins had divulged it. The swordplay between him and Blake had been carefully orchestrated by Robert Cecil, as had today's chance meeting.

If Haskins lied and his daughter's husband, The O'Hara, were not true to the crown, if Rory hadn't entered England as an exile but as a spy, what better way to be rid of him than in a duel? It wouldn't be the first time James Blake's ready sword proved politically expedient.

While Robert Cecil's eyes followed his every move, Rory threaded his way through the crowd, oblivious to the admiring glances of women, both young and old. At last he found Lord Haskins and allowed the old man to draw him aside into the privacy of an arbor.

"I've talked with Cecil."

"And?"

"He will arrange an audience with his father and, if your news has weight, he will present you to the Queen. He seems elated that you are in London."

Rory chuckled. "And well he should. After my brother's escape, I will prove a ready hostage should Hugh pursue his rebel ways."

"All the more reason you must convince Burghley that your only mission here is to usurp your brother and claim Tyrconnell for yourself out of loyalty to England." Here Haskins cast his eyes downward and ground the toe of a booted foot into the grass. "And that should prove easier now."

Rory sensed something amiss in the old man's tone. "How so?"

"I've got word only an hour ago that O'Neill is hard pressed to hold your brother, Red Hugh, from war."

Rory shrugged. "My father controls my brother's wildness."

"No longer," Haskins said, clamping a wrinkled hand on the younger man's shoulder. "Black Hugh lies buried these seven days at Donegal Castle."

And while Rory made his way through the hedges to mourn in private, Elizabeth, Lady Hatton, lay like a stone in her bed.

She really hadn't known what to expect...pain, pleasure, ecstasy, degradation. She just knew that she had expected something, and found nothing. Now, lying on her back, her breasts rising and falling gently with her breathing, she found herself frustrated and committing the sin of lascivious thought.

With her husband wheezing beside her and only a dull ache between her naked thighs, she found herself thinking of Rory O'Donnell.

Sir William rolled from the bed and gazed down at her naked body. His small eyes took in the firm swell of her breasts, jutting impudently ceilingward even though she lay on her back. They moved down across the gentle rise of her belly to her full thighs and the fine taper of her barely parted legs.

"You are beautiful, my dear, and the answer to an old man's dream."

"Bonnie in bed and at board, m'lord. I am now your

wife." Elizabeth was surprised at the calmness in her voice.

"That you are," he wheezed, pulling on his breeches. "And a fine one you'll be."

She rolled her head around to face him, making her eyes avoid his paunch and the sunken whiteness of his chest.

"Just remember, m'lord, that there will be more to this marriage than the mating of two pairs of naked legs."

CHAPTER TWELVE

RORY SAT JUST OUTSIDE the range of flickering candlelight. Carefully he listened and weighed every word uttered by Haskins and the other two men seated at the table before him.

They were in a tiny, poorly ventilated room under the chamber stairs in an Old Street house just behind Golden Lane. The house belonged to a wizened old lady named Mistress Rigby, and the secret room had harbored many a Jesuit martyr on his flight from the Queen's justice.

Rory had already learned much from the three men's talk. The Catholic underground was much larger than he had suspected. The number of Catholic exiles outside the country and of sympathizers inside were legion.

Clandestine directives to Catholic insurrectionists flowed daily into England from France, Spain and the low countries. In Brussels a council of state, made up of well-known English gentlemen exiled from their native land, met each day to argue over plans to restore Catholicism to England.

Two of the most powerful revolutionaries were Henry Garnet and Robert Southwell, the men at the table with Haskins.

Much of the current debate between Haskins, Southwell and Garnet centered on the movement's activities. It interested Rory little. He cared not a fig for Catholicism in England. His only interest was in the freedom of Ireland.

There came a lull in the debate and Robert Southwell turned to Rory. Of the two men, Southwell was more somberly dressed in a plain, dark broadcloth doublet with black breeches of a like material.

"Your ideas have merit, Master O'Donnell, but Henry would balk at allying our cause with the rebel Irish and the English ruffians of the road."

Rory thought for a moment and turned his gaze on Henry Garnet. Unlike Southwell, Garnet dressed the times. At his throat he wore an expensive ruff, and his doublet was satin, wrought with golden roses embroidered on a field of blue. His Spanish-leather shoes were slashed to better display the white silk stockings beneath them. Even his satin breeches were padded out with bran to make him more a dandy, or more imposing.

Rory though it was probably the latter.

Rory's voice, when he spoke to Garnet, was low and toneless. "Would Master Garnet be implying that only gentlemen of rank should be allowed the faith? Is he saying that the Jesuit cause is solely an Englishman's province?"

The wiry little man with dark piercing eyes was ready with a quick answer. "Nay, Irishman, but the Pope himself has withheld aid from you Irish rebels. Why then should we join our faith to your cause?"

"Because we all have the same faith!" Haskins sputtered. "And neither the intolerance nor the stupidity of the Pope can deter me from my faith!"

"Sacrilege!" Garnet hissed.

"Gentlemen, gentlemen," Southwell murmured, lightly slapping the table with his palm. "Let us converse as thoughtful men rather than as howling dogs." Again he turned to Rory. "There *is* merit to your idea of a minor rebellion created by the poor and the outcasts. If nothing else, because there are so many of them. I am of a mind for tolerance only. Let the Queen keep her throne, but let there be two faiths side by side in England."

Rory knew that this was the point where Garnet and Southwell differed. Southwell would have peaceful toleration, while Henry Garnet would settle for nothing less than the Queen's head and a Catholic king upon the throne.

Rory cared little which happened, and told them so. "I want nothing more than unrest in England to buy time for Ireland. To do that I'll need your help. You have avenues for moving messages, means of obtaining seditious pamphlets and other propaganda, and contacts in high places for information."

"And in return," Southwell mused, "you'll give us an army from the streets."

"A rabble," Garnet muttered.

"A rabble perhaps," Rory replied, "but numbers you don't have now."

"A moment." Southwell rose. He and Garnet moved to a corner and spoke in low tones.

Haskins leaned closer to Rory and whispered, "Beware of Garnet. He would have us all in Ludgate or the Tower."

"I know. Southwell seems a man of reason as well as compassion. He will see the advantage of many tiny thorns in the Queen's side instead of a sword at her neck."

"Think you that you can amass this rabble army?"

Rory smiled at the old man. "I don't really know."

The two men returned to the table. Garnet was scowling, his dark eyes beaming dislike at Rory. Southwell's lips had curved into a faint smile.

Rory knew they had a bargain.

IN THE WEEKS FOLLOWING HER WEDDING, Elizabeth quickly discovered that marriage, particularly to Sir William, was more palatable than she had expected.

With a huge staff and practically unlimited funds, she found it easy to run Hatton House. Sir William's demands on her time, both in and out of bed, diminished with each passing week. As the summer wore on he spent more time away from London at Bath. Elizabeth accompanied him the first few times, but soon grew bored of the place and the company. To her delight, Sir William didn't object.

Elizabeth was elated with her freedom and enjoyed it to the fullest. She quickly made friends near her own age in society and at court. Days were spent in the vast open country that spread northward behind Hatton House. There were orchards and sheepfolds but few hedgerows, so one could ride like the wind to the baying of the hounds.

Sir William paid little or no attention to her extravagances, so she indulged. She rode well, and bought horses and hounds in the same random fashion that she commissioned new clothes. Her wardrobe grew apace with her growing reputation as a London hostess. She entertained lavishly, and still Sir William complained only of his gout and his other aches while paying her bills without a murmur.

And on the afternoons she wasn't riding with a favorite hawk on her wrist, there was always a witty group assembled for bear-baiting or the theater. This latter was frequent, because all of London was thrilling to the genius of Henslowe's new protégé at the Rose, one Will Shakespeare.

Evenings were spent in lavish suppers and clever conversation at Hatton House. Elizabeth felt no guilt at this, for she deemed herself a good and diligent wife. Her husband's friends of state were entertained with private feasts and banquets as sumptuous as any she gave the young gallants and ladies who flocked to the hospitality of Hatton House when Sir William was away.

And true to her marriage vow, Elizabeth remained bonnie in bed as well as at board. Not once did she deny Sir William his conjugal rights when his heavy tread would sound in the hall and his rasping voice would inquire of her mood.

Her mood was always one of acceptance, and never once did she complain of his method or his quickness. Indeed, she thought little of it, steeling herself to stifle or remove the passion that lay like a dormant volcano in her breast.

Rarely did she allow herself an unfaithful thought. This even when handsome young gallants were more than open in their admiration of her beauty, and their propositions were barely veiled.

The only times that this proved untrue were the times of chance meeting with Rory O'Donnell.

With the close proximity of Hatton House to Haskins House, it was inevitable that they would see each other on the street in passing. But Elizabeth soon realized that these meetings were more than chance. Each time she would quit the house for the country, for shopping, or for a day gossiping at Whitehall, the Irishman would appear.

Her coach would barely reach the Strand before she would look out to see his darkly sardonic face smiling at her. Quickly she would look away to stop the flutter in her breast. But not before she saw the insolent desire flashing in his dark eyes.

All through the day the memory of his face, his tall lithe body and those daring eyes would unnerve her. Over and over she told herself, *I am married. I am the titled wife of a nobleman. This is preposterous,* until by day's end she had convinced herself that the strange beating of her heart was mere foolishness. He was no different, he meant no more to her, than the foppish gallants who daily paid her court.

But on her return there he would be, again to dash her resolve.

It was even worse at the theater, sitting in her box and enjoying the admiring stares from the nobles in boxes around her and from the gallants in the pit below. Then in the sea of faces she would find his; smiling, always smiling, with his white teeth gleaming and his dark eyes asking.

He seemed to be everywhere, a lone rider in the distance on a hunt, a face among faces along the Strand when she boated on the Thames, a broad back across a room during the galas at Hampton or Whitehall.

Everywhere, like a genie or an Irish fairy come to haunt her.

Often she found herself daydreaming, envisioning herself in his arms with her face tilted up, her lips meeting his. She could feel his strong thighs meld to hers as his arms pulled her closer until her breasts ached against his chest.

Once in the early morning hours she awakened shaking in a pool of perspiration. It was the result of a dream, a dream that remained all too clear.

She was under a tree somewhere in the country. Rory was there. He took her in his arms and brought her body flush to his. Wrapped in the vise of his arms, she surrendered willingly to his kiss. His lips were hot, demanding, and Elizabeth felt her senses stir as never before.

She felt the throb of his heart against hers, and then his hand was trailing fire along her throat and down to her breasts. He loosened the stays of her bodice until her breasts spilled into his waiting eager hands. His touch sent jolts of desire through her body and swelled her veins with need.

Gently, deftly, he removed her dress and then her chemise. Her naked body in the moonlight radiated a lust she'd never known as he laid her in the grass. Her stomach muscles rippled wildly as his velvet hand caressed and then parted her legs.

She felt his bare flesh as his body covered hers. And then her mind rebelled at her body's surrender. She began thrashing wildly beneath him, beating his broad chest with her small fists and closing her legs to deny his entrance.

It was then that she awoke in a cold sweat, her arms pressed tightly across her heaving breasts, her knees locked painfully together.

A cool breeze wafted from an open window and she made for it. Near nude she stood in the opening, her breasts rising and falling in the thin gown as she inhaled deeply of the fresh night air.

A movement below by the stone wall skirting the gardens of Haskins House arrested her gaze.

She peered down, following the figure's stealthy movement through the garden. A burglar? It must be so. Why else would such stealth be required, and why else make an exit over the garden wall as opposed to the open gate in the front leading to Holborn?

Then the figure leaped, gained a handhold, and mounted the wall.

It was he, tall in the moonlight, silhouetted against the darkness. His cloak was thrown back, and the ruffles of his white shirt were parted, baring his chest.

He looked up and saw her, and the ever present slash of a smile spread across his dark face. The tips of his fingers came to his lips and then reached forward, throwing an insolent kiss to the window. The lips moved, silently forming words she didn't have to hear to know.

"Someday...someday...someday."

"No, no, no, no!" she moaned aloud, whirling from the window and throwing herself on the bed.

But as she wept into her arms, she knew that the power he had over her was gaining strength. Her body was already willing and her conscience was receding like a fading tide.

Deep in her breast she knew that someday would surely come.

CHAPTER THIRTEEN

RORY WATCHED ELIZABETH'S FIGURE bolt from the window and sighed with a feeling of relief and guilt. Relief that she hadn't lingered long enough to see that he wasn't just taking the air, and guilt because he was using her.

Since the day of the wedding he knew he was being watched. It had been practically impossible to roam the town at will, and the meetings at Mistress Rigby's with Southwell had become increasingly more difficult to arrange.

Hence, he had needed a diversion. And what better one could he find than assuming the role of a love-struck gallant pining after a newly married woman?

It had worked. After weeks of doing nothing but follow the new Lady Hatton's every move, those watching him had become bored with the game. Their vigilance had dwindled, allowing him to sneak away from Haskins House in the evenings. Almost nightly he had visited the taverns in Cheapside, or in Bankside across the Thames in Southwark.

In the taverns and ale houses he had watched and listened as he rubbed shoulders with footpads, prostitutes, beggars, and often murderers.

He had discovered that indeed half the thieves and cutthroats in London were ex-soldiers, unhappy with their lot and open to any suggestions of how to make it better. The love and adoration they had showered on their good Queen Bess during the early years of her reign had now soured as poverty and hunger spread like the plague through the lower classes.

Rory had also visited The Ship Tavern at Lincoln's Inn Fields in Holborn, and other Catholic gathering places. He saw for himself how strong the Jesuit cause was growing.

Across the Channel their holy war had been taken into the enemy camp. English forces under Vere were winning the day, but slowly. Holland's Protestants were still under siege enough to be an expensive thorn. And there was always the chance, however slim, that the Jesuits would win in Normandy. Should that happen, England herself would be exposed to Catholic invasion and conversion.

With a failing treasury and constantly escalating wars abroad, Whitehall would be hard put to handle a peasant insurrection at home. The instigation of such a rebellion was Rory's purpose, and if successful, it might allow victory for Irish insurgence.

Rory jumped from the wall and made his way far out into the moonlit meadows before shifting direction toward the dusty path that would take him around the vast estate of Hatton House. Once there he crossed Holborn Road in the shadows and proceeded down Chtrunceler Lane toward the Strand and the river.

He was at Temple Bar, near the Fleet Street Gate, when he rounded a corner and practically ran into the watch.

"Stand ho!"

A lantern was raised in his face. Behind the chief watchman Rory could see two men armed with brown bills and axes.

"Whar ye bound at such an hour?"

Rory shrugged.

"Are ye deaf, man? Or mute?"

It wasn't the first time that he had been stopped by the watch on one of his nightly forays. He had learned how to evade questioning.

"Qu'est-ce que cela signifie? Je ne comprends pas," he said, his brow furrowed in confusion.

"What's that he's talkin'?"

"He's a bleedin' foreigner," the chief watchman replied, "a Froggy. Be on with ye, man, and watch fer yer throat!"

Rory didn't move and continued to stare uncomprehendingly. At last the other man stepped aside and motioned Rory on with a wave.

"Merci, merci. Bonsoir!"

The watch moved off in the opposite direction. Rory

could hear their words as he passed the Fleet Street Gate and made for the river.

"The devil and a cutpurse take him, it'll be one less Froggy we'll have to kill when the time comes!"

It was only minutes before he was spotted by a boat.

"A wherry, sar?"

"Aye." Rory gathered his cloak and descended the stairs.

"Where be ye headed, sar?"

"Bankside," Rory replied, climbing into the tiny boat. He pulled his long black cloak tighter around him and settled into the cushioned aft seat.

The wherryboat heeled over and caught the current at an angle toward midstream. In the darkness, through the light mist, Rory could see the bobbing lights of other boats, and beyond them the twenty arches and the covered right-of-way of London Bridge, barely illuminated against the night sky.

"At the bridge landing, sar?" the wherryman asked, dipping his oars and pulling hard to reach midstream. Under his red hat the wherryman had a patch over his right eye. His left was like a beacon in the lantern light, taking in the cut of Rory's clothes and the style of his boots.

"Nay, closer by the Clink, this side of the bridge. The Winchester landing will do."

"The Clink it is, sar."

"Aye."

A long grunt-filled pause and then a loud cackle from the wherryman's lips. "Would ye be after a piece of Winchester geese this evenin', sar?"

The oarsman's face was broad, like his shoulders where they strained in the canvas overshirt. The upper muscles in his arms were huge from his trade. Like his arms, his hands were large and powerful, heavily calloused from the oars. They were hands that could snap a man's neck in seconds, and probably had.

Rory shifted further into the cloak and fingered the blade in his boot. "That's not of your business, wherryman."

"Oh, no offense, sar. It's jest that ye have the looks of a gentleman, ye do. An' gentlemens usually prefer the linen-liftin' tribe in Cheapside, they do. The whores there are more buxom and they has less pox, they do!"

Rory took a different tack. "A gentleman I may be, wherryman, but my purse dictates Bankside."

The good eye blinked and lost interest as the powerful arms applied speed and pressure to the oars. Little chance to lift a full purse from this one.

Rory retired back into his own thoughts.

Again using Lady Hatton's movements as daytime cover for his own, he had found that the royal fleet, even the Queen's flagship *The Ark Royal*, was in sad disrepair from lack of funds. At balls and banquets he had followed Elizabeth's every move as if she were the sole reason for his attendance—but his ears were constantly alert.

He found out that the feud for royal favor between Essex and the Cecils was escalating. With the help of the Bacon brothers the Queen's on-again, off-again favorite had established his own network of spies. A careless word from an Essex confidante had given Rory an intelligence coup.

Anthony Standen had been chased out of England to Spain. Caring more for gold than for his faith, Master Standen had taken advantage of his position as a religious refugee to gather information at the Spanish court. Among the facts he gleaned were the names of Irishmen visiting Spain, all of which he reported back to Essex in London.

A swift cryptic message was sent from Rory to O'Neill, and Master Standen mysteriously disappeared in Madrid.

Overall, Rory was pleased with what he had accomplished during his months in London. But there were moments when guilt brought him up short.

The cause of his uneasiness was Elizabeth, Lady Hatton.

As he hounded her every move, he couldn't forget the warmth of her lips during that first meeting in her carriage. He could close his eyes and still see the swell of her firm breasts as she had cleansed his wound. He had kept the scarf, and many evenings since then he had lain awake, gently rubbing its silken texture across his cheek and inhaling the sweet scent.

Often in contemplation he had quarreled with himself over his motives. Had he chosen her as his ruse because of her status? Since she was a married woman he could moon over her from afar and there was no chance for involvement.

Or was there?

Lately he had sensed a yearning, a vulnerability in her glance when it met his. At first she had barely looked at him, but now her gaze lingered longer and longer.

And more and more Rory found himself reaching out to her with his eyes, returning the desire he thought he detected in hers. His concentration on his work would falter as he studied her many moods, listened to her lilting laugh, and watched the graceful movements of her full-figured body.

Despite her modish full skirts he could imagine the line of a hip, the curve of a cheek, the smoothness of a thigh, the soft dampness of her secret places.

During these times he had often become embarrass-

ingly aroused. Even the tips of his fingers would tingle
with a desire to caress the molded flesh of her bosom
where it rose and fell seductively above her bodice.

Merely lust, he told himself.

Since arriving in London he had imposed upon
himself a rein of celibacy, and it was beginning to take
its toll. Since his youth Rory had amply sampled the
sweets of Donegal milkmaids, serving wenches, and
even a few distant cousins. That kind of regularity,
suddenly denied, fired temptation.

And temptation there was aplenty, from one of the
Queen's handmaidens at Whitehall, to a few bored
country wives, to a buxom serving wench at Haskins
House. All in one way or another had offered the handsome young Irishman their charms.

The temptation was great, but none was so great as
Lady Hatton herself. Rory couldn't help but wonder,
as the tiny boat passed close to the cacophony of London Bridge, what he would do if that lady ever made
the offer.

"The Clink, sar!"

Rory gave the wherryman a few coppers and stepped
from the boat.

At wharftop he passed two idlers who eyed his
clothes much the same way as the wherryman had. Just
beyond them he paused and glanced over his shoulder.

The boatman's one good eye looked up and then
quickly away, but not before Rory had caught a shake
of the head he had given the two idlers.

Two less footpads to worry me, he mused, turning
his back on the river.

Across the cobbled stones of Bankside the light from
the wharf's torches barely pierced the maze of tiny
alleys and streets leading into Southwark. Using the
Rose Theatre and the building housing the bearbaiting

pit beyond it as landmarks, he took a deep breath and plunged into the labyrinth.

"Take a fancy, dearie? Naught but a few pence. C'mon now, dearie, let's feel what ye got!"

A hand brushed Rory's groin. He slapped it away and looked down into the old whore's toothless, crimson grin. Even in his agitated state of celibacy she was no temptation.

He shrugged her away and moved on through the narrow winding streets. His boots echoed loudly on the stones, joining the muted sounds of voices in dark doorways and occasional raucous laughter from an open tavern window.

He had never crossed to Southwark in the daytime, but he could imagine its scurry and bustle. With the sun above, these streets would be clogged with hackneys, pedestrians and vendors; all excitement, noise and confusion.

But at night it was eerie, with only tiny pools of light spilling from taverns or the shuttered windows of living quarters in the upper stories.

He passed few people; now and then a tipsy gentleman was preceded by a linkboy with his lantern aloft. "Make way, make way there! An armed gentleman passes!"

A few footpads in search of victims, an occasional whore smelling of sack as she breathed her invitation, and the ever present goldfinders carrying their tubs of night soil to the Thames to be dumped made up the nighttime population.

At an intersection of many streets, he paused, again taking his bearings from the top of the Rose.

"A copper, sar...a few coppers fer an auld so'jer...."

"Be off!" he said, then he caught a glint of steel in the beggar's hand.

"I'd have more than yer coppers, sar, since ya don't care to help an old man."

Rory looked down at him in disgust. Filthy rags barely covered the old man's scrawny body, and his hand shook with palsy as he brought the dagger up.

Rory ducked sideways. The blade missed his belly by a foot. He flattened his hand against the scrawny chest and shoved, sending the frail figure sprawling across the stones.

"Leave off, you old fool, lest you make me gut you with your own blade." Shrugging into his cloak, Rory hurried on.

Behind him the old man threw a final, futile jibe. "I charge you, in the Queen's name to kiss my tail!"

As it had on many of his nightly excursions, the filth and poverty of London disgusted Rory. At least the green countryside of his Ireland was clean and the poor still tried to scratch an honest living from the land. They had not yet been reduced to the level of animal survival that he saw here. And, God help him, they never would be.

Carefully he maneuvered his way past piles of horse droppings that the goldfinders hadn't found yet. A few minutes later he spotted the small swinging sign he sought: The Hound and Hare.

Stepping inside, Rory blinked at the sudden glare of lantern light as well as the haze of smoke that filled the room. If, as Haskins often said, the Germans sought to bring England to her knees with their beer, Rory guessed that her own native son, Raleigh, would do it quicker with tobacco.

The center of the room was occupied by a few doxies and some bleary-eyed, sullen men sitting around two long wooden tables with benches attached. A mongrel beneath one of the tables raised his head and growled, as if he sensed the newcomer didn't belong.

Rory moved forward. The dog growled again and rose up on its haunches. One of the women kicked it soundly in the side.

"Here now, scud, whar's yer bloody manners?" The dog flopped back to its belly with a whine and the doxy rolled her red-rimmed eyes up at Rory. "What can I get ya, sar?"

She folded her arms under her breasts and leaned forward until they spilled from her bodice. Rory eyed the darkness of her nipples. A tiny twinge of desire passed through his loins, but it faded quickly when he looked up at her smallpox-disfigured face and matted hair.

"A tankard. . .sack," he said, "back there!"

He made his way around the large tables to a smaller one at the rear. As he passed the curtained booths along one wall he heard the ripple of cards and the clink of dice.

The curtains of the last booth were open. A merchant gentleman, better dressed than the other customers in a ruff and a suit of good broadcloth with lace at the sleeves, was loudly extolling the virtues of the plump doxy sitting across from him.

Rory could see why. This one had gone a step further than her sister at the long table. Her bodice was unfastened to her waist and pulled wide. Both her breasts rested on the table, where the gentleman was liberally sprinkling them with wine from a tankard at his elbow. As he moved on by and sat at a table with his back to the wall, Rory could guess the man's intent.

He couldn't help comparing the nudity he'd just seen in an English tavern to the innocent nudity in an Irish booley. *And they call us savages,* he thought.

A tankard thudded to the table. "Will there be any-thing else, sar?" The doxy's smile revealed blackened teeth.

"Not unless you're Annie."

The smile disappeared and she straightened up to eye him warily. "Annie, is it? That's not me name. How do ye know Annie?"

"I don't. But we both have the same friend. It's him I'm here to meet." He reached up and dropped a coin into the hollow between her breasts.

She rubbed it down to the sash around her belly and, still eyeing him coldly, stalked away. He watched her totter up a rickety staircase along the wall opposite the booths, and with his eyes followed her course along a narrow overhang until she disappeared through a door.

The tankard was half empty when she reappeared with a slip of a girl. They both started down the steps, but the girl stopped halfway. Even from a distance Rory could see that she was more child than woman, with elfin features and a nearly flat bodice.

Her eyes were vacant, two hollows made darker by the shadows in which she stood. She stared at him for a full minute, then with a slight movement of her head she turned and walked back up the stairs.

Rory stood up, walked across the room and made his way up the stairs.

"I'm Annie. If you're the one, then you'll have the note I sent."

"I do."

"I'll have a look at it."

Rory produced the slip of paper he'd received from a youthful messenger that morning at Haskins House.

Satisfied, she nodded and pointed at a door. "Can't be too careful, you know, with the Queen's men and the watch an' all. In there!'' She moved around him and went down the stairs.

Rory opened the door and stepped into a small dimly lit room.

The man he had been trying to find for two months sat at a table in its center, ripping meat from a huge leg of mutton.

"Ah, my Irishman!" he roared. "Shut the door and sit down, laddie!"

Rory shut the door and sat in the only vacant chair.

"Now," came the booming voice again, "what in Christ's blood makes you want to see Ned Bull so much that you'd risk a neck-stretching by asking about me in every tavern in London?"

CHAPTER FOURTEEN

"WINE, James?"

"Thank you, Sir Robert."

Robert Cecil chose a decanter of port from the sideboard and poured Blake a glass. He knew the man's tastes ran to the exotic wines from across the Channel. Such wines were harder to come by and therefore, to a man like James Blake, more desirable.

"Is our Irish aristocrat to bed?" Cecil asked, passing the glass.

"Aye...and there's been no change in the past week," Blake replied, raising his glass to Robert and then sipping the aperitif with relish. "Ahh, excellent."

Robert smiled. "I know your tastes, James." Robert knew more than James Blake's tastes. He knew that Blake had committed murder in France, Spain and the Netherlands, and more than once on English soil.

Usually this was done under the guise of a duel. But if the victim couldn't be baited into a duel, Blake had no compunctions about outright assassination.

Much of Robert's success, like his father's, stemmed from his ability to weigh men's souls and recognize a weakness. Blake's weakness was ambition.

Unlike Robert himself, who made his own ambition a strength, James Blake pursued his from frustration and let it eat at him until it warped his every thought and action. He sought by any means at hand to take what he considered his rightful place as a peer in an aristocracy that shunned him.

He had been born to a titled father, but the clandestine marriage was outside the law. His parents were married in a private home, without benefit of clergy or witness.

When his mother died during his birth, his father had remarried. The new wife bore two sons, and soon after that her husband died. With his death, Blake's step-mother claimed the inheritance for her own offspring and used the courts to prove the first marriage illegal. As a result of her efforts young Blake was declared a bastard, with no right to lands or title.

His blind desire to correct this injustice had made him a ruthless man, one who would seek any avenue to regain his title. Such a man made a perfect pawn for those who could use him to further their own ends.

"Methinks our fears may be unfounded, Sir Robert. O'Donnell appears to be what he seems: an Irish aristocrat in exile, pursuing the Queen's favor and a dalliance or two while he waits it."

Robert nodded. "And is his object still my niece?"

"It would seem so."

Robert detected a slight change of tone in the other man's voice, and he hadn't missed the momentary cloud that passed over James's aristocratic features. Robert had surmised the reason for this weeks before.

Because of O'Donnell's open interest in Elizabeth, Robert had made it simpler for Blake to watch the Irishman by providing his entrée into Hatton House. Elizabeth had accepted Blake as she had the other gallants who fawned more over her skirts than what they hid.

She had never dreamed that the notorious James Blake was any different from the rest. It hadn't entered her head that there could be anything more than harmless flirtation in the man's intent.

Robert had assumed the same, until a few weeks before. Then, slowly, it came to him that James Blake had evidently caught the same disease as Rory O'Donnell; they were both desirous of Elizabeth. Whether it was for love or lust Robert wasn't sure, but for his purposes, it didn't matter.

Blake's interest in Elizabeth gave him one more hold over this volatile, dangerous man, and another reason for the swordsman to apply his art if the need arose.

Blake was speaking again. "I think the good fellows I employ with m'Lord Burghley's coin would be better put spying on Jesuits or the Frenchmen who stream in and out of the city."

"Perhaps. But the winds of war in France are clearer to the eye, and the lines of division open to scrutiny. The same with Spain. Not so with the Irish devils.

"O'Donnell's brother, Red Hugh, now preaches open rebellion from his Ulster lair. Lord Deputy Fitzwilliams, who has replaced Perrot, as you know, summons O'Neill to Dublin almost weekly to question him about the rumors of clan unification."

"O'Neill smells of traitor to me. What says he to Fitzwilliams?"

Robert sipped his wine thoughtfully and continued as if speaking to himself. "He fawns and pleads his fealty to the crown with a golden tongue. Methinks that beneath those words he would lick the Queen's hand while removing the rings from her fingers. He claims that O'Hara and the Maguires remain neutral. Only the hothead, O'Donnell, continues to tweak our noses."

"If that be true," Blake mused, "I can see where the O'Donnell in England could be used to equalize the O'Donnell in Ireland. But is it necessary? The odds have it that after a skirmish or two the fools will go back to killing each other."

Robert shook his head and began to pace. The old injury to his back and his leg began to throb as if to warn him of a weather change. He heeded it, for his aches and pains often warned him of a change in political fortunes, too.

"I don't think so...no, not this time. My nose tells me there's more to Red Hugh O'Donnell's rhetoric than revenge for his years in Dublin Castle."

He stopped in front of Blake and rolled the ruby liquid around in his glass.

"As for necessity, my dear James, you tell me. What figures do your vagabond turncoat spies in the Ulster countryside give you on the clans?"

Blake thought for a long moment before lifting his eyes to meet Robert's. "Should the clans come together—O'Donnell, O'Hara, the Maguires *and* O'Neill—their strength would number upward to fifteen thousand foot and near four thousand horse."

"And there's our answer," Robert sighed, adding a humorless chuckle. "Though our countrymen still rejoice these four years and more over our defeat of Philip's Armada, the war with Spain goes on and the treasury sinks. Add to that the Netherlands and

France, and the Queen's purse breeds moths instead of gold."

He paused, shivering slightly in his cambric shirt before continuing. "Methinks if there's rebellion in Ireland we could field no more than four thousand foot and horse combined. It would, I think, be a short war, and at its end the Irish would be running Ireland again."

James Blake dropped his eyes to the crystal goblet in his hand. Part of the fee for his services had been a grant of five thousand acres of prime land in the second Munster plantation after Desmond's final defeat in the south.

Income from that land could let him live like a gentleman for the rest of his days. If all went well he might even secure a title through it.

And James Blake's plans for the future didn't stop there. Sir William Hatton's twelve thousand acres in Munster abutted his. Sir William Hatton was a gout-ridden old man with few years left. His widow would bring wealth as well as beauty to her second marriage.

Blake already intended to be the groom in that second marriage.

But all would be lost if Ireland was lost. No, that couldn't happen. It couldn't happen, and he, James Blake, would make certain it didn't. If he had to he would kill both O'Donnells as well as Hugh O'Neill to make sure of it.

"Damn the bloody Irish!" he hissed, his fingers applying enough pressure to shatter the goblet in his hand.

"James," Robert said, "damned if you haven't wined your breeches."

"And cut my hand," Blake said in disgust.

"Why, so you have. But no bother...it's not your sword hand."

NED BULL stuffed the last bit of meat from the mutton leg into his mouth and washed it down with sack. With his eyes on Rory he strained the powerful muscles in his forearms and snapped the bone in half. Noisily he sucked the marrow as he spoke. "How do ye find London, lad?"

"Dirty," Rory smiled. "And full of vermin."

The shaggy mane of black hair was thrown backward as the wide throat rippled with laughter. "Dirty, is it? How would ye know, livin' in the rarefied air of them fine houses along the Strand?"

"There's a sickness in that air as bad as the plague in the streets."

Ned Bull's eyes took on the cunning gleam Rory remembered from their first meeting. But the Irishman also saw them flash with amusement as the big highwayman leaned across the table.

"Damme, if I'd known I had a prince of Ireland in me hands that night, I would'a shot first!" He dropped half the leg bone and began sucking the other.

"You hate the Irish so much, Ned Bull?"

"Nay, the opposite, lad. I admire ye. Ye're a bunch a fightin' bastards." His lips slid back into a smile. "That's why I would'a put a bullet through ye rather than cross swords!"

Now it was Rory's turn to laugh. Putting his elbows on the table, he, too, leaned forward until their faces were inches apart. "Then I think I've sought out the right man."

"How so?"

"I want to do a bit of business."

"Gar, with me? What sort of business can a gent do with the likes of me?"

Rory took a deep breath and lay his hands flat on the table. It was now or never. Only one man, Lord Haskins, knew of his real purpose in London. Rory was about to increase that number to two. If he was wrong in his judgment of Ned Bull, he would be in the Tower by morning.

"I've seen around London an army of masterless men, driven from the countryside for lack of work on the farms. Most of them have become rogues or vagabonds, thieves and murderers."

"Aye, an' most of them not likin' the trade."

"Does that include you, Ned Bull?"

Another roaring laugh. "Nay, I was born to be a captain of the road, lad. I was liftin' purses before they pressed me to serve, fightin' your crazy Desmond in Munster!"

"In other words, you were born to hang."

"I'd say that."

"Then, Ned Bull, I'd like to let you hang a rich man."

"I'll drink to that, lad!" He stomped to the door, opened it a crack and bellowed into the tavern. "Annie, lass, sack.... Two tankards and be quick about it!"

By the time he regained the table the elfin girl had scurried into the room and thudded two tankards onto the scarred table. As she turned to the door Ned Bull grabbed her arm.

"Nay, Annie, stay! Put yer butt in the corner, I would have ye hear this." Rory's eyes widened in surprise. "Just a precaution, lad. I'd trust little Annie with me life. Ye might have spared mine once, but I'd still like a witness to what ye've got to say."

Rory had no choice. A sideways glance at the girl earned him a vacant, noncommittal look in return. He took a deep breath and launched into it.

"If you had coin to spread around, Ned Bull, could you get willing men to organize others?"

"To what ends? Footpads are a loose group and they trust few."

"When the time comes I would have them organized into a mob to harass the gentry, to plague the army, what there is of it, and to prickle Whitehall with the needle of peasant revolt."

Again Ned Bull's heavy lips curved into a smile. "A rebel ye are, Irishman. What ye're askin' be treason."

"Only treason for you, Ned Bull. Your Queen's not mine. I owe her no allegiance."

Rory sat back with a silent sigh. There, it was out. If what he'd said went beyond this room, he would be a guest in the Tower, hung, or both.

"And when would ye be needin' this revolt?"

Rory shrugged. "Six months, a year... maybe longer."

"Hmm, time enough to form a guild of thieves. I've often thought of it." Ned Bull scratched the graying stubble on a scarred cheek and leveled a steely gaze on Rory. "And ye say ye can produce the coin it would take to woo the recruiters?"

"Aye."

"How much?"

"As much as you'll need," Rory replied. "And what your rogues can steal in groups instead of running alone will sweeten the pot."

Ned's hand came down on the table with a resounding whack and he lurched to his feet. Rory slid his fingers into his boot for the dagger. He was sure of an attack.

He was wrong.

The big man's hands clapped him on the shoulders and lifted him from his chair in a hug.

"I thought I detected somethin' of the savior in ye, lad. Damme if I can't give ye an army of rogues when ye need 'em!"

"Then we're agreed?" Rory asked, shaking himself as his feet regained the floor.

"What think ye, Annie?"

The girl rose and came into the pool of light at the table. Instantly Rory saw a change in her. The eyes were alive now, darting to the two men in turn. They had lost the dark vacant quality he had seen in them before and now shone with a look of cunning not unlike Ned Bull's, a look that spoke of maturity far beyond her years. Her smile was no longer elfin, but suggested a devil deep inside her thin body.

"Methinks, Ned, that the rebel Irishman would have us make war with the Queen here in London so her army would be less fit in Ireland."

"My thoughts exactly, darlin'," Ned said, and grinned at Rory. "Smart little doxy, ain't she? An' only thirteen! That's why I keeps her. She kin even read and write!"

The fact that Ned Bull's mistress was so young only mildly shocked Rory. The idea that he would ask the girl's opinion on his business carried more weight.

Even now her parted lips and brazen stance told him that his first notion of her had been wrong. Annie was much more woman than child.

Suddenly Ned was leaning forward, his face near Rory's ear. "Lad, I can tell from your look...."

"What?"

"I've an inkling that you have need of a woman."

Rory blushed and pulled his eyes from the girl's.

"My Annie, she'd tune you like a fiddle, lad. An' I do believe she's an eye for it. What say ye, Annie?"

The child-woman grinned speculatively. "Aye."

"Christ's blood, the both of you," Rory said, pulling away from Ned Bull's grasp. "You'll have me red from my nose to my toes!"

Ned's roaring laughter filled the room.

Annie's chuckle was low and husky as she flounced between them to the door. "We'll see, Irishman. Peel away the fancy silks and satins an' we're all sisters. I'll be gettin' some sack to seal the bargain."

"Then we have a bargain?" Rory said, willing the embarrassed flush to leave his cheeks and glad to return the conversation to the business at hand.

"Aye, Rory O'Donnell, we've a bargain," Ned nodded, the smile fading from his face to be replaced by a look of stolid determination. "For I've a certain date to keep at Tyburn Tree, and when it comes it matters not why the noose is knotted."

CHAPTER FIFTEEN

THE COLD WINDS OF MARCH gave way to the blossoms of April. It was spring, 1593, and after a year in England Rory O'Donnell was finally to have his audience with the Queen.

And none too soon.

Blindly the Queen's men in Dublin went ahead with plantationing Munster in the south of Ireland. They paid no attention to the new rumors of unrest, secretly spawned by O'Neill's agents. And they were turning their eyes to the north, to the lands of the Maguires and the O'Donnells.

By now The O'Hara had been pardoned, through Haskins's intervention with the crown in England and O'Neill's wily arguments put forth at Dublin Castle. Although Shane, Deirdre and little Rory had long since returned to Ballylee, their lands and titles were now returned with official sanction. But as a condition of his pardon it was understood that he would pay his tithes to Dublin and prevent rebellion rather than spawn it. He was charged with keeping a tight rein on the warrior urraghs and the clan septs under his rule.

"A curse on their damnable English titles! The only title I need or care to have is The O'Hara. Ballylee bulges with a year's supply of grain. My pigs, sheep and cattle are fat within the stalls. I've two hundred fighting men under my roof who can turn back two thousand English foot under seige. Let it begin!"

But O'Neill knew better. In England Rory was doing his job well. The forges and armory of the Tower were turning out a new cannon, a forty-pounder. With such a weapon for seige, even the heavily buttressed, formidable walls of Ballylee would crumble in time.

O'Neill urged patience.

Outwardly O'Hara appeared to acquiesce, but inwardly he seethed, as did Hugh Maguire and Red Hugh O'Donnell. The time was quickly approaching when these two clan leaders would openly oppose the crown parceling out their land to English settlers and adventurers.

Many skirmishes had already taken place. The Queen's lord deputy, Fitzwilliams, had taken Monaghan, the strategic county just below Fermanagh. Even now they were beginning a plantation in Monaghan and preparing to move on north to capture the eastern shore of Lough Erne.

Should this happen, Fermanagh would fall, giving

the English forces an open pass into Donegal and even
Tyrone. This constant hammering on the door to the
north had forced Hugh Maguire to openly declare that
should it continue, war would result.

A curt message from O'Neill to Rory conveyed the
seriousness of the problem.

O'Hara is like a raging bull in his desire to join
Maguire. Your brother has already sent men south
to Fermanagh, and threatens to join them himself
soon. We are not ready. Philip of Spain has promised shot and men, so we must wait. But further
waiting would be a disaster if a path is opened to
Ulster.

You must convince Burghley, and through him
the Queen, of Fitzwilliams's rashness. She must
believe that ambition and greed are your motives,
and that you have the common sense to see that
English rule is inevitable. You must convince the
crown as well that you alone have a strong voice
with all the clans, including mine, and can urge
restraint—restraint that would be impossible if
Dublin insists on the folly of invading Ulster at
this time.

Deirdre sends her love and best wishes, as does
her wild husband. Little Rory is a year now, and
already eyeing the hilt of his father's sword instead
of his toys. He will be a true son of Ireland, and, I
hope, a free man by the time you return.

I see Deirdre often, even under the noses of
British spies. They think she travels to Dungannon
as liaison between O'Hara and myself. And indeed
she does. But the messages she conveys are my urg-
ings to O'Hara for patience for the coming war,
rather than for no war at all.

She has truly been an asset, so much so that I've forgotten her birth altogether. Not so my own shrew, Mabel, who remains British to her core. Beware of these aristocratic Englishwomen, lad, for I fear there are few Deirdres and many Mabels.

O'Neill's last words had eaten at Rory's brain for days. He had even left off his haunting of Elizabeth Hatton, because he felt himself falling deeper and deeper under the spell of those flashing yet somehow sad green eyes.

One day they met by accident on the commons by St. Paul's. It was impossible not to speak.

"Good morrow, m'lady."

"Good morrow, Rory O'Donnell," she replied, extending her hand.

He grasped it gently and brushed its warmth with his lips. The slight tremor he felt in her body was unmistakable. It made him want to do much, much more.

Her face was slightly flushed when he again stood to his full height and looked down into her eyes.

"What think ye, by this time, of our London?"

"I think...." He paused, then his teeth flashed in a wide grin. "I think that God made the English countryside and ran out of time when he got to London."

"A wily answer, but maudlin for such a beautiful day."

"True."

It was indeed a beautiful day, with the sun bright and warm, making even the gray of the buildings appear cheerful. Slashes of color flowed from window pots to gardens and assaulted the eye. The Thames was alive with gaily bedecked boats, and the swans were everywhere like white bursts from a master's brush.

They took it all in, as much to avoid the other's eye as to enjoy the sights of the day.

At last Rory broke the silence. "I look around at these imposing towers, I hear the tumult of scurrying people, I breathe the scents of commerce and flowers, and I am in awe."

Elizabeth turned at once, her eyes finding his chiseled profile. Never before had she heard such a strange sonorous tone in his voice. Always he had been light and witty, sometimes condescending to the point of arousing her anger. Now she detected more of the weary philosopher in his voice than the insolent gallant.

"How so...this awe?"

"Because in all I see and hear I sense history hurtling forward. I sense the pageants of chivalry, the pomp and circumstance of kings, the strife of progress, the sounds of armies...and the petty schemes of statesmen."

"A pithy speech, Rory O'Donnell."

"A mood...forgive me." Now he turned and their eyes met fully, speaking beyond their words. "Your England is a part of the world."

"Is it so different from your Ireland?"

"My Ireland, my Ulster, I'm afraid, is a world all its own behind its lakes, its mountains, its bogs and rivers."

"And Irishmen?" she said, her voice barely a whisper. "Are they, too, a world apart?"

Rory found himself swimming in the depths of those green eyes. He wanted to crush her in his arms and tell her that there was but a brief channel of water that separated them.

But he couldn't. The gulf was more than water. It was a mountain so high that its peak couldn't be found.

"A vast world apart, m'lady."

Her early words had seemed banter of the kind he'd grown used to hearing from her lips. But now a sudden cloud passed over her exquisite features, and she grew serious.

"Why do you haunt me, Rory O'Donnell?"

"Haunt you, m'lady?" Her scent filled his nostrils. Her questing look unnerved him, so much so that he averted his gaze. In keeping with the current style, her doublet was cut low at the bodice, to the point of immodesty. The rounded swells of her heavy breasts stirred his desire beyond bounds. "Nay, m'lady, I fear it is you who haunts me."

The words were out of his mouth before he could stop them. They were rash words, and he knew it. So did she. When she made to reply, he excused himself and moved quickly on, not looking back.

For two days he cursed himself, knowing that he had made matters worse. He took to wearing her scarf inside his doublet, close to his heart. It was foolish, but it would also serve him as a warning should they meet again.

He even went so far as to make a vow to himself that they would not meet again. For a diversion to benefit the hounds that seemed to sniff his every movement, he would look elsewhere. The night of the carriage must never happen again, lest he find her lips sweeter than his cause.

Then word came from Robert Cecil, summoning him to Whitehall and to his audience with Her Highness the Queen of England.

And the same day, Haskins informed him that the Queen had announced her schedule for this summer's progress. One of the houses she would visit was Sir William Hatton's estate at Holdenby.

Rory breathed an even bigger sigh of relief than he

had at Cecil's invitation. The news meant that Lady Hatton would be spending the summer outside London, and the danger of his temptation would be removed.

CHAPTER SIXTEEN

THE PRESENCE CHAMBER was astir with anticipation. This would be the first morning of court since the recent close of Parliament. It was said that the Queen was pleased with the subsidy given her, but in a tirade against those who had opposed her.

In the lower house Francis Bacon had made an ass of himself by demanding that the Queen openly declare war on Spain if she wanted money to wage war. This wasn't Gloriana's way. Everyone knew that Bacon was merely the mouthpiece for his protector, Essex, in the House of Commons. The gossips, therefore, were looking forward with glee to the new rift between the Queen and her favorite.

The other main topic of conversation was the dexterity and deftness with which the Cecil faction, led by Sir Robert and by the speaker, Edward Coke, had turned aside Essex's pleas and demands for declared war. Robert Cecil had won the day, and with it even more power.

All this and more flowed into Rory O'Donnell's ears as he stood tall and silent amid the chattering, gossiping lords and ladies in the huge presence chamber. Over their fans the women flashed looks of curiosity or outright flirtation at the tall dark-eyed Irishman.

He remained immobile, impervious to the invitation

in their eyes, as around him swirled a glittering parade of silk, velvet, taffeta and brocade.

It was good that the room was large, for nearly a hundred souls awaited the Queen and the women needed room to move—or rather glide, Rory thought.

The newest designs in farthingales were distended with whalebone. He had heard them called cartwheel farthingales, and they were as wide at the waist as they were at the hem. Though they were all the rage, Rory thought their appearance not unlike gaudily decorated teapots mounted on tiny wheels.

But no matter how much he might scoff at the design, he had to admit to feeling awe at such a display of wealth. Fine brocade and velvet skirts 'heavily embroidered with gold and silver thread graced the farthingales, and the doublets above them were as richly made, many of them bordered with fine lace and sprinkled with pearls.

He couldn't help but compare Whitehall to Bankside; it was a marked contrast between rich and poor, splendor and squalor. Even though he had passed through the gates of Whitehall more than once in the past year, the opulence of the citylike palace and those who frequented it still made him uneasy.

The men were even more richly garbed than the women, and Rory himself was no exception. His doublet was a deep turquoise-malachite Genoa velvet patterned with golden thread. Down the front was a row of costly silk buttons narrowly spaced and ending at the matching upper hose. These extended to his knees and were fastened to his stockings with velvet garters also trimmed in gold. Under his arm he carried a plumed hat, also matching.

When Haskins had first brought in the simpering

tailor Rory had bridled. He preferred the outdated but more comfortable clothwear of the street.

"Not at court, m'boy," Haskins had warned. "The court is not only a marketplace of conspicuous consumption, it is a battleground for recognition and favor. The weapons used are dress, a love of gambling, a townhouse with a well-equipped staff, and the means for lavish hospitality. Most you don't have, so we'll dress you better than the best of the peacocks and let your well-turned leg and handsome face do the rest."

If he felt uncomfortable in the courtly dress, it was quite the opposite with his tooled Russian-leather boots. They were by far the most comfortable he had ever worn.

General movement and a lowering of the voices to whispers brought his attention to the door of the privy chamber. Rory knew that beyond that room lay the Queen's apartments.

Then the doors were flung wide, and Rory was struck with the full pomp of English royalty.

First came barons, earls, and Knights of the Garter, all richly dressed and bareheaded. Behind them shuffled the aging Lord Burghley. Since the lord treasurer's townhouse, Exeter, lay in a straight line between Haskins House and the Strand, Rory had seen the old man many times from afar, mounting his carriage. Now, at closer range, he could discern the pains of age in the seamed and bearded face. The shoulders were slumped as if they did indeed carry the weight of England on their narrow width.

At his side but a step behind walked his son Robert, with open concern in his eye at his father's faltering steps.

Yes, Rory thought, the secret of success would be the creation of friendship with Robert Cecil. He would surely control the purse strings as well as the future of England when Burghley was gone.

Next came the chancellor, bearing the seals in a red silk purse. He was flanked by two squires, one of which carried the royal scepter, the other the sword of state in a red scabbard studded with golden fleurs-de-lis.

A blast from the pages' trumpets silenced the room and announced the Queen.

Rory took his cue from those around him and dropped to one knee. There was a moment's hush, with Rory straining his eyes from under a bowed head, and then she swept dramatically and majestically through the door.

Even with her sixty years and the distance of the room, he sensed the aura of supreme power that emanated from her presence as she stood surveying the assemblage.

"Good morning."

There was a general chorus of greetings from the group. Rory heard "Hail, Gloriana!" and "Long live the Queen!" from individuals scattered across the floor.

"The damnable chill of winter is gone at last," came the voice, bell-clear and powerful. "The signs of spring we saw from our chamber window this morning gladdened our eyes. We are in a gracious mood."

Rory detected a general round of sighs and a mumbled "Thank God" or two.

As she moved forward everyone stood up. Slowly she moved between the two lines of subjects marking her passage, stopping occasionally to chat with someone who caught her eye. To certain courtiers and gentlemen of the court she offered her hand.

As she came nearer Rory could better see her features and dress. Her face was oblong and handsome, but discernibly wrinkled under heavy layers of cosmetics. The lips were thin but mobile, capable of parting in a wide smile or tightening with obvious disdain. Her nose was rounded and slightly beaked. It was a bit overlarge, making her eyes appear smaller than they were. The eyes themselves were very dark, almost black, as they flashed and darted with a nervous quickness from one person to the next.

It was her eyes and the way she used them that gave Rory the feeling that under the red periwig there was indeed the calculating mind of a monarch.

She was dressed in white silk bordered with pearls the size of beans, and over it hung a mantle of black silk shot with silver. As if to enhance the style she had already set, her bosom was bared even more than those of the other ladies in the room

Then she was in front of Rory, those dark eyes challenging as they took in the cut of his clothes and openly admired the line of his jaw. Bravely he met her gaze, telling himself that as well as being the most powerful ruler in the world she was also a woman. But to meet her gaze he had to look straight down. He hadn't realized how small she was.

Small?

No. It was then that Rory realized he was by far the tallest man in the room. Where Gloriana herself approached nearly eye level to her court and courtiers, Rory O'Donnell's height made the great woman crane her neck backward.

"Is this the Irish rebel?"

"Yes, Your Majesty," Robert Cecil said, moving to her side. "Rory O'Donnell, son of Black Hugh and brother of Red Hugh—"

"Who is himself the rebel, Your Majesty," Rory interrupted, surprised at the calm sureness in his voice.

"And who would band the northern clans together to achieve his own ends and to see me in Dublin Castle in his place."

"And mayhap *we'll* see you in the Tower instead."

"As it pleases Your Majesty," Rory said, flashing what he hoped was his most winning smile. "I'm given to understand I would be in fine company...with some of the highest peers in Your Majesty's realm."

Gasps followed his statement and heads craned to get a better look at the Irish upstart.

Elizabeth herself blinked, returning his gaze coldly for a moment and then lifting her chin with laughter.

"A wit...by Christ's blood, the Irishman has a wit!"

Rory remained unmoved, letting his smile broaden and his eyes meet hers with what he hoped was a mischievous twinkle. He didn't let his face register her words, for he knew that when she chose to shock, Gloriana could swear like a stablehand.

"What hear you from my monster of the north, that glib and dissembling Tyrone...The O'Neill?"

Rory feigned a puzzled look. This was a baited trap that he had no intention of falling into. "The O'Neill, Your Majesty? I had no idea the Earl of Tyrone had taken the mantle of The O'Neill. I thought it was your express command that he shouldn't."

"It was," she replied dryly.

"Then, Your Highness, I am sure he has not. And as for communication, I've had none since my exile."

"What would you have of us?"

"Beyond the leave to serve you? Only the O'Donnell lands of Tyrconnell when my brother ends his days."

"And what would you give us in return? Besides your undying loyalty, of course."

"I think this would be better discussed in the council

chamber, Your Grace." Robert Cecil's words were a whisper in the Queen's ear, but they reached Rory.

"I quite agree, Your Majesty," Rory said, lowering his own voice. "But I think I can guarantee to calm Maguire, hold O'Hara in check, and serve as a balm to Tyrone."

"And your brother?"

Before Rory could reply, the doors to the guard chamber swung wide. The crowd parted, and through them stepped a man as large and broad of shoulder as Rory himself. He approached the Queen with a firm long stride and dropped to one knee as his hand reached for hers.

"Your Majesty, I require an immediate audience on the gravest of matters."

Elizabeth balled her long fingers into fists and pulled them out of his grasp. "You would what?"

Without being bidden to, he stood up. His black eyes glared at the Queen with such anger that Rory thought it impossible that he had not already been commanded from her presence.

"I beg you, Your Majesty, to let me explain the recent events in Parliament...."

"Enough!" she barked. "Can't your eyes perceive that we are busy? This Irishman—"

"*Irishman?* By God's blood, you would—"

"I *would* do what pleases us." With vehemence she turned to Rory. "Your arm, Rory O'Donnell. I would hear more of what you think of our Irish problem. Perhaps it is time someone outside my court advise me on the problems those inside it create."

Rory was stunned. He could feel sweat rise between his shoulder blades and trickle down his spine. In the presence chamber were the Lord Mayor of London, the Earls of Suffolk and Putnam, as well as fifty other

high-ranking lords and ladies of the court, all waiting
to see the Queen.

He had fully expected to be the last of the long line.
But now he was raising his arm, and upon it the Queen
of England rested her hand.

"Good day, m'Lord Essex," said the Queen.

The sweat turned to ice and Rory felt a sudden chill
as his eyes met those of the Queen's favorite, Robert
Devereux, Earl of Essex. What he saw in the other
man's stare could only be interpreted as unadulterated
hate.

And beyond Essex, Rory saw Robert Cecil with his
kerchief raised to hide a smile.

Rory had previously tinkered with the idea of courting the Earl of Essex's favor. The man's hope for an
openly declared war with Spain to further his own
heroic ambitions would fit nicely with O'Neill's desires
to keep England occupied outside of Ireland.

But the balance of power was now clearly on the
humpbacked shoulders of Robert Cecil.

So, Rory thought, adding a jaunty arrogance
to his step to match that of the woman at his side,
*I've perhaps made a friend, and most assuredly an
enemy.*

Now it remained to be seen if the seed of friendship
could blossom into the tree of advantage.

CHAPTER SEVENTEEN

RORY GUIDED his handsome Galloway mount under the
wide arch of Whitehall and past the Queen's tennis
courts and tiltyard, then turned right toward the
Thames. His mind was already befogged, and by the

time he reached the Strand and veered right toward
Fleet Street and the city it was reeling.

One of the reasons for his confusion was his encounter with the Queen. In an audience that lasted
more than two hours, Rory had learned much about
the woman and monarch he had been taught to hate.

Her knowledge and grasp of affairs had astounded
him. And her cleverness had unnerved him. With
rapid-fire questions mingled with light banter, she soon
had him telling her about his youth at Donegal Castle.
Before realizing it, Rory had related his part in bygone
skirmishes with the Queen's men and the other clans,
battles that had started when Rory was only fifteen.

"'Tis a pity that so fair a youth—for fair you must
have been, Rory O'Donnell, to grow into such an appealing man—'tis a pity that your youth be wasted and
your life spent, mayhap shortened, by war."

Herewith she had launched into a recitation of her
own wars—England's wars—in France, the Netherlands, on the lands and seas with Spain and Scotland. It
was when she began to praise the people of Wales and
the lowland Scots that Rory perceived her aim.

Besides reminding him of England's wealth, her vast
power, her military might, she was scolding him and
the Irish for not following the example of the Welsh
and prospering under England's rule. She was drawing
a picture in words, and drawing it well, of the futility of
future Irish wars.

She almost convinced him, until Rory remembered
O'Neill's words: "The English armies dwindle daily,
raked by the damp of what they call their Irish ague.
Because of their officers' perfidy in lining their own
pockets, the common soldier either deserts or sells his
musket and powder for food. Morale is low and will get
lower. In time they will be ours."

But Gloriana was going on to compare the sleek, swift, tall-masted galleons Rory had seen so often on the Thames to the slow oar-driven ships of Grace O'Malley at Clew Bay. "That is not to say that I don't admire your famous Irishwoman pirate, for I do. She makes her way, and she makes it well in what men think is their world. But like Spain's Armada, O'Malley's ship would be mere kindling under English naval guns."

Rory had met the embattled old woman, Grace O'Malley, only once, but he had never forgotten the experience. She might be a woman, but she fought like an Irishman for her clan. Her spirit was worth those of a hundred Englishmen. If her ships sank, O'Malley would somehow escape to build more.

With the roughness and impetuousness of what he was—an Irish warrior lord—Rory debated Her Majesty on the question of how Ireland differed from the rest of her empire. To further his own plea he gave her an example of the Irishmen's ways.

"On the question of church, Your Majesty. . . I often wonder if the common man in my country is anti-English because he is papist, or if he remains papist because he is anti-English."

Inflammatory words, perhaps rash, but true; and she saw the wisdom in them at once. "So, my young Irish philosopher, you would have the lords and princes of Ireland rule the common man without benefit of English titles?"

"Aye, Your Majesty, for then the common man can keep faith with his lord and believe, right or wrong, that he is ruled by Irishmen and his soul is protected."

"You have a clever and devious mind, Rory O'Donnell. We will weigh your words and your other requests. My good Sir Robert shall keep you advised on our moods and desires.''

Rory left the council chamber in an ambivalent mood. The verbal sparring had gone against his grain as a man of action, but he felt he had acquitted himself well. He was positive the Queen believed that his only desire was peace, and that his only motivation was his ambition to share his rightful inheritance in Donegal.

He was equally ambivalent over this woman who worked so hard at being a ruler and a coquette at the same time. He knew her to be an elderly, vain and capricious female, but he had also learned this day that she was a sharp-eyed, sharp-tongued Queen who indeed ruled an empire.

As he dodged around the hackneys and carriages moving between the town, Whitehall, and Winchester beyond, Rory tried to bring into focus all that had transpired. He was using and being used, that he knew. But he also knew that the audience had been more than a battle of wits and words. Elizabeth the Queen had been trying to tell him something, had been trying to plant a seed in his mind with her words, but as yet her purpose escaped him.

A carriage rumbled to a halt by his horse's flank. Rory turned in the saddle and stared into the solemn face and brooding eyes of Robert Cecil.

"Come, share my carriage, O'Donnell. I would speak with you more and, besides, the ride will save your nose from the offal of the city."

"You're for the Tower as well, Sir Robert?"

"Aye, a trifling bit of state business Her Majesty would have me perform there."

Rory smiled and stepped from his horse, handing the reins to a waiting footman.

Trifling indeed, he thought; Sir Robert Cecil did

nothing trifling. Rory guessed well this "coincidence." The Queen's last suggestion—nay, command—had been that he visit the Tower armory and acquaint himself with her armies' latest progress in arms. And she'd suggested that while he was there he tour the Tower as well.

The import of this wasn't lost on Rory. To any man toying with treason, the mere sight of the ominous fortress was a warning. Many entered its walls as prisoners, few came out.

Rory felt sure that Robert Cecil had "just happened along" to make sure Rory had the full experience of the Tower.

"The Queen was much impressed with both your carriage and your thoughts," Cecil said as Rory settled into the opposite cushion.

"I'm glad."

The two men sat weighing each other in silence as the granite cobbles of the Strand shook and rattled the carriage. The one sat high in the seat, filling it with his shoulders; the other was hunched, his diminutive size even smaller by comparison. Rory, with his aristocratic, almost Romanesque features and his beardless, olive-skinned face was a marked contrast to Cecil, whose sharp angular face was made longer by a dark spade beard.

"You *were* on your way to the Tower?"

"Aye," Rory nodded. "I've seen Tyburn Tree, and the rotting heads on London Bridge. I've heard the miserable souls howling in the Fleet Prison and I've been told tales of the dying martyrs. I welcome a visit to the Tower with the knowledge that I can walk out as well as in by the Queen's grace. After this I feel my criminal education will be complete, and the Queen's point well made."

Cecil's laugh was flat. It echoed without humor off the wood-paneled and velvet interior of the carriage. But nevertheless it was a laugh, the first Rory had heard the man utter.

"Your candor is like a brisk and refreshing breeze, O'Donnell. I'll try to match it."

"I say what I think...sometimes too often."

"I've noticed. Methinks you've made an enemy of m'Lord Essex."

"Oh? Just from the Queen using me to tweak his nose?"

"Our valiant Welsh lord has taken far more umbrage from far less provocation."

Rory hooded his eyes and grinned into Cecil's stare. "Then m'Lord Essex may ask me out, and all your problems with his warring ways will be over."

Another laugh came from the smaller man, this time strong enough to shake his frail body. "No, that would never be. M'Lord Essex, like you, is impetuous but not stupid. He might incur the Queen's displeasure, aye, even wrath, by constantly dunning her for a war to fight, but never by dueling with a foreigner."

"Foreigner, Sir Robert? I?" Rory mocked. "How can I be a foreigner when I am Irish, and Ireland is England but a span of water away?"

"Damme, but you do war with words as well as Tyrone. But to the meat of it." The carriage jolted over a particularly rough spot and pain slid over Cecil's features. He readjusted the swollen hump of his back in the cushion before continuing. "It's true Essex wants a war, and if the past sway the future he will probably get it. If that be the case in France or Spain, we would have Ireland quiet."

"I doubt that means you would leave off the conquest of Ireland,'' Rory said, a jaunty, gibing tone in his voice.

But Cecil was serious and his own tone became harsh. "Total conquest, as you call it, of Ireland is not our desire...conciliation is. Indirect control of Ireland through the clans is far cheaper and therefore much more appealing to Her Majesty."

Now it was Rory's turn. He lowered his voice to a guttural growl and leaned forward so that even seated he towered over the smaller man.

"Then I restate my case...our case. We Princes of Ireland, chiefs of our clans, are no different than you lords of your shires who devote your life to gain by convincing an old Queen she is young and a failing monarch she is strong. To do what you would have us do, rule for you, we need the people. And we can't have them with English titles and English laws!"

With a deep sigh Rory threw himself back into the cushion and waited for an answer. When none came he looked out the window and thought about his own words.

Suddenly, as if he had convinced himself, it all made sense. Maybe war wasn't the only way out. Maybe through indirect rule Ireland could rule herself with England's help. Perhaps peace with compromise could be a reality.

Could it be that the words and arguments he was using to create a cloud for his real purposes weren't really false? Was there a way Ireland could remain England's colony, and her people prosper as Irish?

But then he remembered the graft rampant in Dublin's government, the English lords hungry for Irish land. Once they obtained it they became absentee landlords, with overseers who made slaves of the Irish peasants.

And what of the Irish lords, himself included? Battle was a way of life. It was all they knew, and that would take generations to change. In that case, as O'Neill said, it was better that Irish begin killing English instead of each other.

The idea of possible peace and compromise was stillborn in his mind.

The carriage was approaching Ludgate, and Rory let the sounds of the bustling city clear his mind.

"Buy! Buy! What d'ye lack? What d'ye need? What'll ye buy? Buy! Buy!" The hawkers' cries mingled with the screech and rattle of carriages and carts across the cobbles.

Suddenly they were nosing their way between two rows of tiny shops and open stalls, all with apprentices urging the sale of their master's wares.

Rory was noting the price of fresh mackerel and hot sheep's feet as Cecil's voice tried to reach him through the cacophony of church bells tolling the hour.

"Sorry, Sir Robert, my mind wandered."

"I said, 'twas a sensible and well-wrought speech."

"But not to your liking."

Cecil shrugged, pulled at his beard, and spoke again. "Do you think you can impart as much sense to the clan leaders—keep them on their own lands, in their own castles until I can convince the Queen and Parliament of the worth of your proposals?"

"I know I can," Rory replied, keeping the anticipation out of his voice. "I will need free rein and open lines of communication, and I'll need to know what Whitehall and Dublin are doing at all times in order to convince the chiefs that I indeed have the Queen's ear."

"You ask a lot."

"I know. Perhaps I would fare better in the Essex

camp. If I could guarantee him no war in Ireland, he could better press his wars elsewhere."

Cecil shook his head. "Foolish thinking. Mark ye this, O'Donnell, and mark it well. M'Lord Essex is popular with the people, like Drake and Raleigh before him. He is perhaps even more popular than the Queen. But popularity does not power make. I daresay that one day this very popularity will be his downfall. Nay, my Irish lord, the power is with the purse, and the purse is with the Cecils."

Rory made a mock bow from his waist. "Then it stands that I am automatically in your camp."

"It would seem so, but remember this—even with our differences, M'Lord Essex and I are both Englishmen. We serve our Queen."

"As do I."

"As an Irishman?"

"What else, Sir Robert? You have my case. What say you?"

Rory held his breath as Cecil's eyes narrowed, boring into his as if to plumb the depths of his soul. Then, slowly, the little man relaxed and Rory began to breathe again.

He had won. He knew it. He could read agreement on Cecil's face.

"Very well, you have it—the run of London and all of England, if you need it. Give me the names of your couriers and I'll see that they come and go as they please."

"And just one last thing," Rory said. "Call off your sniffing hounds."

"What? Why, my dear sir, how can I do that and keep up with the latest gossip?"

His tone was again light, bantering. Rory didn't comprehend and his face said as much.

"If I do that," Cecil chuckled, "how will I know when you've put horns on m'Lord Hatton?"

Rory could feel heat flush his face as the carriage lurched to a halt. "Sir Robert, I—"

Cecil shook his hand in dismissal and chuckled low in his throat as he stepped down. "No matter. The Lady Hatton is my niece but quite her own person. As one man to another, I can tell you that she will do quite as her mood pleases her. And I'm afraid we English are not unlike you Irish in these matters. Have not the O'Neills, the O'Haras and the O'Donnells been famous in their time for carting off other men's wives?"

Rory nearly stumbled as he stepped from the carriage himself. Was Cecil advocating his niece's adultery?

He gained the smaller man's side, and was about to assure him that his attentions had only been flirtatious when again Cecil interrupted with a wave of his hand.

"Oh, that does remind me. . . the Queen was indeed taken with your person. So much so that she bids me tell you that she would have you along on her summer progress with the court."

Rory was dumbfounded. The Queen's pygmy fox was outfoxing him at every turn. Cecil wouldn't need spies to check his movements if he was in the countryside with the court. And worst of all it meant that Rory would be spending a whole month in the same house with Lady Hatton.

Had Cecil planned that, too?

"Sir Robert, what the Queen asks is impossible."

"How so?"

"I must be in London."

"Why so?"

"How can I carry out your desires in the country?" Rory found himself sputtering but also found it impossible to stop.

"I'm sure you'll find a way."

Rory stopped short and drew himself to his full height. "No!"

Cecil turned. His head barely reached Rory's chest, but his demeanor was as strong and his face as glowering as the bigger man's.

"It is the Queen's request, and as you well know, Her Majesty's requests are as commands. Besides, a summer in the country is a small thing."

Small thing? With the most desirable, most beautiful woman in the world doors away and practically his for the asking?

Small thing? To create a scandal at court that could bring his whole reason for being in England down around his ears?

Small thing? Inside Rory was fuming. He knew full well that the "request" had been planted in the Queen's ear by the man before him. And the look on Cecil's face seemed to say that he wouldn't budge.

He tried a different tack. "Sir Robert, I ask you . . . nay, implore you—as a cohort, as one who has mutual desires of monumental import, as a newly made friend—"

"A piece of advice my father once gave me I pass along to you, Rory O'Donnell. In trying times be sure to keep some great and powerful man thy friend for favors, but trouble him not for trifles."

CHAPTER EIGHTEEN

" 'TIS JUST PAST SIX, m'lady."

The chambermaid's words, accompanied by the swish of the opening drapes, brought Elizabeth to a

half-wakened state. *Another few minutes,* she thought.
Yes, please, just a few more minutes. Her whole body
felt as if it was inflicted with ague. She hadn't stopped
for as much as a tenth of an hour in the last four days,
getting Holdenby ready for the Queen's visit.

"The whole household is atwitter over the court's
coming!"

Elizabeth let one eye creep open to survey the quilted
canopy above the large ornate four-poster.

"Does m'lady wish a bit longer in bed?" Honor's
wide pleasant face appeared at her side and hovered
there.

Yes, m'lady would like to sleep 'til nine. Then she
remembered all that must still be done, and most of it
without Sir William's help.

With a sigh she threw off the light coverlet. A groan
followed as she stretched one last time in the soft abundance of three feather mattresses piled one on the
other.

"Your hand, Honor."

"Yes, m'lady."

Gently, cautiously, Elizabeth walked the four steps
down from the bed. She flexed and relaxed the muscles
in her legs and revolved her upper body until most of
the ache had left her.

Her cambric nightdress was overshot with black silk.
The lace at the throat had snaps at the front and back.
Honor unfastened the clasps with deft fingers, and with
a shrug Elizabeth let the gown slither to her feet.
Naked, she stepped to the window.

"Would m'lady like her clothing warmed?"

"Nay, Honor, my body will do it soon enough, for I
smell heat in the day already. Not too hot with the bath
water."

"Yes, m'lady."

Elizabeth heard the girl scurry to pour more cold water into the wooden tub that stood in front of her bedroom fireplace.

While she awaited the bath, Elizabeth breathed deeply of the fresh country air wafting through the open window. Her nipples distended from just the hint of an early morning chill.

The sky was the lightest of blues, dappled here and there with charcoal clouds. A few stars were still visible, but fading before the coming dawn.

A perfect time, she thought, realizing how much she had missed country mornings this last year in the city.

From her window she looked down on the formal gardens with their granite-cobbled walks and tall, perfectly manicured hedges. They covered five acres directly behind the great house, and the two center pools caught the morning light and reflected it to her eyes.

Beyond the enclosure there were more gardens, rimmed with giant oaks that led to the vast meadows and recently tilled and seeded fields of Holdenby. She could see movement, people already scurrying toward the fields in the first break of dawn. The dairy herd, numbering nearly five hundred prime head, had already been milked. Now they plodded their way along the hedgerows toward the day's grazing.

She had seen much the same at Wimbledon House as a child, but not on so grand a scale. Holdenby was vast, its great house huge with over eighty rooms, its outbuildings too numerous to count, and its tenants and workers a small army.

She felt a thrill seeing it all come to life and knowing that she had a large part in managing it. Sir William was still the lord, but more and more he had come to rely on Elizabeth's judgment in nearly all the Hatton affairs.

For all his kindness to her and for all his attempts at business, Sir William was not his uncle, Christopher Hatton. Elizabeth had learned that much quickly, and had thrown herself into the breach lest her good husband lose much of what had been gained by his inheritance.

She had started by suggesting two small investments, which Sir William had heeded. Both of them had been wise and were already proving profitable. It was she who had thought of purchasing all the remaining lands on the Isle of Purbeck around Corfe Castle, which they already owned. Her reason had been the boom in building she could see all around them. Purbeck marble from England's south coast soon became part of that boom.

Bit by bit Sir William sought her counsel more often, until he began to draw away from business affairs altogether and permit his wife, with her quicker mind, to run the greater portion of the Hatton holdings.

Elizabeth found that she not only enjoyed it, she was also good at it. Organization seemed to be her forte, and the growth of Hatton wealth her reward.

And poor Sir William, gentle, sickly man that he was, drew away from more than business. It had been months since he'd sought her bed. It was with no small guilt that Elizabeth had admitted to herself she didn't mind. She had discovered deep within herself a boiling cauldron of passion that her aging husband could only stir and not satisfy. Consequently his visits to her bed had left her more frustrated, as well as vulnerable to the knowing looks of the younger gallants around her.

Chief among her admirers were James Blake, now Sir James thanks to whatever strange service he had provided the Queen, and the young Irishman, Rory O'Donnell. While one was blatant with his speech and manner, forward to the point of arrogant impudence, the other was sad and gentle in his obvious desire, and seemingly afraid to express it.

Elizabeth felt herself being drawn to both men.

With Blake her mood was one of underlying intrigue and danger. The man's dark eyes flashed with a will to conquer her, to strip her body bare and force submission from her loins. His presence was as exciting as it was fearful.

Rory O'Donnell brought out the other part of her, the part that was feminine, womanly; the part that was neither Cecil nor Lady Hatton. In the Irishman's dark brooding eyes she saw the same smoldering desire and sensed the same volatile rage as Blake possessed. But in O'Donnell she also sensed the gentleness of love, the capacity to make a woman throw everything to the winds in order to spend her days and nights in strong as well as loving arms.

In recent weeks she had found the temptation almost too great to bear. She had listened to ladies at court openly discussing the ruses they used to horn their husbands. Adultery had become such a common vice across the land, from lords and ladies of Whitehall to country yeomen and their wives, that the ecclesiastical courts hearing such cases had been jokingly renamed the "bawdy courts."

The idea of giving in to her own passions had begun to creep into her every waking thought.

But fate had intervened. Blake had been sent overseas on the Queen's business, and Elizabeth had left London to prepare Holdenby for the royal visit. She kept telling herself that with O'Donnell far away in the city, all temptation would be gone by the end of the summer.

Even so, her mind still tricked her now and then with the question of "what if...?"

"Your bath, m'lady."

"Thank you, Honor."

Elizabeth accepted the girl's hand and stepped into the tub. The water, as usual, was just the right temperature and scented perfectly.

"Your soap, m'lady."

The soap ball was liberally scented, like the bath, with oil of almonds. Elizabeth used it freely and then passed it so the girl could wash her back.

"Oh, not so hard!"

"Sorry, m'lady...I'm so nervous. I've never seen the Queen, nor all the fine lords and ladies. They say the retinue will number more than a hundred!"

Elizabeth chuckled. "And think of all the handsome young footmen and grooms. See that you lock your door securely at night, Honor. I'll not have you with a belly full of child before me!"

The girl's face turned scarlet but she giggled at the warning. "Such a thing, m'lady...never! I'm promised already and I've the good fortune to love my father's choice."

Elizabeth's eyes shot up to meet the maid's. Honor knew the circumstances of her lady's marriage. She also knew, as did every other servant in the house, that lately Sir William never spent a single night in his wife's bed.

Elizabeth looked for malice in the girl's frank, open stare but saw only innocence.

Touchy, Elizabeth thought, *I'm too touchy.* But it was ironic that this girl, lowborn with little or no expectations and probably no dowry, should be able to marry for love.

"I wish you well, Honor. My only regret is that I might someday lose you."

"Thank you, m'lady."

Elizabeth returned the girl's wide smile and averted her gaze. Honor had been a find. She *would* hate to lose her.

The maid was a pretty buxom girl with long hair the color of straw and open features always graced with a ready smile. Elizabeth had been taken with her at their first meeting. She had chosen Honor as her personal maid less than two weeks after the girl had joined the huge staff at Hatton House.

How different we are, and only two years apart, she mused. Honor was the seventh child in as many years, born of an Islington blacksmith, while Elizabeth was a Cecil and a Hatton. The price of the ivory-and-boxwood combs that Honor would soon use on her mistress's hair, or of the cosmetics Elizabeth would soon apply, could keep Honor's family for a year.

But Honor was going to marry a virile, strapping young lad one day soon, and she would marry him for love.

Shaking the thought from her mind, Elizabeth stepped from the tub and allowed the girl to dry and powder her body. She took linen cloth and tooth soap to her teeth until they gleamed. Then she sat at a huge oaken vanity and applied her cosmetics while Honor saw to her hair.

While she worked she checked over the day's schedule, at the same time considering everything that had already been accomplished.

Beef had been laid in, more than a thousand pounds, as well as like quantities of veal and mutton. The cellar house had been larded with huge quantities of milk, butter and cheese.

Knowing well the Queen's taste for sugar meats, Elizabeth had brought a pastry cook from London to plan and execute elaborate desserts. There would be gilded marchpane cakes made of pounded almonds, pistachio nuts, sugar and sweetened flour. Elizabeth herself had seen to the building of the table decorations made of sweets; huge molasses-and-sugar animals molded together with orange paste. As if that weren't enough, huge platters of sugarplate, sugarsops, and eringo would be at everyone's fingertips constantly to sweeten the breath.

And the entertainment would be no less lavish, with hawking and hunting by day, fetes, masques and games by night.

The cost? Elizabeth wouldn't think of it. But it would be worth it. The new Lady Hatton intended that Holdenby should prove the highlight of this year's progress. Through the years of her reign Gloriana had been known to favor most those in her court who were unstinting in their hospitality. Elizabeth planned on using this year's royal visit to cement forever her place at court.

She knew only too well how highly the Queen had regarded her husband's uncle, Sir Christopher. In going through the papers of Hatton House she had found a copy of the letter Gloriana had written to the Bishop of Ely to settle forever the question of ownership between the Church and Sir Christopher Hatton.

Proud Prelate:
    You know what you were before I made you what you are; and I would have you to know that I who made you can unmake you. If you do not

immediately comply with my request in the matter of Holburn lands from Ely to Hatton, by God I will unfrock you.

Elizabeth R

Sir Christopher Hatton got the lands he wanted to expand his London house.

That was power.

Elizabeth knew that her husband, Sir William, would never have that power. But she, with careful strategy, might regain a part of it.

Honor's quiet voice brought Elizabeth's thoughts back to the bedroom and the matters at hand. "M'lady is pleased?"

Elizabeth perused her rich auburn coif and smiled. "Perfect."

The way she wore her lustrous thick hair was the one area of fashion Elizabeth refused to bow to. She saw no reason, with such a mane, to cover it over with a powdered periwig as was the latest style. Now it was layered high in wide curls and ringlets held in place by two strings of pearls.

For the day she chose a copper-colored velvet doublet to go over a matching blouse bordered at bosom and wrists in dark green. She decided on a narrower-than-stylish farthingale to make movement around the house and grounds easier. Over the farthingale she pinned a sea green skirt dappled with copper brocade.

She let Honor choose the decorative pins for her cuffs and bodice and then, after selecting two handkerchiefs for her brow, she started the day.

Housemaids, scullery maids, chambermaids, cooks, grooms, stablehands, stewards, couriers, huntmaster and falconer all received their last-minute instructions for the Queen's arrival directly from Elizabeth.

She inspected each room in the great house personally, paying special attention to the two-hundred-foot-long gallery where meals would be served. Each painting was straightened and dusted. Each tapestry was tapped for tautness where it graced the high walls. She commanded the floor to be strewn with fresh rushes even though it had been done only a week before.

Next came the gardens and the selection of flowers for each room. Particular care was taken with mixed bouquets of roses, lavender and hyssop for the bedroom Gloriana herself would occupy.

That done, and mounted on her favorite mare, Lady Hatton rode to the far end of the gardens where she inspected the almost completed renovations of the summer cottage. The little house was nearly hidden in a grove of oak and yew trees far from the main house and the estate's other buildings.

Elizabeth had fallen in love with it the moment she had seen it, which was shortly after her wedding. Builders and decorators had been commissioned at once to make of it a comfortable and secluded hideaway for m'lady.

It was small, only five rooms and a solarium, but that was the way Elizabeth wanted it. When completely finished it would be her own place, a private retreat for reading and thought away from the great house with its army of servants.

Already she had instructed every one of the servants, including Honor, that she was not to be disturbed in any way when she was secluded at the cottage.

The private refuge was part of what Elizabeth regarded as her "other self." It was the part of her that still bridled at Robert and her grandfather for arranging her marriage. It was the part of her that cared nothing for the court and its gossip and intrigues. It was the part of her that was sad and lonely and lacking in ambition, the part of her that was womanly—and that she managed to keep hidden.

By noon, with the sun high in a now cloudless sky, all was in readiness, including the two opening entertainments: a sea pageant for that afternoon and a masque for the evening.

Elizabeth was tired. Her legs felt like leaden weights and her head pounded with worry. Had she forgotten anything? Would everyone be in their proper places? Had the gold and silver plate been polished to a mirrorlike sheen? Was her gift to the Queen, a golden toothpick and fork, properly wrapped?

She was at the lake seeing to the fireworks that would follow the masque that evening when she heard the clarion call of the royal trumpets. New raw energy surged through her veins. Her eyes lifted to the far hill, and there, topping a rise on the Bedford road, she saw the first riders in the Queen's retinue.

Suddenly the headache was gone and her heart began pounding wildly within her breast. Her legs were filled with renewed vitality as she lifted her cumbersome skirts and sprinted for the house.

"Honor...*Honor!*" she called, not realizing that the girl was right behind her, panting at her heels.

"Here, m'lady...right here."

"Good. Hurry, girl, we have but minutes!"

And only minutes were needed to change into somber black and white in deference to the Queen's arrival. Honor quickly reshaped her coif, brushed her fresh doublet and placed a clean handkerchief in her gloved hand.

Elizabeth stepped back and critically checked every detail of her appearance. Out of the corner of her eye she saw Honor. The ever present smile was on her young face, but Elizabeth detected a tear running down each cheek.

"Honor, what's the matter?"

"Nothing...oh, nothing, m'lady," the girl blubbered. "It's...well, it's just that you're so very beautiful."

"Why, thank you, Honor," Elizabeth replied, and turned back to the mirror.

Yes, it's true, she thought, *I am beautiful...but then, I am a Cecil and a Hatton.*

CHAPTER NINETEEN

AN OVERCAST MORNING had turned into a balmy day of bright sunshine and country-fresh breezes.

Rory rode in the foremost group. Behind him, in the procession stretching for over a mile, were a hundred other riders, their horses prancing, their jangling bridles creating ripples of sound up and down the line like ebbing and flowing waves in the sea.

Besides the horsed nobility there were servants, some on foot, some riding in small carts. Fifty four-horse wagons carried the Queen's goods. And in the center of the whole parade rolled the Queen's coach, constantly attended by fawning courtiers.

O'Donnell's rankling ire at Robert Cecil had abated somewhat when he realized how pleasant the summer would be, away from the congestion of London with its constant noise and the horrible smells of open sewers.

He had to admit there was a charm to the English

countryside, with its green lanes and thatched cottages, its meadows glorious with wild flowers, its gray-stoned, moss-covered bridges spanning winding rivers swollen and sparkling with spring rains.

And attending the Queen on her progress would not be a total loss. The last week spent at Lord Burghley's Theobalds mansion had added to his education. In spite of the fetes, the dancing and the mood of frivolous, lighthearted gaiety, the Queen and her court remained in constant touch through couriers with London. Almost hourly Rory was reminded of the duality of this woman and her people.

Even at her age she could dance and gamble until the morning hours, and then repair to her apartments and attend to state business until dawn's first light. He quickly discovered that the effeminate foppishness of the court gallants was often only a facade. For in tiltyard games they were adept and vicious with sword, lance and rapier. Their skill as horsemen matched or bettered his own, and with musket many of them had an unerring eye.

It was this practiced use of new arms, added to what he had already learned in London, that unnerved him. All over the city he had seen that the gunsmith's craft had usurped the bowman's. Soon English generals would be able to field an entire army capable of fire power.

Even powder was now being manufactured on English soil, while O'Neill depended on recalcitrant Irish chieftains, a France fighting its own wars, and a wavering Spanish king for supplies sorely needed to equip a modern army.

All this knowledge accumulated in Rory's mind until he was beginning to understand the veiled warnings beneath the Queen's words. He began constantly to compare their two worlds, and his beloved Ireland fared poorly.

Even the architecture of English palaces reflected the national confidence with their lack of moats, their wide glassed windows, and their internal construction made for comfort rather than defense. It had become all too clear to the Irishman that the English never expected to be put under siege on their home territory.

Reluctantly Rory had to admit that, if the luxury of their day-to-day lives and their modern methods for war were anything to go by, victory and eventual domination of Ireland would go to the English.

Moment by moment the Queen's words began to carry more weight.

The summer progress alone represented a marked difference between the two cultures. While the Queen frolicked across the countryside with her entire court, O'Neill, O'Hara, Maguire and Red Hugh sat chafing behind their fortress walls wondering when attack or treachery would come.

Not so the noblemen in England. This summer the Lords Norris at Rycote, Burghley at Theobalds, Montagu at Cowdray and Hatton at Holdenby would dig deep into their purses for the pleasure of entertaining their sovereign. Each would spend thousands of pounds for food, drink, gifts and entertainment for the Queen.

The septs of Tyrone, Fermanagh, Donegal and Ballylee would be hard-pressed to supply the food and arms their clan chieftains would need to begin a war, let alone finish and win it.

Even the conversation around Rory on the ride from Theobalds to Holdenby was lighthearted and trivial.

"Hast thou heard of one Cotegrieve, a yeoman miller, near around here?"

"Nay. Humorous?"

"Aye. 'Tis said he was brought to book for making a child upon an honest maid in his employ. Nay, he says, the child's none of his. But besides the maid, there was a witness who claims he saw Master Cotegrieve take her against the mill door."

"And what said Cotegrieve to that?"

"Od's blood, the fool says, can a man get a maid with child astanding? For I never had anything to do with her but standing!"

The sound of trumpets and the echo of fireworks announcing the Queen's arrival brought Rory from his reverie.

"Holdenby," said a voice at his shoulder.

It was as if the sight unfolded before him at that precise moment just to reinforce his thoughts.

Holdenby was awe-inspiring.

The arched gatehouse was a palace unto itself with its twin round towers on a level with the lines of tall stately oaks beyond it. The trees bordered a wide avenue leading to the rambling four-storied great house. It was impossible for the eye to take in all at once the splendor of its octagonal turrets, its ornate gables and balustrades, and its myriad stacks of chimneys.

The long line came to a halt while the Queen shifted her person from coach to litter. Then, borne aloft by eight nobles, she led them in a procession of state under the gatehouse arch and up the long avenue.

The next half hour was a blur to Rory as the Queen and each member of the court were welcomed by Sir William and Lady Hatton. As he moved slowly through the receiving line, he couldn't remove his eyes from Elizabeth's face.

There, in front of this vast palace, her features were more beautiful and haughty than ever. As he grew

closer and closer to her he realized how foolish his
earlier thoughts had been. Seeing her in London in the
milieu of Hatton House, was one thing but here,
amidst this pomp and enormous wealth, he suddenly
knew how unattainable she was.

It was because of this realization that, by the time he
stepped in front of her, he was totally composed and
able to flash his old sardonic smile. "M'lady, allow me
to thank you beforehand for your hospitality."

"O'Donnell."

She said only his name, then her eyes widened for an
instant before she closed them tightly. Her body began
to sway gently. Her hand closed tightly over his before
he could brush it with his lips.

He wasn't sure, but he thought that if he hadn't
gripped her hand to steady her, the Lady Hatton would
have crumpled in a swoon.

THE AFTERNOON WAS SPENT seeing to a hundred and
one things necessary to delight the Queen. The water
pageant was held in two parts. In the first part,
Aureola, the fairy queen, was drawn across Holdenby
Lake in a pinnace by sea gods. The second was taken
up by Father Neptune himself who, attended by
nymphs, recited a small poem hailing her as Queen of
the seas.

The idea of Aureola being the embodiment of Gloriana herself was lost on no one, much less Her Royal
Highness, who applauded and heaped enthusiastic
praise on the players.

Between the afternoon entertainments and the evening's feast Lady Hatton had little chance to think of
Rory O'Donnell. It was at the conclusion of the meal,
when the great gallery had been cleared for dancing,
that he again entered her thoughts.

Had he somehow maneuvered an invitation from the Queen? And if so, had it been done to further his own ends?

Or had it been done to see her?

As she danced, Elizabeth weighed the pitfalls; not of having an affair, but of having it with an Irishman. Her Uncle Robert had mentioned several times in her presence of late how O'Donnell could be of great value to the crown, that he might have the means and support of his savage clan brothers to suppress war and bring peace at last to a wild unruly Ireland.

Savage?

She thought Rory O'Donnell anything but savage. True, his speech was strange and his manners sometimes crude. And now and then she had seen in his eyes and sensed in the aura of his person an unbridled wildness.

But never savagery.

Not even the night many months before, when he had been so forward as to steal a kiss on their first meeting.

The thought of that night, and the many dream-filled nights since then, made Elizabeth search for him in the crowded room.

When she couldn't find him immediately, she felt slighted that he had retired before dancing with her at least once.

And then her gaze fell upon him standing by one of the tall leaded windows that led out to the torchlit gardens. He was chatting and openly flirting with the ladies around him.

She was admiring the striking figure he made in a black doublet shot with silver thread when she realized that he *was* flirting with the obviously admiring women around him. Worse yet, the smile he passed from one adoring feminine face to another was the smile that Elizabeth had begun to think he reserved only for her.

"So sorry, m'lady," said her partner.

"What? Oh, that's quite all right, my fault really."

And it was. Her mind had not been on her feet, making her crash into her partner on a roundelay. It required all her concentration to pass around the floor again. But when they once more came near the little group by the window, she couldn't keep her eyes averted.

Their eyes met, and now the wide smile was directed at her. The mockery on his lips told her he knew that he had been the cause of the recent faux pas.

Elizabeth felt the heat flush her face and flood down her throat to her breasts. Quickly she turned away, only to again crash into her partner, Lord Hebert.

"So sorry, m'lord."

" 'Tis nothing, m'lady, but...."

"Yes?"

"The music has changed. The dance is no longer a pavane. It is now the saraband."

The flush deepened until Elizabeth was sure her face and breasts were a darker hue than the purpurice she used to redden her lips.

"Why, so it is." She covered her embarrassment by moving into the squat lord's arms and moving with the rhythms of the new fad, in which men and women danced together.

Hebert's lips were near her ear. "You know, m'lady, that the Puritans claim this dance entices wanton and obscene behavior and is meant to inflame lust."

Elizabeth jerked her head back and stared into the man's jowly, pock-marked face. *My God,* she thought, barely suppressing a giggle, *the man really means it.* Her eye traveled from Hebert's paunchy frame on its spindly legs to Rory O'Donnell. The vision of the tall Irishman, with his immense shoulders, his clear dark complexion, and his heavily muscled thighs, made the comparison ludicrous.

Her gaze returned to Hebert. "I'm sure, m'lord, that any lust involved in the dance is more in the mind of the viewer than in the tired body of the dancer."

"Uh, yea, of course, of course." It was his turn to sport a flushed face as the music ended and he excused himself to scurry away.

"Here." Elizabeth motioned to a servant carrying a tray. She was just lifting the glass of wine to her lips when the music suddenly stopped altogether. The reason for its demise was the Queen's voice, raised high in anger and ringing down the length of the hall.

"You would do well, m'Lord Essex, to practice subtlety!"

"I assure Your Majesty—"

"Fie on your damnable assurances! They are like foul wind from a cow's arse, fleetingly there when chased by a light wind!"

Heads turned away from the warring pair. Light conversation continued to buzz through the hall, but all ears were attuned to the Queen and her sometime favorite.

The reason for the outburst was well known. Essex had been badgering the Queen for days about the upcoming appointment of attorney general. It was a powerful position, and Essex wanted it for Francis Bacon.

The recent Essex-Bacon faux pas in Parliament had grown into a serious loss of prestige for the earl, which threatened to sway the loyalty of his followers.

"Such matters," continued the Queen, "are in the

province of m'Lord Burghley, and I have his word that he leans toward a man of age and experience.''

"And would that man be Edward Coke?" Essex bellowed, moving toward the state of petulant rage everyone knew so well.

The Queen smiled, her darkened teeth gleaming almost cruelly in her chalked face. "I do believe it would."

"And I say age is irrelevant to the appointment! If Coke's beard ran gray with the knowledge of antiquity he would still be no match for Francis Bacon!"

The Queen's smile never wavered, but her voice became taut. "I would remind m'Lord Essex that his Queen will not be badgered into yielding to a brash youth's every whim."

"Brash... *youth*?" Essex sputtered.

"And I would further remind m'Lord Essex that had he spoken such brash words to my father Henry, a less offense than this would have caused a man to be banished from the royal presence forever."

"Your Highness, I only want what's best for England and—"

"And m'Lord Essex!" She leaned toward her would-be tormentor and spoke in a lower tone, but one that still carried well. "A good lesson to learn is that youth does have certain lessons to learn from age."

Essex stomped from the hall and Gloriana turned to the orchestra. "Play! I would have music rather than the sound of baying hounds!" The wide smile once again graced her face.

Everyone in the hall, except Essex himself, knew that his angry departure was exactly what the Queen had wanted and had maneuvered him into.

The music swelled into another lively saraband, and an arm slid around Lady Hatton's waist.

"May I, m'lady?"

It was O'Donnell. She had no choice, they were already moving.

"I see why foreign courts call England a paradise for women, a prison for servants and a hell for horses. I see also that the attitude of your good Queen doth set the pace for the independence I see in English-women."

It was all Elizabeth could do to still the beating in her breast caused by their touching hands and his strong arm at her waist. It took all her concentration to match his light tone with her own voice when at last she could speak.

"In England, civilized attitudes toward women prevail."

"Perhaps, but they're hardly practical. I think you spend too much time out of your husband's sight, riding to the hunt, playing at cards, gossiping with friends and making merry at churchings and funerals. In Ireland we make good wives by properly beating and bedding our women regularly."

Elizabeth reacted to his words by stiffening her spine. She tried to pull away, but his arm was like a vise. Instead of furthering the distance between them, she found her breasts pressed to his chest.

"Methinks, Irishman, that you would have wives be no more than young men's mistresses, middle-aged companions and old men's nurses. For myself I would have more."

The firmness of his hold relaxed slightly and his face moved until he was staring down at her. "Oh? And what more would you have, m'lady?"

You, she thought, and immediately cursed herself for thinking it.

She was lost for an answer, and he read it in her eyes.

The old grin returned around the perfect flashing teeth; impudent, insolent, and forward.

How changeable he is, she thought. For months after their first meeting in the carriage, after the kiss that had made her mind soar even before her wedding day, he had deviled her with his brashness and his open stares. He had been so sure of himself that he had challenged her with his silent words, "Someday, m'lady, someday."

And then his demeanor had altered. His eyes had softened. Rather than daring, they had become pleading, reaching out to her even in her dreams.

"No, m'lady, methinks it is you who haunt me," he had said that day. Those words had brought them close, had suddenly made her want to throw caution and position to the winds and glide into his arms.

Now he was his old self, sardonic, brazen, challenging rather than pleading, unreachable rather than vulnerable.

Well, she thought as the music ended and she took a step backward out of his arms, *I'll have none of it.*

"I think you've learned a knee and mayhap a bit of our English dancing, Rory O'Donnell, but you've mastered naught of our manners, nor the skill to tell the difference between an Irish workerwoman and an English lady!"

Instead of anger flooding his handsome features, the grin grew wider. "I beg to differ, m'lady. I think I've learned all too well the difference between an Irish warrior's wife and her pampered English counterpart. An English wife finds herself too often bored. She must create diversions for herself, and too often those diversions put horns on her husband and fill the bawdy courts to overflowing."

All color drained from Elizabeth's face. He had

struck the chord, too close. Both fear and embarrassment filled her mind, and her body shook.

If there were words, she couldn't find them. Doing her best not to waver on her feet she turned and walked as quickly as possible away from him. She had to lose herself, to hide from him—and from the confession she knew was clearly stamped on her face and in her eyes.

Had she turned the second before she disappeared into the crowd, she would have seen the smile fade from Rory's face and the look of sadness she had seen before return to his eyes.

And now, m'lady, my love, he thought, *let us hope that it will be easier to keep some distance between our yearning bodies in the weeks to come.*

CHAPTER TWENTY

THE QUEEN'S MARSHAL, Henry Bagenal, swung wide the heavy iron-barred gate and stepped back.

Sir James Blake's vacant eyes stared down the narrow spiraling stairs and his nose twitched as the dank odors wafted from the dungeons of Dublin Castle below and reached his nostrils.

"Watch your step," Bagenal growled. "The damp is everywhere and the drafts make it difficult to keep the torches lit."

Blake nodded. Part of the smell emanated from the burning animal fat used in the torches, which rested every few feet along the moisture-dripping wall. He pulled a kerchief from his sleeve, held it over his nose and started down.

The gate clanged behind him and the narrow passageway echoed with Bagenal's heavy tread.

Blake had just met the newly appointed Queen's Marshal, and there had been an immediate rapport between them. Unlike his father and predecessor in the office, who had tended toward conciliation with the Irish lords, Henry Bagenal would have their heads and be done with it.

The stairs ended and they entered a long corridor wide enough to again allow them to walk side by side.

Bagenal immediately returned the conversation to the subject the two had been avidly discussing on the upper level.

"I tell ye, it gets worse and it will not get better. The harpers and poets are brave again. They smell rebellion and they've started chanting their martial songs across the country, stirring the rabble!"

"It isn't rabble," Blake offered, "that wins wars."

"In Ireland I'm not so sure, me friend. O'Neill gains power almost daily, and we have no one to blame but ourselves."

"Ourselves?" Blake countered. "Come, Bagenal, you mean our Queen, do you not?"

Bagenal shifted his eyes to Blake's, liked what he saw and nodded.

"Aye. The latest instructions from Whitehall and the Queen's hand differ naught from others these months past, and are as impossible to administrate. She would have us increase the Irish revenues without oppressing the Irish. She orders me to reduce my armies without impairing their efficiency. She would have Bingham in Connaught punish rebels without driving them to desperation, and reward loyalists without cost to the crown!"

"And without the Queen's writ, Henry Bagenal, what would you do?"

"Do? I'd drive their bloody arses into the sea and drink a tankard watching them drown!"

Sir James Blake agreed with Bagenal.

He didn't agree with Robert Cecil, and had told him so in the brief conversation they had had before he left London.

"Sir Robert, we have spies in all the known world," he had said. "We have every Spanish move registered. We know the mood of the Netherlands as well as Italy. We know within the hour what wench Henry of France has bedded. Yet in Ireland our intelligence is like a lost ship in heavy fog."

"What would you have us do, Sir James?" Robert had replied.

"Assassinate the Irish lords, one and all. Without the heads the bodies will do our bidding."

Robert Cecil's features had contorted into a grimace of distaste at the suggestion. "We preserve the lives of the Irish earls as a matter of policy—"

"That policy, Sir Robert, will have an Irish king on the Irish throne."

And that Sir James Blake didn't want. The ownership of his Irish lands depended on English rule without *any* Irish control. O'Neill, O'Hara and O'Donnell were all striving to be great Irish lords. Blake was not so naive that he didn't realize that to be great Irish lords they must also, by necessity, be great Irish rebels.

And in time all rebels rebel.

They came to a second arched, iron-barred gate. At a motion from Bagenal it was opened by a guard and they stepped through.

"This way!" Bagenal guided him through one cavernous chamber into an even larger one, brightly lit by blazing torches all around the gray stone walls.

Three men were standing together near the far wall.

All three of them were stripped to the waist, and their upper bodies gleamed with perspiration in the dancing light from the torches.

A fourth man was stark naked. His body, which also gleamed in the torchlight, was suspended three feet off the stone floor by manacles attached to his wrists. The manacles in turn were attached to chains that ran up into the darkness twenty feet or more above them.

"How long has he been hanging?" Blake asked.

"Two and a half, perhaps three hours this time."

"And nothing?"

"Nothing."

Blake's eyes moved slowly over the man's lean frame. The muscles of his shoulders had long ago knotted, and there were discolorations all up and down his arms. Blake was a skilled and experienced interrogator. He knew just how much pain to inflict to get the information he desired, and could usually gauge how much pain a man could take before he gave it.

This man had already withstood a great deal more pain than was normal. Blake guessed that it would take more than the iron manacles biting into his wrists or the stretching of his body to make him talk.

His eyes wandered around the chamber with familiarity. The room was little different from other rooms like it in London Tower, the Gatehouse, the Marshalsea Prison, or the Clink.

Blake had used them all.

He spied a rack in a far corner. In the center of the room hot coals gleamed in a forge used for the heating of irons. A Spanish chair complete with straps, and with iron boots specially made to hold hot oil, sat in yet another corner.

He rejected them all and turned to Bagenal.

"Do you have a scavenger's daughter?"

In the darkness of his beard, Bagenal's pink lower lip disappeared between his teeth in a moment of hesitation before answering. Manacles were one thing. The use of the ultimate torture device was another.

"Aye, sir, we do. But by law the Queen's warrant is needed—"

"My dear fellow, I know the law only too well. The Queen's warrant is needed in all cases where it is necessary for the Queen's men to obtain a confession or information using extreme devices that could cause death to the prisoner. I also know that we are not in London. We are in the wilds of Ireland and far from the Queen's ear. Can these men be trusted?"

"Aye."

"Then ready the scavenger's daughter!"

As hard and cruel a man as Henry Bagenal was, even he flinched before the flintlike coldness he saw in Sir James Blake's eyes. He knew the man's reputation with the rapier and dagger at his belt. He had only heard rumors of the darker side of the man's character, and the deeds that had been attributed to it.

Now, although he stood a head taller and a third wider in body, Bagenal felt insignificant under the man's icy stare.

"I'll have it done."

Blake nodded in satisfaction and moved to the prisoner. He waved the three men away and retrieved a filthy rag from a basin of water.

Gently, with deft fingers, he mopped the blood, the grime and the sweat from the man's face.

One swollen, blackened eye opened, struggled, and finally focused.

"You're called the harper," Blake said in a gentle voice.

"Aye."

"Cormac, the harper."

"Aye."

"Of what clan are you, harper?"

"None. I'm a man of the forests and mountains, a free man. I owe no clan nor man allegiance."

Blake smiled. He dipped the rag into the basin's murky water and finished wiping the man's face.

"Of what clan are you, harper?"

"None. I'm a man of the forests...."

The harper's words dissolved into an ear-piercing scream.

Blake had put his arms around the man's waist and added his own weight to the harper's, to suspend them both by the manacles attached to Cormac's wrists.

He remained so for nearly a minute before letting his own feet regain the floor.

The scream died.

"I require much information from you, master harper. I would have it from you and leave you alive if possible. You could do our good and gentle Queen a great service alive, back in your forests and mountains You do love our Queen, do you not, master harper?"

There was no answer.

"You have been carefully watched, harper. You travel a great deal between Maguire at Enniskillen and the castles of Ballylee and Donegal. Do O'Donnell and O'Hara plan on joining Maguire?"

Silence.

"You were caught with an Irish party buying powder and muskets from the Scots. To which great Irish lord were you to deliver those arms? O'Donnell? O'Hara? Maguire? Or perhaps they were bound for the Queen's great ally in the north, The O'Neill himself?"

Again the eyelid levered open to study its tormentor. But the harper didn't utter a sound.

Blake slid a hand inside his doublet. When it reappeared he held a printed penny sheet.

"Several of these were found in your pack, harper. Are you an educated peasant? Do you read English?"

A mumble.

"What?"

"Aye, I read the heathen tongue."

"But I doubt you write it this well." Blake turned the paper to his own eyes and read:

"Englishmen and truemen of the Catholic faith. How long must we starve for landlords who wear their lands upon their backs and let the fields stay fallow? How long must we bow to an aging Queen who turns her ears to foppish advisors, who in turn have no ears for their starving people? Must our daughters become whores and our sons thieves to survive...?"

Blake folded the paper and replaced it in his doublet. "There is more, much more. But you know that, do you not, harper?" Again he stared deeply into the harper's swollen eye.

"This is seditious treason, here or in England. But it is curious to me that you should have it. Why is that, harper? Why is an Irish vagabond harper carrying such filth in Ireland? And where did it come from? Are there more of these sheets, and if so, where are they bound? Surely not the booleys of Tyrone and Donegal. A great many questions, and I would have answers, harper... now!"

Again Blake's weight was applied to the harper's middle, and again the chamber echoed with an agonizing scream. This time Blake hung for a full minute before releasing him.

"Tell me, harper, and save yourself more pain!"

The lips moved but not to form words. The harper gathered all the spittle he could muster from his dry throat and mouth, and sprayed Blake's face.

Sir James didn't flinch. His thin-lipped smile remained, and his coldly staring eyes never wavered.

"You are indeed a brave man, master harper, but foolish. The manacles and the rack are nothing to a man like you, and I know it."

Bagenal appeared at his elbow. "It is ready."

"Good. We shall test your bravery and your body now, harper, in the scavenger's daughter. Ahh, I see you know the device. Good. Braver men than you have fainted at its mention. Bring him down!"

The three half-naked men lowered the harper's body to the floor and began removing the manacles.

Blake turned to Henry Bagenal.

"Do you have fresh water and a clean cloth? The scum's sweat has stained my doublet."

THE AIR WAS CRISP. Early morning haze wafted from the damp meadows as they guided their horses free of the hedgerows and into the open meadows.

Rory rode alone just behind Sir Robert Cecil and Lady Hatton. Sir Robert had arrived the evening before with papers from London for the Queen's signature and news of some interest to the Irishman.

O'Neill's only source of supply from the sea were the ships of Grace O'Malley. Those same ships could be used to shift arms and men from one point to another.

But not now.

Richard Bingham, the Queen's lord lieutenant in Connaught, had pacified the Burkes. This left Grace O'Malley stranded and forced to sue for peace in order to survive. The Queen had already given Cecil the authority to grant Grace O'Malley an audience at Whitehall at the end of the summer progress.

Rory could do nothing about the pirate Queen's defection, but he could and did rail against Sir Richard Bingham's army moving north out of Connaught into Ballylee and Donegal.

So far his objections had been to no avail, but Sir Robert was wavering.

Elizabeth Hatton's merry laugh reached his ears through the morning air. "Surely, uncle, you jest! Your Barbary is a male, and as any falconer knows, inferior to the female for the hunt!"

"Ahh, my dear, perhaps true in some cases," Sir Robert replied. "But I do believe I have an eye for training, as well as the bird to train. And this male Barbary will fly higher and stoop faster than your peregrine."

"We shall see," Elizabeth laughed.

Sir Robert turned in his saddle. "The Barbary is an Irish bird. What think you, O'Donnell? Male Barbary or female peregrine?"

"Indeed, Sir Robert, it is an idle match, as a hawk against a dove. True, the peregrine, being female, is more vicious and more maneuverable. But the Barbary, being larger, stronger and swifter, would prove the victor."

"The victor in what, may I ask?" Elizabeth said icily, without turning to face Rory.

"Why, in a hawk to hawk match, m'lady."

Sir Robert guffawed and pulled his horse up short. "What say you, niece? A hawk to hawk match? The male against the female?"

"It would be an idle match," Elizabeth replied. "They would do naught but soar."

"I think not," Rory said, reining around to draw up

with them. "With no game in the air, they would turn on each other."

"He is right," Sir Robert said, gently caressing the huge bird on his wrist. "What say you, Elizabeth, to a thousand pounds?"

Elizabeth's green eyes flashed anger at O'Donnell, and then turned to her uncle in defiance. "'Tis a wager. And 'twill be a pity, uncle, that you have no bird for the rest of the day's hunt."

"We shall see," Cecil chuckled. "O'Donnell, set us off!"

Rory backed his horse enough distance from the pair so he would be no distraction for the birds, and gave the first command. "Ready your hoods!"

Both of them unfastened the leather thongs holding the hoods over the falcons' throats, all the while singsonging to the birds the gentle phrases used by their respective trainers during feeding time.

"Hoods!"

The hoods came off. Both birds blinked at the sudden light, but quickly adapted.

"Go!"

Elizabeth's arm lifted slightly before Cecil's, and the peregrine was first off, swooping low through the trees and then rising.

Sir Robert's Barbary lifted from his wrist and climbed immediately. Quickly the magnificent falcon gained an altitude high above the peregrine and began gliding in ever widening circles.

"Useless," Elizabeth said. "They only look for game."

Rory looked up at her face, alive with the hunt, her eyes bright with the anticipation of victory.

"M'lady does love the hunt," he said.

She glanced at him and smiled, momentarily forgetting the strained animosity that had grown between them during the past week.

"Oh, I do. I would have every morning like this. I love the baying of the hounds and the hawk's bells, and I would have it always thus."

"I have the feeling, m'lady, that for you there will always be fine horses, good dogs, and the tinkle of the falcon's bells on your wrist."

But Elizabeth hadn't heard a word he had said. Her face was again lifted to the sky and the peregrine.

"The Barbary has spotted her!" Sir Robert whooped.

"No matter," Elizabeth said, but her heart began beating faster.

Indeed, the Barbary had spotted the smaller bird. Finding no movement of game on the ground, his attention had turned to the sky around and beneath him.

His effortless circle grew wider and wider, while the peregrine continued to tire herself swooping just above the trees in a vain search for a kill.

Then the Barbary's huge wings folded and he dropped like a stone from the sky. The soaring body was corrected in flight by the tail, and he was directly above the peregrine and dropping faster.

"He's got her!"

"Not yet," Elizabeth cried. "Fly, little bird!"

At the last second the peregrine sensed the danger above her. She beat her wings furiously, catching an air current and swooping up in an arc away from the Barbary.

But it was too late.

The huge wings came open, stalling the Barbary in the air. The talons splayed open and the peregrine seemed to fly right into them.

The talons closed and the Barbary's lethal beak came

down swiftly. There was a barely discernible screech from the peregrine and it was over, with the Barbary sailing back to where Sir Robert sat his horse, twirling the lure around his head on a leather thong.

The falcon dropped his prey at the horse's feet and caught the lure in his beak before settling on Sir Robert's wrist.

Rory retrieved the peregrine, and looked up from it into Elizabeth's flushed face.

"Alas, m'lady, I think you can see it was no match. The Irish male has vanquished the English female."

She spurred her horse and nearly knocked Rory to his knees before bolting through the trees.

"An odd analogy, O'Donnell," said Sir Robert.

"Merely a jest, Sir Robert. But I'm afraid not well taken."

THE SCAVENGER'S DAUGHTER was the brainchild of Leonard Skeffington, who had lived during the reign of Henry VIII. It had a twofold advantage in the art of interrogation. Because of its size it was much more portable than its predecessor, the rack, and it accomplished its desired ends much more quickly.

In method of operation it worked exactly the opposite from the rack. Where the wheel of the rack stretched the body, drawing the joints apart, the scavenger's daughter constricted and bound the body into a ball. The lower legs were pressed to the thighs, the thighs against the chest and belly, and the arms to the sides. Around the whole went two large iron clamps that were regulated by a corkscrew vise.

In the guardroom adjacent to the chamber, Blake was explaining the various successes he had had in the past with the device when they heard the harper's first screams.

Bagenal immediately shifted the conversation. Blake let his lips curl into a slight smile and sipped his wine. For all the man's bravado, Bagenal was obviously squeamish about the darker side of backstairs intrigue.

"Did you know, Sir James, that the Irish service is so dreaded by English soldiers now that the rogues will venture any punishment or imprisonment to escape it?"

Blake nodded but heard few of the man's words. His attention was on the pitch and frequency of the harper's screams. His ear had become so attuned that he could tell when too dangerous a pressure was being applied, or when the man was about to break because of the right amount of pressure.

"What? I'm sorry. My mind wandered."

Bagenal repeated his statement. "Their tactics are strange, these Irishmen. They don't fight like regular armies in the field. They break up into small bands and strike like snakes. Before you can mount a counter-attack the devils have disappeared back into the forests."

Blake rolled his eyes upward. "Then the proper counterattack would be to cut down all the trees and scorch the forests. Then they would have no place to hide."

Bagenal's eyes widened. "Aye, now there's an answer. Have you had much time in the field, Sir James?"

"None," Blake replied, pouring himself a second glass of wine.

And he wouldn't have, Blake thought. The field of battle and a bloody death on the end of a lance were for heroes like Essex and Bagenal. Blake had no intention of dying, let alone in battle.

And he also had his own theories about the Irish

wars, if they came. He sensed that they would be won not by foot and horse and cannon, but by treachery.

Bagenal was about to speak again when Blake held up his hand. "I think our harper has reached his limit."

The words had barely left Blake's lips when one of the guards appeared beneath the arch separating the room from the chamber.

"He's blubberin', sir, but speaking somethin' like words."

"Good." Blake stood up and motioned to Bagenal. "Bring your wine, Sir Henry, we'll have a chat."

But for his size, the harper could have been a fetus still ensconced in the womb, so compressed were his limbs to his body.

Blake knelt, placing his smiling face close to the harper's. Even though the bands around his body had been eased, the man's features were still contorted in a mask of agony.

"A little wine, harper... for the throat?"

The man drank.

"Good, you'll feel much better now." Blake's voice was soothing, the words intoned softly in the harper's ear so the others had to strain to hear. "Shall we begin now?"

"I... I am but a harper, not a soldier, so I know little." Each word was punctuated by a gasp for breath.

"We shall see what you know. We know Maguire is planning a major battle at Enniskillen. He would stop Sir Richard Bingham from moving farther north. Will O'Hara and O'Donnell come to his aid?"

"No. O'Hara wants nothing more than the Queen's peace. He would live at Ballylee and let the war, if there is a war, pass him by."

"And Red Hugh, The O'Donnell?"

"Red Hugh would fight, but only if Bingham moved into Donegal and tried to shire his lands. O'Donnell looks to O'Neill for council, and O'Neill bids him to keep the peace. Red Hugh also fears his exiled brother, Rory, who would have his titles and lands if he fights at Maguire's side and loses."

Blake pondered this for a moment. He knew of the arrangement between O'Donnell and Cecil, giving the Irishman free rein to act as liaison between Whitehall and the clans. He had thought it naive and foolish, but so far it seemed to be working. If the harper's words were true, it would continue to work.

"The arms you were buying from the Scots, harper. . .where were they bound?"

"Hugh Maguire. I am of the Maguire clan."

A natural answer, Blake thought, *and probably a lie.* Maguire had already openly declared himself a rebel. His illegal purchase of powder and shot was expected.

"And now the penny sheets. From where did they come?"

"I don't know."

"I do, harper. . .Brussels. Who was their author?"

"I don't know."

"How come you by them?"

"The Scots."

"You lie, harper. The gallowglass Scot, like all mercenaries, cares naught about the smuggling of paper. They can neither fight with paper nor eat it, so it has no value. Where, harper, and are there more of these sheets?"

Again the harper was silent.

Blake stood and motioned the guards back to the vise. "You tell me nothing, harper. We shall try again." He drew Henry Bagenal to the side. "Stay with him. Apply the bands in ten-minute intervals. I would have some supper. Call me when he has had enough.''

Blake moved back into the guardroom and climbed the steep spiral stairway to the upper quarters of the castle.

He had just finished a light meal of roast capon when Bagenal, his face slightly ashen, entered the room.

"Well?"

"He blubbers. I think the man knows not of what he speaks. Mayhap we've squeezed too much blood from the body to the brain."

"But he did speak!" Blake barked, suddenly finding Bagenal's squeamishness tiresome.

"Aye. Red Hugh has already sent two hundred foot south in small groups to reinforce Maguire."

Blake felt elation soar through his body. The scavenger's daughter never failed. "What else?"

"The printing on the sheets *was* done in Brussels, by Sir Brian Russell."

"I know of him," Blake nodded. "A Jesuit sympathizer who puts his faith above his Queen and country."

"And the sheets are bound for England as part of a plan to raise the street rabble in rebellion."

"Where are they now?"

"Bound in the hold of the *Bridey Mae* in Clew Bay...about five thousand of 'em."

"The *Bridey Mae*?"

"A pirate and smuggling ship captained by Grace O'Malley."

"So that's how they'll get them into England," Blake said, his fingers rubbing his chin as he thought.

"I'll send a messenger at once to Bingham, so he'll know Maguire has been reinforced."

"No...no, I'll take care of it. I'll have to go to Connaught anyway ιo deal with this business of the rebel literature.''

Blake's mind was whirling. One of the reasons he had begged Cecil to send him on this trip was to find some way to convince Whitehall that further Irish rebellion should be stopped now, before it started.

What better way than to have Sir Richard Bingham outmanned and routed at Enniskillen?

He dabbed a linen napkin to his lips, dropped it on the table and rubbed his hands together. "Let us go back down, Bagenal, and find out what other gems of knowledge our harper has!"

'' 'Twill do no good, Sir James. The harper's dead.''

THE HUNT HAD BEEN GOOD: two cranes, several small birds and a bag of hares.

Riding back to Holdenby, Sir Robert was in high spirits. It seemed to Rory the perfect time to press his needs.

"I would to London on the morrow, Sir Robert.''

"Why so?''

"Methinks I've been too long without word from my couriers, and your news of Maguire troubles me.''

"Have your couriers ride to the progress.''

Rory had been close to Cecil long enough now to fathom the man's brilliant deviousness. "Should they do that, Sir Robert, you would know them well and have their every move watched. 'Twas part of our agreement that that should never be, else they would not trust me.''

"True,'' Cecil said, chuckling, "but hold a while longer, lad. You have won the Queen's eye with your dancing, and her ear with your quick tongue. She would have your company on progress a few more weeks.''

"In a few more weeks we might have war in Ireland and all our work would be to no avail."

"Fear not, O'Donnell. It would seem you have done your work well."

"Oh?"

"Aye. Do you remember Blake?"

"Aye."

"He's done a bit of good work in Dublin. I've word that the rebel Maguire will get no help from the northern clans. With Maguire defeated, I give you my word that Bingham will do no shiring of the land beyond Lough Erne."

Well enough, Rory thought, but a pathway to the north would then be open, and he knew his brother would never allow that, no matter what O'Neill said.

Rory had come to expect Cecil's method of shifting the conversation when a certain subject no longer interested him. He did it now.

"How goes your skill with a rapier?"

Rory turned in the saddle, leveling a glaring eye on the smaller man. "So you haven't lifted the hounds from my trail."

Cecil lifted a hand, palm outward. "None of it, I assure you, lad. I know of your schooling innocently, through the fencing master in Blackfriars, Thomas Bruskett."

"Has Master Bruskett come running to court with news that the Irishman, O'Donnell, would learn the rapier?"

"Nay. Bruskett's real name is Brushetti. He is a foreigner—Italian—and a Catholic. As such he must report himself and his students weekly. I know of your nightly attendance by hearsay only, I assure you."

Rory breathed an internal sigh of relief. Cecil's words of explanation rang true. Before leaving London

Rory had been using the frequent excursions to Black-friars not only to master the rapier, but also for clandestine meetings with Robert Southwell and Ned Bull.

"What think you of the new French weapon, now that you know it?"

"I think," Rory replied, "that the slender rapier and dagger will replace sword and buckler in a gentleman's fight."

Cecil nodded. "I agree, though I'm an expert at neither. The rapier is as elegant and deadly as its predecessors were sturdy and brutal. Know you of James Blake's prowess?"

"I've heard."

"Then know something else, O'Donnell. It is said that in a gentleman's duel with rapiers, the tall man will be spitted like a rabbit by the shorter one." So saying, he turned and looked nearly straight up at Rory.

Rory returned the man's steady look with a smile. "Would that be a warning, Sir Robert?"

"Aye, lad, in truth it would. Never believe that what you see is all there is of a man. There is more to Blake than your eye can find."

"Methinks, Sir Robert, that you truly care for my welfare!"

Suddenly Cecil smiled, and his whole manner changed, becoming almost jovial. "Aye, that I do, and admire you as well. I believe you an honest man, Rory O'Donnell, and a brave one, like all Irishmen. I admire your O'Neill as well. In fact he fascinates me. . . for he thinks like an Englishman."

"Oh?"

"Aye, he has a great and ruthless mind, as do I. Tell me, is it true he strangled his own cousin when he was but fourteen?"

For the fifth or more time that day Rory felt he was

being baited. But he had no choice but to go along the path Cecil led. "I believe it so."

"I suppose that's what fascinates me. And in a way makes me slightly envious...O'Neill's great mind in the body of an equally great warrior. You know, of course, that I have never been in battle."

"Then I envy you, Sir Robert."

The smaller man paid no attention as he guided his horse away from the path and the rest of the party. "A shortcut." Rory followed. "Indeed, I've never killed a man. I often wonder how much skill and bravery it requires for one man to kill another."

"It takes neither skill nor bravery, Sir Robert. It takes a will to survive."

"Well said."

Deeper and deeper into the trees they went, until the sun was all but blotted out by the foliage overhead.

"How old were you when you killed your first man, Rory O'Donnell?"

Coming from Cecil it seemed an odd question, but it made Rory think. In truth, he found it difficult to remember, and began to see a reason for the little hunchback's questioning.

"I think...I think I was just fifteen."

"Hmm, a boy, but only a year older than O'Neill was."

"Sir Robert—"

"'Tis said that O'Neill could entertain our Queen with a simple meal under the pines at Dungannon, and enchant her with English grace and manners as well as verse. And then at the end of the meal he could turn from Her Majesty and order one of his henchmen to murder a peasant for entertainment."

"Perhaps, Sir Robert, that is what makes O'Neill great."

"Yes, perhaps it is." Suddenly the little man was up in the saddle, standing in the stirrups with his arms extended. "What ho! There!"

"What?"

"A stag. . . a beauty!"

Rory spotted it, a large brown buck dappled with gray. He stood about thirty yards in front of them, pawing the pine needles and shifting his huge rack as if he might charge.

"What luck!" Cecil cried gleefully. "Let us make the hunt complete."

"But—but. . ." Rory stammered, "we have no bows, no muskets."

"Then we'll improvise, man. Ride!"

Sir Robert spurred his horse forward at a gallop. Rory had no choice but to follow. The deer turned and leaped away.

It was all Rory could do to maneuver his mount behind the other rider. Ahead of him Sir Robert had melted into the saddle. The upper half of his twisted body was so far forward that the hump in his darkly cloaked shoulder seemed to be one with the horse's bobbing, foaming neck.

"Around, around!" Sir Robert cried, frantically waving an arm. "Head him off! Make him skirt the trees once he reaches the clearing!"

Insanity, Rory thought, *and useless.* What did the man hope to achieve? Nothing could be gained but running the stag and tiring the horses. It was a one-way match.

But he kneed his mount around and broke for the large clearing to which Sir Robert had pointed. It was obvious that the little man was using the trees to herd the stag in that direction.

But then what, Rory wondered. Once in the clearing

they had even less chance of catching him. And once they did catch him, what would follow? A bloody wound for the horse's flanks, most likely, should the stag decide to turn and use his rack.

The clearing was about two hundred yards across. Rory reached its center, wheeled his mount around and waited.

He had to admire Cecil as a horseman. The man used only his knees to guide his mount, for he was waving a plumed hat in one hand and a short sword in the other.

Slowly but surely, in a zigzag pattern, stag and horseman made their way toward the break in the trees, the clearing, and Rory.

And then they were there, the stag wild-eyed and snorting as he lowered his powerful head.

"Charge him! Turn him, lad!"

My God, Rory thought, suddenly getting an inkling of Cecil's intent, *the fool thinks he's in a tiltyard!*

But not to be outdone, Rory laid spurs to his horse's flanks and met the stag's charge.

At the last second the huge deer bolted, pausing a moment before veering. Rory veered with him, and the stag's hesitation gave Cecil enough time to reach him on the other side.

"Close in! Flank him with your mount!" Sir Robert screamed.

Rory did, until the froth on his horse's flank was nearly mixing with the foam running from the stag's sleek coat.

Three abreast they thundered toward the wall of trees on the opposite side of the clearing. Cecil was again up in his saddle, his body leaning far out over his horse's head.

"You fool," Rory cried, "watch his points!"

The jagged spurs of the stag's rack danced all around

Sir Robert's head. But the man seemed impervious to them, and Rory swore that he actually heard a cackling laugh erupt from his throat.

"Turn him...turn him in!"

Rory reined his horse to the left. The collision was made and the buck veered in an arching turn.

They were headed back toward the center of the clearing when Cecil left his mount. Like a misshapen black arrow he hurtled through the air and hovered for an instant above the stag.

And then, like the Barbary falcon, he dropped on his prey. The little man's left hand shot forward, miraculously missed impalement on a point, and found the core of the stag's right horn.

He yanked. The big buck's head came around to the right and his body followed. Like a dervish, man and deer whirled. At the completion of the second circle Cecil's right arm came down in an arc.

The aim was true, the cut deep. And then Cecil deftly pulled the short sword back for the final death wound.

The stag bellowed once and then pitched forward.

Again Cecil was in the air, gracefully leaving the stag's body and rolling over and over in the grass.

Rory sat his horse in awe. No man could say that what he had just seen was possible. But his eyes hadn't lied.

By the time Rory slid from his horse, Cecil was already on his feet, standing over his kill.

"Are you all right?" the Irishman said, rushing to the other man's side.

"Fit...I'm fit!" His grin was almost boyish as he turned his face up to Rory's. "What think you the Queen's pleasure for fresh venison tonight?"

"I think you would garner the Queen's wrath were she to know how it was killed."

Cecil shrugged and laughed aloud. "Perhaps, but no matter." He reached up and clamped a hand on Rory's shoulder. "You thought me a fool, did you not, lad?"

"Aye, and still do. The risk was greater than the reward."

"Was it? Perhaps." His grin faded and his dark eyes pulled Rory's until they met. "But now you know."

"Know what, Sir Robert?"

"You know never to believe that what you see of a man is all there is."

CHAPTER TWENTY-ONE

IT WAS NEARING the third week of the Queen's stay at Holdenby. The lavish entertainments of the first two weeks, the elaborate water pageants, firework displays and masques, had given way to more frequent hunts, an occasional bearbaiting, and forays into the countryside to let the people see their Queen.

But if the staged entertainments had slackened, the huge feasts, the dancing, and the evenings spent gambling at gleek and other games continued unabated.

Rory had practically given up receiving any news from London until the end of summer, but then he was contacted by Ned Bull through one of his rogues. The old highwayman had managed to place the man at Holdenby as an extra stablehand during the Queen's stay.

On two different occasions O'Donnell had managed to slip away from the hunting party. The first time he met Ned Bull himself, and the news was good.

Working through his hired lieutenants, Ned had managed to unify a good number of the rogues and

street people of London. With some system and
organization, they were terrorizing London by night
and making it just slightly less fearful by day.

Haskins had received word from Ireland that
Russell's penny sheets inciting rebellion would arrive
aboard the *Bridey Mae* at the time of Grace O'Malley's
audience with the Queen. Ned himself would see to
smuggling them off the ship and getting them into
Southwell's hands.

But something was bothering Ned and, upon hearing
what it was, it bothered Rory also. The Jesuits were using the unrest created by Ned's little army to revive talk
of assassinating the Queen. Already the city was rife
with rumors, and they were spreading.

Since her reign had begun there had been sixteen attempts on Elizabeth's life. Rory had openly admired
the woman's courage and spirit in London, and even
now she rode in open carriages through the streets of
towns and along country roads alike, without seeming
to fear for her life. She even stepped from her carriage
on occasion to mingle with the crowd.

Rory guessed that this new talk of assassination
stemmed not from the moderate, mild-mannered
Robert Southwell, but from his cohort, Henry Garnet.

Ned voiced the thoughts of both of them. "'Tis
treason I do, and I know it, lad. And if I hang for it,
that won't put me in hell any more than the other deeds
I've done. As fer killin', I've done my share of that,
too. But I draws the line when it comes to the killin' of
kings and queens."

As did Rory, and he told the old outlaw so. "The
cause I fight for would be worse off than it is, Ned, if
the Queen dies anywhere but in her bed. Believe me."

He scribbled a note to Haskins, telling him to talk to
Southwell, and instructed Ned to have Garnet watched.

"An', lad, there's another thing...a favor I'd ask of ye."

Ned's rugged seamed face took on an expression Rory had never seen before; a look of care, almost sadness. It somehow made him realize how close the friendship between them had knitted in the months since their meeting at the Hound and Hare.

"Anything, Ned, you know it."

" 'Tis Annie, lad. She's wild and no saint, but she's a young one an' what she is be not her fault."

"Aye."

"I've a love for the wench, I think ye know."

"Aye, I know."

"Then promise me, lad, on yer mother's name... should anythin' happen to old Ned Bull, ye'll take care of her. Even if it means takin' her back to the wilds of Donegal with ye. 'Twould be far from what she knows, but better'n what she's got without Ned Bull."

Rory's body shook with an involuntary chill at the man's words.

Nothing could happen to Ned Bull. The man was indestructible. But in his eyes Rory saw a pleading that spoke of both friendship and trust. Readily the Irishman gave him his assurance.

"Should it ever happen, Ned Bull, little Annie will have her own corner of Donegal."

IT WAS THREE DAYS LATER when the stablehand informed Rory of the second meeting. This time it would be Annie herself he was to meet, accompanied by one of Ned's stout lads. They would be in a glen near the tiny village of Wickmore, posing as young lovers on an afternoon picnic.

Thankfully, on this day Cecil had returned from London once again with pressing matters for the

Queen's attention. Gloriana insisted that the outing take place without her. This left everyone to his own devices.

The hunting party quickly fragmented into small groups, whose intent soon became gossip and play instead of the hunt.

It was easy for Rory to slip away.

Wickmore village was a fair distance from the path of the party, but Rory traveled there in less than an hour. He gave Wickmore manor itself and the workers in the fields a wide berth, and entered the long, lonesome meadows beyond.

The day was warm, but heavily overcast and threatening rain. Using the landmarks given him by Ned's man, Rory reined his mount to a walk and searched for the couple among the primroses stretching in their golden ranks before him.

In less than ten minutes he spotted them near a stand of yew trees by a tiny stream. Annie was clad in the simple dress of a milkmaid, and her "beau" was attired as a tradesman.

Rory had barely left the saddle before the lad grasped his horse's rein and had the beast tethered. Wordlessly he then climbed to a tiny knoll to make sure they wouldn't be disturbed.

"What ho, Annie?"

"My, now, ain't we got to be the dandy!"

Rory's dress had grown even more elaborate since leaving London on progress. This day he knew he looked something of the dandy in his fine wine-colored doublet with huge slashed sleeves, and his breeches of golden cloth. The half cloak that flowed from his wide shoulders was velvet and dashing, in deep blue tones.

He grinned and made a leg. "All the better to cut as

fine a figure for my little milkmaid as I do for the Queen, m'lady.''

She moved toward him, fidgeting with trembling fingers at her skirt. It was then that Rory noticed the added lines between her wide-set eyes. Her lower lip was trembling and her eyes were misting as if they were about to sprout tears.

"Annie. . . what is it?"

Suddenly she was against him, her arms wrapped tightly around his waist, her cheek against the soft velvet at his chest.

"I'm afraid, so afraid!" Her voice was a whisper.

"Why? What is it?"

His first instinct was to draw away, meet her eyes, perhaps shake her by the shoulders. But he didn't, for he could feel the trembling that racked her frail body.

Instead he folded his own arms around her shoulders and ran a comforting hand along the back of her head and down the silky hair that hung down her back. "Is it Ned?"

"No. . . no, not yet at least."

Good God, lass, what is it? he wanted to scream. But he held his tongue and continued to stroke her head. Though he heard no sobs from her lips, he knew that she was crying. Her body seemed to vibrate like a tuning fork against his, and her thin arms gripped him like a vise.

"Annie, lass, get your wits," he whispered. "What has happened?"

"My Ned," she blubbered. "He was nearly taken by the Queen's men leaving Mistress Rigby's."

"How so?"

"Methinks betrayal."

"But he escaped."

"Aye. 'Twas a meeting to settle the place for handing over the pamphlets when they arrive."

"I know. Garnet and Southwell were there as well."

"Nay! Master Garnet never arrived. My Ned barely escaped, but he has a ball in his leg!"

Now Rory did hold her from him, staring into the eyes filled with fear—eyes bleeding huge tears that ran down her cheeks to drip from her chin.

"M'Lord Haskins?"

"Away free. That's how Ned got the ball, leading the Queen's men on a merry chase away from him."

"Then Ned was recognized?"

Annie nodded. "Most likely."

"Where is he now?"

"Hiding at an inn near Mile End. A safe place."

Rory's mind was racing. Garnet wanted martyrs to further his cause. He hadn't shown up at the meeting. Most likely he was the one who'd alerted the watch.

"Annie, you must go back. Tell Ned to stay out of London and in hiding. Tell his lads to cease the nightly robberies and the talk of rebellion until they hear differently. Everything must stay calm until this storm passes over."

She nodded, looking like a little girl again as she rubbed a sleeve across her cheeks.

Damn the Jesuits, he thought. His plan to turn Englishmen against Englishmen in the streets without the rubbish of religion had been sound. Involving Garnet and Southwell had only muddied the water.

Southwell.

"Annie?"

"Aye."

"What of Robert Southwell?"

"Taken by the guard. He lies now in the Tower."

ELIZABETH HATTON FRETTED and constantly shifted her back to a more comfortable position against the tree. Around her the ladies chattered and played at gleek. The only sound that broke the hum of their gossiping voices was the twitter of birds in the trees overhead and the occasional riffle of the cards.

She was bored.

She almost wished one of the birds overhead would spoil one of the fine satin dresses or cloaks. At least it would be a moment of levity and a break in the dullness.

What was it he had said? "You English women ride too much to the hunt, play too long at cards and gossip your time away."

Perhaps he was right.

"More wine, m'lady?"

She nodded at the servant and held her goblet up. He poured and moved on to the group of finely dressed ladies perched on tiny cushioned stools a few feet from where Elizabeth sat.

Even with the velvet padding Elizabeth's own stool was beginning to hurt her backside. She wished Bess of Hardwick, the Countess of Shrewsbury, had not been taken with a headache. With Bess Elizabeth never became bored. The woman and her stories of personal success fascinated Elizabeth. She was a living study on the management of a great house and estates, and a model for Elizabeth's goals concerning her own future.

Born lowly, the daughter of a Derbyshire squire, Bess had used a combination of beauty, tenacity and business acumen to forge for herself a small empire.

True, Elizabeth thought, the lady had carefully cultivated her wealth through four husbands, the last of whom—the sixth Earl of Shrewsbury—was near to being the grandest peer in the kingdom. But unlike so many widows who squandered their husband's wealth after his demise, Bess of Hardwick had multiplied hers.

Besides the huge houses of Chatsworth, Hardwick and Chelsea, she had made shrewd investments in lead and ironworks, as well as accumulating vast land holdings through the purchase of mortgages.

Until now no woman in the kingdom other than the Queen herself could be compared with Bess. Lady Hatton had aspirations of being the first.

The thought brought a smile to Elizabeth's lips. Wealth and power were the things a woman needed to be able to direct her own life. And, by God, she would have them. One day she would have them!

But what of her life between now and that day?

This thought erased the smile from her lips and spawned a tear, which squeezed from the corner of one eye. Quickly she applied a kerchief to her cheek lest one of the other ladies see it.

Here she sat—her great wide farthingale spread around her, her bodice of green and gold and her open throat revealing her high proud breasts—among a group of gossiping, idling women. Here she sat, only half a wife and half a woman.

But it need not be so.

She felt an unexpected jolt of desire race through her body like tickling fingers.

The reason? Rory O'Donnell.

It had become obvious in the past few days that the Irishman was avoiding her with a purpose. It was equally obvious that his sarcastic and arrogant, almost cruel, manner was being resurrected between them deliberately, like a mason builds a wall. And Rory O'Donnell was steadfastly playing the master-mason's role.

But why?

Just the previous evening she had swallowed her pride and brazenly approached him during the dancing.

"I'm afraid, m'lady, that my feet are more attuned to outdoor dances, such as a jig, a hornpipe or a round," he had replied.

A lie, and meant to be an insult. For he had just executed a perfect galliard with Lady Pembroke, who said the wild Irishman acquitted the dance nearly as well as Lord Essex himself.

"Thank you, m'lady," he had said with a bow. "A compliment I hope I deserve. Would I some day be an English prince of Ireland, I would hope to bring the manners of the dance to my native land."

With Pembroke he flirts, speaks sweetly and slavers over her hand. And me he insults! Why, she wondered.

The reasons escaped Elizabeth, but the mystery of it intrigued her. His churlishness on the one hand, and the way he looked at her on the other, only served to spice her passion; a dangerous passion, but one Elizabeth was finding harder and harder to keep in check.

She had lost track of the times she had stolen a look in his direction, only to find him gazing raptly in hers with the look in his eyes she remembered. *I think, m'lady, it is you who haunts me....*

Why, why, why, her mind cried, and again the kerchief went to her cheek.

And today where had he gone? She had seen him wander away from the string of riders. At first his direction had seemed aimless. But the longer she watched his broad back diminish in size, the more direct and southerly was his route.

Had he found a wench to bed somewhere in an open sea of cowslips? Or had one of the fine ladies in the Queen's retinue also slipped away to join him? Were they even now clasping each other naked somewhere in an open meadow beyond the far hills?

The thought brought a jolt of anguished pain to her bosom, even though she knew it was silly and possibly even dangerous. Jealousy didn't fit the picture Elizabeth had of herself, especially jealousy over an arrogant Irishman who was providing only a harmless flirtation at best.

Oh, how you do lie to yourself! she thought, and stood up abruptly.

"Come join us, Elizabeth!"

"Nay, thank you. I'll have some wind in my face for a change." She moved from the quilts onto the grass and crossed the short distance to the tethered horses. "Master steward, ready my mare."

"I fear rain, m'lady. Already there is the smell of it in the air and a rumble in the sky to the south."

"No matter. I would have a short ride. The air here is still and has become stifling with prattle."

The steward suppressed a grin and turned to the horses. In the months since Lady Hatton had been his mistress he had learned only too well of her strong will. If she would become drenched in the coming downpour, so be it.

Elizabeth entered the changing tent. Honor awoke with a start and jumped to her feet, rubbing the sleep from her eyes.

"M'lady?"

"The narrower skirt, Honor. I would ride."

Honor closed and fastened the flap of the tent, but not before casting a wary eye to the darkening sky.

"The coming storm will likely bring a fair downpour, m'lady," the girl said, her fingers rapidly working at the stays of Elizabeth's dress.

"Od's blood, girl," she hissed, "I can see! And what

if a drop or even a bucketful drenches me? I'm not
made of sugar, I'll not melt!"

"Yes, m'lady...I was just thinking of your hair."

Angrily Elizabeth pulled the many combs from her
coif and violently shook her head. The thick mane of
auburn hair flew in every direction, to eventually settle
in a wavy cascade along her shoulders and down her
back.

"There! Now 'twill perforce have to be redone
anyway, will it not?"

"Yes, m'lady."

Five minutes later, Elizabeth, dressed now in a narrower farthingale and skirt for riding, emerged from
the tent. The steward held her favorite horse, a big bay
mare, at the ready a few paces away.

"She smells the storm, m'lady," he said, bending a
knee for Elizabeth's boot. "Watch out should she be
skittish."

"I will," Elizabeth replied in an undertone, and accepted the leg up.

She reined her mare around the changing tent
and headed her toward the open meadow. She
was about to tap the horse's rump with her quirt when
there was a searing flash across the sky, followed by a
peal of rolling thunder that cracked like a barking
whip.

The mare reared high, her nostrils flaring as the
forelegs pawed at the noisy but unseen danger.

Like the excellent horsewoman she was, Elizabeth
skillfully kept her saddle and brought the mare back to
the ground in a comfortable lope.

"Easy, girl, easy," she intoned, patting the trembling flank with a gloved hand. "The gods are not
angry with you and me."

Free of the tents, she broke into a canter and let the

wind lift her hair, which flowed like a tongue of soft fire behind her.

What a picture I must make, she thought. *It will take them all of five minutes to get back to their game of gleek!*

And she could imagine the comments.

"Brazen, riding off by herself at the head of a storm!"

"Foolish."

"Dangerous!"

"Silly and uncalled for, I say."

"Have you heard of Lord Harrell? They say he and Mistress Lindsay..."

Elizabeth cared not a whit. Like Bess of Hardwick, she would be her own woman. If she felt like having the wind in her hair and the rain in her face, then she would ride and let them all be damned!

Once out of sight over a hill, she turned south and urged the mare into a gallop.

RORY PAID LITTLE ATTENTION to the first stinging drops of rain. His thoughts were turned inward, to what he was sure was Garnet's treachery. The man would go underground himself now and spew venom from his pen until he got his way.

And what of Southwell? How would he hold up under the torture of Richard Topcliffe, the notorious Tower inquisitor? Rory was fairly certain that Garnet would count on Robert Southwell holding his tongue, even if he knew Garnet was his betrayer.

Rory wished he could be as sure.

The rain was heavier now, and he suddenly realized that his clothing was soaked. In disgust he wrapped the sodden half cloak tighter around his shoulders and leaned into the rising wind.

He passed a small thatch-roofed cottage on his right. It was covered with woodbine and roses, and it looked cozy and warm. He considered stopping and begging for shelter until the storm passed, but dismissed the thought. What use; he was already soaked.

With the sun blackened out and the rain descending in blinding sheets, it was difficult to maintain direction. Once he was north of the village it was nearly impossible to find the landmarks that had guided him originally.

Another bright flash of lightning and a peal of ominous thunder made his horse dance sideways beneath him. The rearing head almost caught him in the face, and it was all he could do to hold his seat as he leaned out of the way.

It took nearly a minute to calm the frightened animal and to rein around again.

It was then that, in the well of a narrow glen, he saw the riderless horse.

He was about to call out in search of the rider when his eye caught the green-and-amber filigree trappings on bridle and saddle. They were familiar to him.

"Lady Hatton...Elizabeth!" He spurred his mount in a dead run toward the mare, which shied and bolted away at his approach, revealing a woman's figure sprawled on the ground.

It took a second for Rory to realize what had happened. Beyond Elizabeth's sprawled figure was a huge old oak. One large limb had been struck by a bolt of lightning and now hung by a thread of fibrous wood from the main trunk. Its leaves raked the ground at the whim of the wind. Elizabeth must have been passing near the tree when it was struck, he surmised. The horse had shied and thrown her.

He slid quickly to the ground and dropped to his knees in the pulpy earth beside her. "Elizabeth!"

She was lying on her back in a grotesque position, her eyes closed and both arms flung outward. Her cloak was open, and he could detect no movement in the bulging softness of her breasts above her bodice.

Gently he covered the top of her left breast with his hand and willed his own heart not to beat.

She was alive!

Carefully, shielding her body as much as possible from the driving rain with his own, he slid his hands under her. Gently he moved his exploring fingers up and down her back and then over her ribs.

He couldn't be sure through her many layers of clothing, but he didn't think anything was broken.

Her left arm was a different story. Her wrist was already swelling over the cuff of her belled and slitted sleeve. Taking the dagger from his belt, he inserted its tip under the cuff and shredded the material to her shoulder.

The pink flesh was blotched in several places, and the wrist appeared to be badly sprained. She had probably used her left arm to help break her fall from the horse.

A quick inspection of her neck and the back of her head under the wetly matted auburn of her hair told him why she was unconscious. There was no blood, but by morning Lady Hatton would probably have a lump the size of her fist where her head had hit the ground.

Rory sighed with relief as she moaned and her eyelids flickered.

"Elizabeth."

"Oh...oh, my...." And then she squealed in pain. She had rolled her head toward the sound of his voice, and had put pressure on the throbbing knot.

"Lie still." He bundled up part of her cloak, lifted her head, and slipped it under to act as a pillow.

"Hurts..." she groaned.

"Where?"

"My head."

"Anywhere else?"

"I...I don't think so."

Carefully she began moving different parts of her body to make sure. Satisfied, she said, "No, just my head. Dizzy. You...everything's a blur...."

"Can you stand?"

"I'll try."

Slowly he helped her up. She had barely regained her feet when the dizziness overcame her. She fell against him, and instinctively his arms wound around her.

A strange thought struck him as her body melded to his. How different from frail little Annie she was. Less than an hour ago he had held the other girl the same way.

Elizabeth was full figured, with the delightful softness and abundance of a woman. Her breasts against his chest and the sweet scent of her damp hair in his nostrils made him giddy. Rather than simply hold her, he wanted to crush her in his arms and tilt that beautiful fine-featured face to his.

"I...I don't think I can ride...quite yet."

Her words broke the spell of his desire, and he cursed himself for his own foolish and callow thoughts.

Her body shivered in his arms, and he realized that she had been taken with a chill. They could ride his mount double, but it would take at least an hour to get back to the hunting party. That is, if he didn't lose his way in the pelting, landscape-obscuring rain.

Suddenly he made his decision.

Sweeping her up in his arms, he lifted her into the

saddle. With an easy graceful leap he mounted the horse's rump behind her.

He answered the questioning look in her misty eyes with a tight-lipped smile. "I passed a herdsman's cottage a short piece back. We'll get you warm and wait out the storm there."

She nodded, but a tiny cloud seemed to pass over her eyes. Rory wondered if the same thought was running through her mind that was in his.

Would the herdsman be in his cottage?

Or would they be alone. . . .

RORY HAILED TWICE as they reached the cottage, with no answer.

"If they have sheep, they'll be with them," Elizabeth said. "The lightning. . ."

He agreed with a curt nod and swung her from the saddle like a feather. He called out one more time at the door, but when he received no answer he lifted the latch and carried her inside.

The cottage contained two rooms, and was obviously inhabited by a bachelor. Both rooms contained rough-hewn oaken furniture and no traces of a feminine hand.

He sat her in a high-backed chair by the open hearth and then stood up, shaking the water from his head as an animal would.

And that's how he appeared at that moment to Elizabeth; like a tall, lean, darkly furred animal. An involuntary shudder passed through her body, and she knew it was caused as much by his presence as by the chilling dampness of her clothing.

"You'd best remove your cloak. Here, this will do until I can get a fire started."

Elizabeth let her cloak slip from her shaking shoulders and accepted the homespun woolen mantle he handed her. It was obviously the herdsman's, for it had an earthy masculine scent as well as a slight odor of sheep.

Rory, too, cast aside his cloak, as well as his soaked doublet. The finely embroidered cambric shirt stuck to him like a second skin. Every line of his upper body, from his narrow waist to his broad chest and muscle-corded shoulders, was defined. He reached for the buttons of the shirt and then stopped, with an awkward look at her.

"I'll. . . build the fire."

He found kindling and logs in a woodbox and, it seemed to Elizabeth, went to his task with a vengeance.

When the fire was licking noisily in the grate, she moved closer to the hearth and opened the mantle so that her dress, and hopefully her body, would absorb the warmth.

The thought of removing the dress passed through her mind in a quick rush, but she couldn't bring herself to be *that* brazen.

Rory had been scouring the cabin, opening drawers, looking into cabinets. Now he returned with two wooden tankards.

"I'm afraid our host has hardly the tastes of royalty. There is only sack."

"It will do. Anything." Gratefully she took the tankard and drank, letting a large draft of the biting liquid flow down her throat.

"How came you to ride in the rain, m'lady?"

"I felt like it. And the storm had yet to start when I set out."

"A bit foolish."

"Perhaps, but then I've been accused of being a woman of impulse."

"An admirable trait at times," he murmured. "And sadly lacking in many women I've known."

Something in his tone drew her eyes upward. From where she sat he looked like a giant. He stood with his back to the fire, his legs apart and his head bent slightly toward her.

His eyes were like two coals of black fire burning into her body. They drew her to her feet.

The sadness and the yearning she had seen before in those eyes had returned.

She took a step toward him. Rory didn't move, but she could sense the tautness that suddenly came into his body, as if he were about to spring.

Wordless thoughts passed between them through their eyes, and they both knew, knew that the inevitable was about to happen. Fate had dealt them a strange hand, and now they would play it out.

His voice when he spoke was low and husky with desire. "Even as a drowned sparrow, with your hair like matted wool and your cosmetics streaming, you are to me the most beautiful woman in the world."

Elizabeth felt her breath catch in her throat. "My impulse to ride was calculated," she said, her voice breathy, her full breasts expanding above her bodice with each gasp for air. "All else would be a lie."

"Methinks 'tis foregone, this."

"I have thought so for a long time," she whispered, "and fought it the best I could."

"As have I, sweet Elizabeth."

A peal of thunder rattled the windows and seemed virtually to shake the whole of the little cottage. The wooden floor beneath their feet vibrated through their bodies, and she was in his arms. It was as if the hand of God had given her a gentle shove.

His lips came down on hers, both caressing and

mauling. Willingly, lustfully, Elizabeth molded her body to his and accepted the insistent probe of his tongue between her lips.

"My sweet," he breathed heatedly against her neck, "you are so beautiful, so woman."

Her senses came alive with his kiss, his every touch. There was a moment of panic, of guilt, as his hand caressed the fine line of her neck and moved down across her bosom.

And then it fled as the cauldron of passion in her body responded to his probing fingers. Deftly they released the stays of her bodice, and his hand was cupping her warm bare breast.

Then her bodice was open, the top of her chemise was pushed down and her heavy breasts spilled forth. There was no holding back now, no reserve as her hands found his head and guided his lips first to one tautly erected nipple and then to the other.

She moaned in open desire as she leaned far back and arched her breasts as an offering to his passion.

"Oh, Rory...Rory...."

"Elizabeth, my sweet, my love." His lips were a firebrand as they moved hotly, insistently, over her smooth creamy flesh.

Now the full insistence of the male came out. He took one of her hands and brought it down between them. Elizabeth moaned when she felt how ready he was. Her mind was spinning and her throat was clogged with need, or else she would have cried out aloud for him to take her at that very moment.

Then his own hand was feeling beneath her skirt, crawling up over the garters that held her silken hose. The fiery trail of his touch moved from the bare skin of her upper thigh to her belly as if her undergarments had already been peeled away.

And then downward with probing fingers, and he was there. She clamped her thighs over his hand and ground herself to him like a wanton.

She didn't care. This touch, this feel, this rapture of total consent was the stuff of which she had dreamed.

His face was buried in the soft warmth of her neck. Her lips found his ear. "Rory, my love, my love, make of me the woman I know myself to be!"

"I will, I will, my love," he groaned, and lifted her into his arms.

"Someday" is here, she thought, her heart soaring. She threw her arms around his neck and again felt the loving and gentle warmth of his lips between her heaving breasts.

But someday was not to be. Rory had taken barely three paces toward the other room and the bed it contained when the sound of a horseman outside the cottage brought him to a halt and Elizabeth struggling from his arms.

For a moment they looked at each other in shock and alarm. These feelings rapidly turned to despair and flushed embarrassment.

"The herdsman, *damn* the herdsman!" Rory choked.

Surprising herself, Elizabeth quickly gained control, even though her legs felt weak and there was a sickness in the pit of her stomach born of unleashed but unsatisfied desire.

She turned away and fumbled back into her clothes.

"Perhaps it is just as well," she gasped, barely keeping a sob from her voice. "If I am to become a wanton, I would have it done under more romantic conditions."

CHAPTER TWENTY-TWO

FOR TWO DAYS Elizabeth lay in bed, thinking about the touch of Rory's lips on hers, the gentleness of his hands as they had caressed her breasts and moved knowingly over the rest of her body.

She closed her eyes and dreamed that it had happened. She had wanted it to happen.

And then she would open her eyes to study the canopy above her bed, and realize that she had been relieved when the sound of the herdsman outside the door had interrupted them.

An affair, yes. But with an *Irishman*?

What of her position? She was, above all, a woman of position. One day she would wield great wealth and power.

Isn't that what she wanted? Of course it was.

That half of her personality, the ambitious half, was fearful of the liaison all the while she was willing it to happen. She had overheard her uncle and the Queen. The problems in Ireland grew worse, and there were strong rumors that Hugh O'Neill, the Irish earl so adamantly loyal to the crown, was not quite the loyalist Rory O'Donnell made him out to be.

Would it not stand to reason then that Rory, apparently a peacemaker, was in fact a traitor and a rebel himself?

And where would Elizabeth's place at court be, what would become of her bright future, should she become entangled with an Irish prince and warlord who in his heart plotted the death of England's Queen?

But her body, like her mind, was divided, and the

other half cried out for the love of Rory O'Donnell.

She was confused, torn and in agony.

FOR THE SAME TWO DAYS, Rory sequestered himself in his quarters, pleading a cold brought on by the chill of the rain. But the ague he suffered was created by something far more serious than a damp rain.

Like Lady Elizabeth, he found that the aftershock of what had almost happened frightening. When reality had again set in, Rory cursed the failure of his resolve.

But had not a great deal of it been Elizabeth's fault? She had admitted that she had ridden after him like a wanton. She had practically stated that consummation of the fire that burned between them was the reason she had sought him out.

And he had been a willing accomplice. Even when he had stepped from the cottage and seen the old herdsman with Elizabeth's mare, he had wanted to strike the man instead of thanking him for his aid.

Was this burning in his breast love for Elizabeth, or was it merely lust for the perfection of her body? And no matter what it was, did he have the right to bring her down with him should he fall? For fall he would, eventually, and he knew it. It was only a matter of time before his tenuous position would lead to betrayal from some quarter.

What then of their love, if indeed it was love?

Rory thought he knew the lady's mind. She was the wife of a peer, and would remain so.

He was a dedicated rebel with the cause of Ireland as a wife.

He knew they were star-crossed, but in his heart of hearts he wanted to ignore all else and make her his.

"AH, LITTLE ANNIE, 'tis a dangerous thing ye do."

"Nay, 'tis your other leg that's wounded, Ned Bull!" she giggled, rubbing her body over his muscular thigh.

"Not that, wench," he growled roughly, tousling her hair with his strong hand. "'Tis yer joining me here that's unwise. For if the Queen's men lay upon me, I'd have ye a safe distance from me!"

"I feel safe only in your arms," she said, running her lips lightly over the stubble of his cheek.

Ned looked into her young-old eyes made hollow by the fight for survival in a world not of her making.

He sighed. "Oh, little Annie, ye're too sad for one so young."

"'Tis sadness made worse by your stubbornness. We've enough coin from our treachery. Let's be off alive to enjoy it!"

"Nay, damme, I've told ye often enough. Our days in England are numbered, aye, so when we're off it must be for France and a new life. For that we'll need more than we've got. I made the choice for the Irishman and I must see it out. 'Tis the only way."

"Are ye not afraid at all, Ned Bull?"

"Aye, afraid I am . . . for ye, little Annie. My road's been there for years and I've known its end."

He felt a tremble all along her naked body where it touched his. Her face was buried in his neck, and her voice when she spoke was muffled.

"Please, oh, please, don't say that. Even if ye must think it, don't say it." Her hand traveled across the dark mat of his chest and the washboard of muscle at his belly until she found him. "Make love to me, Ned!"

"Yer an insatiable little wench, ye are," he chuckled. "Methinks 'tis yer youth that will kill me."

But the pain in his leg and the hurt he felt in his heart at making her face reality disappeared as he rolled his big body over and settled between her thighs.

"Ye're a wench."

"Aye, who wants as much of her man as she can get while she has him."

SIR BRIAN RUSSELL'S LEADERSHIP of the English Jesuits in exile was well known, and he gloried in it. He was a man of intellect and daring. He fought equally well with the pen as with the sword, and dreamed of glory when England returned to the true faith.

Sir Brian was one of the first Englishmen who had schemed to free Mary, Queen of Scots, from the Tower and place her on the throne of England. When that failed he had begun to forge his fellow peers with Jesuit leanings into groups that would one day sprout into rebellion and put a Catholic—any Catholic—on the throne.

But Russell hadn't counted on the vast network of spies controlled by Walsingham and the Cecils. He had been discovered and forced into exile. Since then he had waged his wars in France and the Netherlands, hoping one day to return to a Catholic England and regain his vast properties, which had been claimed by the crown during his exile.

The realization of that hope had drawn much closer with the news of Southwell's and Garnet's success with the masses. A popular rebellion might very well create a breach into which Sir Brian himself could step.

Part of that hope had been dashed by the imprisonment of Southwell. True, Henry Garnet claimed that he had the situation in hand, but Sir Brian didn't trust the man. Garnet was a fanatic, and Sir Brian knew only too well that fanatics occasionally win battles, but never wars.

That was the reason Sir Brian was in Calais one night, having what he hoped was his last French meal for a while. His palate could already taste and savor good English puddings and fresh meat—food he had been too long without.

Beneath his doublet he carried forged papers that would identify him as a Protestant tradesman from Brussels. During his absence from England his hair as well as his beard had grayed considerably. In fact, because of the trying times he had been through, the whole configuration of his features had altered. Only someone who had known Sir Brian extremely well would recognize him now, he was sure.

By this time the following evening he would be in England, gleaning from Garnet the names of his fellow conspirators and lifting from the man's hands the reins of rebellion.

It was with a light heart that he raised his tankard and made a salute toward the quay below, and England beyond.

"Damme, monsieur, you've soiled my best doublet and cloak with your stupid carelessness!"

"Nay, sir," Sir Brian replied in French, matching the language of the strutting peacock before him. " 'Tis you who have jostled my arm and brought the burgundy upon yourself."

"Christ's blood, man, do you take me for a fool? With all the room to move in, you fling your arm around like the scarecrow you appear!"

"*Scarecrow* is it, sir?" Sir Brian came out of his chair so quickly that it tumbled to its side on the oaken floor behind him. He faced the three French dandies before him with a florid face. "You would do well to watch your tongue with a gentleman, sir."

"Would I now?" The man, dressed like his fellows in fine brocaded satins and rich dark velvets, cast a scrutinizing eye on Russell's suit of broadcloth and stout linen stitched with colored cording. "Since when do gentlemen go around dressed like drunken mourners?"

Sir Brian had taken less from the Queen herself at his exile. Now his blood boiled at the popinjay before him, and at the two fellows with him who laughed behind their bejeweled fingers at Sir Brian's expense.

True, there was something about the cut of the man's features and the steely pitch of his eyes that belied the effeminate swagger and the tone of his clothes. But so incensed was Sir Brian that he paid little heed.

"A gentleman, sir, does not need to wear his grace and manners on his back like a strutting peacock."

The man took two steps backward, his long delicate fingers playing over the hilt of the rapier at his side. Sir Brian's hand was moving toward his own sword when his two aides and the tavern's landlord stepped between them.

The landlord groused that he wouldn't have his meeting room turned into a tiltyard, and Sir Brian's aides convinced their master that a duel at such a time, win or lose, would be foolishness.

Their arguments were sane and reasonable, and even though it went against Sir Brian's pride, he backed down.

"Perhaps another day, sir," he huffed, and allowed one of his aides to guide him toward the door while the second satisfied the landlord's bill.

"The man was goading you, Sir Brian."

"Aye, I know. These callow youths with a bit of inheritance to idle with have nothing better to while away their days.''

The encounter soon diminished in Sir Brian's mind as he and his two aides neared the quay and the lights of the ship, bobbing at anchor, that would soon be taking him to England.

They walked swiftly along the narrow street. Emerging from the darkness between the tall two-storied houses, they found themselves on the wide boulevard that circled most of the harbor. The ship was anchored about a hundred yards to their left.

They had covered about half that distance when their way was blocked by the three men from the tavern.

"By your leave, sir," said Sir Brian's tormentor.

There was little doubt of the man's intent now. His face had dropped all pretense of light sport, and his eyes held Sir Brian's with a dark brooding look that the older man could only describe as satanic.

"I'll have no more of it, sir. If you'll stand aside—"

"Nay. I'll have an apology, you stupid oaf, and I'l have it in front of my fellows."

"You'll have an apology of a box on the ears!' retorted Sir Brian, his ire instantly heightened further than it had already been during the previous encounter.

Already a crowd of curious onlookers had gathered, sensing blood in the air. The man exchanged looks with his fellows and then passed his vacant stare over the crowd.

"This man would besmirch my dress with his stupid carelessness and then have the gall to defile my honor as a gentleman with his scurrilous words."

"Sir, I beseech you—" began one of Sir Brian's aides.

"You, stand back! I have no quarrel with you. Nay,

'tis the lout you call master I seek satisfaction from. Well?''

"You'll get no satisfaction from me, you popinjay!" Sir Brian roared.

"Then I am forced to gain satisfaction myself, sir."

The man's hand, quick as a striking cobra, came forward. The stinging slap across his face was powerful enough to wrench Sir Brian's head around and send his whole body back two paces.

The crowd gasped and, as one, moved away to allow room for the inevitable.

"You'll not see the dawn!" Sir Brian bellowed, forgetting himself and speaking in English. His sword glinted in the dull light from the street's torches.

"Nay," the man replied with a leering grin, "I'll see the dawn and a wench to bed, and clean my soiled doublet besides."

The man's rapier made a swishing sound as it left its scabbard and danced in his hand. So fast did it move that the point was a blur. At the end of two passes, there wasn't a soul watching who didn't foresee the outcome.

Sir Brian, dagger and sword in hand, was skilled, but he was slower than the smaller man, who moved like a lithe dancer. It seemed as though the rapier in the other man's hand was never still, and it was unerring as its point danced around and between the heavier sword and dagger of his opponent.

Two more passes and Sir Brian was panting with the exertion. The front of his doublet was in tatters, and he hadn't made a single hit on the bobbing, weaving figure whose boots never seemed to touch the cobblestones.

Another lunge, a parry, and a stinging pain cut the length of his jawline from earlobe to chin.

"A hit, a hit!" one of the aides cried. "'Tis satisfaction enough!"

But the words had barely left the man's mouth when the rapier lifted and thrust a final time.

Sir Brian's dagger and sword clattered on the cobbles. His eyes grew wide in surprise, and a tiny trickle of blood ebbed from the corner of his mouth. With a full length of steel extending from his back, he seemed to be lifted to his toes and suspended there by the slender blade.

And then, as if with the hiss of a snake, the rapier was withdrawn and Sir Brian crumpled to the street.

Instantly the swordsman turned his blade toward the fallen man's two companions. Neither moved, but they stood their ground, their eyes wide and their mouths open in shocked dismay.

Satisfied there was no danger from that quarter, the man drew a linen kerchief daintily edged with lace from his sleeve, and wiped his blade clean before sheathing it.

He then dropped the kerchief beside Sir Brian's lifeless body and rejoined his fellows. Without a word the three of them walked the remaining fifty yards to the ship.

When they were out of earshot of the silent crowd, one of the swordsman's companions said in English, "Think you the watch will detain us before the ship sails?"

"Nay," Sir James Blake replied. "Calais may be neutral, but it is still French. What cares the watch about a beggarly Protestant tradesman from the Netherlands who happens to speak English?"

And that, Blake thought, would be the end of Jesuit propaganda flowing from the pen of Sir Brian Russell.

Behind them a seaman commented to one of his

mates, "Damme, I've never seen a duel come to such a quick conclusion!"

But one of Sir Brian's aides had different thoughts as he muttered under his breath, "A duel be damned. 'Twas outright murder."

IT WAS THE EVENING before the Queen's departure from Holdenby, and there was to be a masque celebrating the failure of the second Armada to reach England's shores. Weeks before, fierce winds had blown the ships back to Spain itself, or had forced them onto unfriendly, rocky shores. Various sea nymphs and the goddess of the winds would be played by ladies in waiting to the Queen.

At the conclusion of the masque there would be a huge supper feast and then dancing.

Even in her desultory mood, and with the aches still in her body from her fall, Elizabeth refused to stay in bed and miss the festivities. She also refused to miss the last night of hostessing the Queen and putting the last touch on her personal conquest of the court.

The thought that everyone, including Rory O'Donnell, would attend didn't escape her, but as she chose the evening's gown she pushed it to the back of her mind.

Honor bathed her mistress with care, and then dressed her from the inside out with equal relish. She wanted her lady to be the most beautiful woman in the great hall of Holdenby that night, second to the Queen, of course.

First came a pale blue chemise edged in lace. Then the petticoat, followed by a whalebone corset with busks. She chose an extrawide farthingale because of the voluminous skirt and underdress that would eventually go over it.

In place of a doublet Elizabeth chose to wear a figure-fitting off-white jacket of her own design. It was cut extremely low at the neck, and the open collar was fringed with point lace. The front was embroidered with the fluted bells of cowslips, designed so that they almost hid their single drop of red as if they were closing their petals against the night. The sleeves were an off-white, full and slitted, with the red inserts edged in gold and covered with lacework puffs. Around the lower edges was another fringe of gold.

Her bodice, a deeper, almost strawberry-colored red, blazed through the triangular cut of the jacket. At the base of her breasts' deep cleavage gleamed four rubies with a centered pearl.

A short red overskirt matched the bodice, with horizontal bands of gold. A blue-green underdress embellished with gold spangles completed the rich picture she made standing before her mirror.

"The blue shoes, I think, Honor."

The shoes added the desired effect. They were covered with white lace, and each had a red rosette on the toe, with a diamond in its center.

Honor had done her auburn hair in a coif of small curls. Atop it she wore a crown-shaped headdress of pearls and rubies. An egret plume flowed upward along the left side of her head, and in her right ear she wore a ruby-and-pearl earring.

Around her neck she wore the pendant of diamonds that had been her wedding present from Sir William.

"M'lady . . . ?"

Elizabeth looked up. "Yes, why not?"

To the point-lace cuff at Elizabeth's right wrist Honor attached a small string of pearls.

Elizabeth did a pirouette and faced her maid with her

arms thrown wide. "What do you think, Honor? Will I dazzle the gallants without paling the Queen?"

"You are so beautiful, m'lady, that for this one evening even Her Majesty will not mind basking in your light."

Elizabeth chuckled. "Let us hope not, lest my place at court be mistress of the scullery!"

ONLY ONCE DURING THE MASQUE did Elizabeth Hatton allow her eyes to search the rapt faces for O'Donnell. There was an instant ache in her breast when she didn't see him, but she quickly shunted it aside. *I must—I must think of myself, my position, my honor!* she insisted to herself.

The supper was lavish, as Elizabeth had planned, with course overflowing upon course. There were fish smothered in delectable sauces, fallow deer and capons garnished with a rainbow of vegetables, and great joints of beef and mutton. The taste of it all was savored with the aid of fine Rhenish wines.

The Queen was pleased, Elizabeth was elated, and, as usual, Sir William departed to his bedchamber before the dancing had begun.

As the evening wore on, Rory O'Donnell, by his very absence, forced himself back into her thoughts. The gaiety of the whirling couples around her paled as she imagined the reasons for his absence. Had he returned to London? Was he remaining in his quarters for fear of what might befall them both if another opportunity such as the one at the herdsman's cottage arose?

By the time the dance drew to a close Elizabeth's fear of facing him had been replaced by the worse fear of not seeing him again.

By eleven of the clock the orchestra had been dismissed, and many of the lords and ladies had already begged the Queen's pardon for their early retirement.

Gloriana herself decided to take the night air before seeking her bed. She led the way into the gardens, where the air was scented with the fragrance of larkspur and laburnum.

Elizabeth was near the end of the long line of courtiers following the Queen. She had no idea how it happened; one moment she was holding the arm of the short, paunchy Lord Hebert, and the next she was dwarfed by the towering figure of Rory O'Donnell.

"You!" Her heart would not hold still.

"I regret missing your entertainments, but Sir Robert retained me the greater part of the evening."

Something in his tone, the brooding look in his dark eyes, alarmed her. "An affair of state?"

"Somewhat. You know of Enniskillen?"

"In Ireland?"

He nodded.

"Nay."

"It lies north of Sligo, near Lough Erne. It is a strategic place, a gateway to the northern lands of Tyrone and Donegal—O'Neill and O'Donnell lands. For weeks it has been held by your Sir Richard Bingham, and under attack by its rightful owner, Hugh Maguire."

"What has that to do with you?"

"It seems that my wild brother, Red Hugh, has declared himself an open rebel to the crown and has marched to join Maguire."

Elizabeth gave a tiny gasp, and a hand came to her breast. "Because of your brother, does my uncle think that you...?"

"That I am a rebel? Probably," Rory replied with a

hollow mirthless laugh. "But Sir Robert hopes to use me as long as he can."

A hundred questions raced through Elizabeth's mind, and the one uppermost was, *are you indeed a rebel to England and the crown?* But she dared not ask it, for fear that he would answer truthfully.

"I fear 'tis folly to think there will not be war in Ireland," he said.

"And if there is," she asked, a lump in her throat threatening to cut off her words, "would you return?"

Their pace had slowed. Other lords and ladies had passed them until they were very near the end of the procession.

"Would it matter a great deal to you, m'lady, if I set sail for the grim wind-beaten shores of Donegal?"

"I. . .I dare not say."

The words were automatic, and she couldn't make herself look at him as she said them. She even tried to let go of his arm, but his grip held her steady and guided her from the path.

Once out of the others' sight, shaded from the moonlight by the spreading vastness of a giant oak, he turned her into his arms.

"Why can you not say what we both know?" he whispered, his breath warm against her ear.

She tilted her face until she could look deeply into his eyes, and willed her heart to stop its wild beating. "'Tis a dangerous game we play, Rory O'Donnell, and one that I cannot take lightly."

"Nor can I."

His face descended and his lips covered the sweetness of hers.

Against her will she succumbed, sliding her hands from his chest around his back. His hard body came against her and she shuddered. She could feel her breasts pillow across his chest as she willingly returned his kiss and caresses.

With his lips still touching hers, he spoke. "My love, your beauty is more than mind and body can stand. And I feel in you the same desire that has robbed me of sleep these many nights."

"Oh, damn," she moaned, unable to keep a sob from her voice, "would that the herdsman had never found my mare and returned. Mayhap then I would not have time, as I have now, to realize the foolish rashness of what we do."

"A countrywoman of yours—Deirdre, wife of The O'Hara—once told me that romance, beauty and gentleness are forever vital, and that love, no matter the briefness of its interlude, is eternal."

Again his lips came down, but this time found only her damp cheek.

"I feel, nay, I fear, that if I let myself love you I am lost," she explained breathlessly.

"I want you," he growled, his voice harsh, matching the power in the arms around her body. "Now!"

Roughly he shouldered her face back to where his lips could reach hers, and he smothered her mouth. Encased in the vise of his arms, she felt as a prisoner must feel, and she rebelled against it.

She managed to get her hands between them, and she pushed on his chest with all her strength. It did no good. He only held her tighter and kissed her harder.

Then one of his hands slid up to caress her breast. Elizabeth could feel the response of her nipple to his touch, and suddenly the memory of the dream she had had flooded over her. The damp grass, the open sky, the spreading tree above them.... His lips relentlessly demanding, his lean body hard against her, his hand violent yet gentle on her breast all combined to assault her senses.

"No," she gasped, "no, not like this."

"How, then?" he barked, holding her at arm's length by her trembling shoulders.

"I . . . not this way."

Her meaning was lost on him. "Is there *any* way with an Englishwoman? With you? Would it be easier for you if I were one of your foppish dandies groveling on bended knee? Not I, Elizabeth. For I am Irish, and a man!"

"Rory—" His face, glowering down at her from his towering height, was like a dark thundercloud, filling her with fear and awe.

"I would have you in Ireland for a night so I could show you the fire a man can feel for a woman! But, alas, we stand in England, where a man's brain can't be filled with fire but must overflow with drivel. For he must recite loving lines and amorous verses to a lady to make her his mistress. He must borrow colors from fields of roses to beautify her cheeks; her teeth must be of pearl, her breath a fragrant balm, her wit that of a genius, and her chastity, no matter how often abused, must be compared to Venus's!"

"Are you through?"

"Nay, but barely begun. This wooer on English soil must learn to lisp prettily, 'kind mistress, oh, so sweet mistress,' as he kisses her hand, the handle of her fan, the netherskirt of her petticoat, the toe of her boot, and even her arse, should the whim take her."

He took a deep breath and plunged on before she could interrupt again. "Nay, if that's the way the lady would have it, then 'tis a wooer she doth need—and a lover I am, a wooer I'm not!"

His hands dropped from her shoulders. Until then

her face had been hidden in shadow. Now she stepped forward into the moonlight and his eyes opened with surprise. For instead of meeting his tirade with an angry scowl to match his own, her beautiful features sparkled with a wide smile.

"If I haven't admitted it before, I do now," she said in a throaty voice. "Yea, it's a man I would have for a lover."

"What say you then?"

"I say," she replied, gliding into his arms, "Rory O'Donnell, I say...yes."

CHAPTER TWENTY-THREE

ELIZABETH'S HEART beat wildly as she slipped Honor's wide skirt and petticoats down over her hips. She shook her body, and the garments fell to the floor at her feet. The narrow-sleeved, laced blouse followed, and Elizabeth stood there, clad only in her pale blue chemise, staring at her reflection in a mirror over the oaken mantle.

What she saw, and the thoughts her reflection caused, brought a bright flush to her face, a flush that quickly spread to the swells of her breasts showing above the low-cut bodice of the chemise.

Remove it, as well? Be totally and wantonly naked for his arms when he arrived?

Nay, that would indeed be one step too far, and the heat she felt in her body beneath the thin material told her so. She was sure that if she slipped the garment off she would see that the flush suffusing her cheeks and breasts had traveled down over the rest of her trembling form.

It had been an hour since she had fled from the garden and sought out Honor where she was sleeping on a pallet at the foot of Elizabeth's bed.

Could she trust Honor to hold her tongue? Could she have faith that the girl would understand her suffering and, as one woman to another, join in her intrigue?

"You would to bed now, m'lady?"

"Aye, Honor, but not here."

"What?"

Taking the girl's hands in her own, Elizabeth with a shaking voice had told her all. She told of her first betrothal and the wretchedness of the subsequent rejection. With rapid words she described her betrothal and marriage to Sir William, leaving out neither the good nor the bad.

And then she told Honor of the love she had in her heart for the darkly handsome Irishman, and what she was determining to do about it.

She hadn't yet finished her tale when she knew that Honor had met her words on the level she had hoped— as one passionate woman to another rather than as servant to mistress.

Quickly the girl had fetched her a change of clothes so that Elizabeth, a dark shawl covering the sheen of her auburn hair, could pass unnoticed through the garden. Then she had scurried off to guide Rory by a little-used path to the summer cottage.

Now, standing in the only finished bedroom of the cottage, her own private place, and waiting for her soon-to-be lover, Elizabeth felt at ease, at peace with herself as she hadn't felt in months. She could no longer curse the treachery of her body, because it cried out, nay, demanded this man's touch.

It was to be, and she could not—would not—deny it any longer, no matter the outcome.

"I'll deal with tomorrow when it arrives," she whispered to the beautiful face staring back at her in the mirror. "In the meantime this night is ours."

The huge bed, with its crimson velvet canopy filigreed in gold, contrasted so much with the bare floor and the darkly paneled walls that it kept drawing her eye.

That bed, this room, my cottage, she thought.

She would greet him by the window, where the blue moonlight would flow through the paler blue of the chemise and outline her body. As he arrived he would see her standing like an offering before him.

He would move to her and kiss her hand and whisper words of love that no one else would hear. Then his eyes would roam across the swell of her breasts and drink in the excitement he had already aroused in her taut nipples. He would bend his head to claim their warmth as his own.

Elizabeth leaned toward the mirror as though offering herself to her own image. She closed her eyes and imagined Rory's strong but gentle hand cupping her breast, while his other hand trailed in exploration over her body, seeking and finding the secret places that needed his touch.

His mouth was at her neck. His lips opened slightly, tasting her skin as they moved down over the rise at the top of her breast.

Then he was there, opening his mouth wide like a suckling child, putting all the pressure of his lips and lungs upon her nipples, drawing so hard that she hurt and cried out.

No, there was no doubt now, none. As a young girl she had dreamed, and now the dream had come true. She was in love.

Just the memory of his hands on her flesh made her

heart beat faster. It took but the smallest effort to feel
his gentle, subtle fingers on her body, bringing it to life
and releasing the boiling passion untapped till now.

Her eyes flew open at the sound of cautious footsteps
on the graveled path.

She flew to the window and carefully peered out.
Slowly moving gray clouds made a patchwork quilt of
moonlight and darkness across the gardens and
meadows. A few stars flickered above the black trees.
The white gravel pathways stretched out from the cottage to lose themselves in darkness.

She listened, her ear straining and one hand pressed
to a pounding breast. Naught could be heard but the
faint rustle of a night breeze through the hedgerows
and the trees.

The window was slightly ajar, and Elizabeth's
nostrils filled with the pungent aroma of passion-
flowers as her eyes bored into the distance, trying to
detect movement.

And then she saw them—two cloaked figures, one
tall, one short—moving stealthily toward the cottage.

Had they been seen?

No, don't even think about it! Honor knew well the
darkest pathways, and even better the nightly routine
of the servants.

The moving shadows parted. Honor ran back to a
place of concealment where she could keep watch and
guard their privacy.

Bless the girl, Elizabeth thought, and felt her heart
skip a beat with the sound of the door below opening
and closing.

Would he remember Honor's instructions? Would
he remember to pull the latchstring inside?

And then her fears were calmed as she heard the
measured tread of his boots moving through the cot-

tage and up the stairs. He moved without hesitation, making not so much as one erring turn.

Honor had instructed him well.

She turned just as he stepped through the door. He found her with one quick, casting glance, and halted abruptly. Even though his eyes were shadowed she knew that they were drinking in the effect she had desired.

"M'lady looks especially beautiful by moonlight."

"Thank you, Sir Irishman."

"Nay, no more are we Irish and English, but man and woman."

The open cloak slid from his shoulders to the floor. He was dressed as he had been on the night she had seen him moving stealthily through the gardens of Haskins House, in tight black riding breeches and a white cambric shirt, its lace front open, baring the darkness of his chest.

No matter how hard she tried, she couldn't keep the quiver from her voice. "Tell me but one thing."

"Aye."

"Do you see me now as you've said you see England—both corrupt and magnificent at the same time?"

"I see you now, dear Elizabeth, as the woman I love."

Before she realized it he had moved. And it was as she had imagined. Her hands were in his, and his lips brushed her palms, her fingertips, her wrists. Then she was in his arms.

"Oh, God help me, God help us both, but I love you as well!"

His kiss was strong, yearning, but very gentle. He held her tightly and she could feel his desire rising to meet hers. She parted her lips and accepted his hot searching tongue between them.

When his hands fumbled with her chemise she helped him, and then it was sliding down her body. Rory stepped back, drinking his fill of her beauty.

There was a quality in his eyes that was altogether strange to her for a moment. Then she realized that this wild Irishman, instead of demanding her body with his own, was asking for it with his eyes.

She responded by lifting her arms to him and spreading them wide. He swept her up like a feather and deposited her in the bed.

His eyes continued to devour her, feasting on her body with love as he stepped back to remove his own clothing. Elizabeth took in every detail of his sinewy form as it was bared.

"You are beautiful," she said wonderingly. As odd as the words sounded to her own ears, she knew them to be true.

For he was. His body was finely honed, like a Grecian statue. It was a fine-boned, well-fleshed body, like her own, and the sight of it swept away everything from her mind but the burning fire between her thighs.

And then he was there beside her, their bodies flesh to flesh. His hands held her breasts reverently as if they were fine porcelain.

Her body arched and yielded, every pore, every nerve end coming alive to his touch. Slowly he let one hand flow down across her firm flat belly. It trailed fire as it moved to her thighs and parted them.

And then his fingers found her. She gasped, and at the same moment a cry broke from his throat. But far from being the animal cry she might have expected, it was the moan of a gentle lover who had achieved his goal.

Again her body arched and sang out as she thrust toward his probing touch. Then his lips added to the tingle of her flesh. Her passion grew wings as his kisses covered her breasts, her belly. The tip of his tongue teased her navel until Elizabeth was sure she would explode into a million tiny fragments.

"Oh, no more," she cried out, "please, no more. Love me now as only a man can truly love a woman!"

"You are all of woman, my darling," Rory groaned, as a naked, tautly muscled leg came between her thighs to open them further, like a flower opening its petals to accept the morning sun.

She encircled his body with her straining arms. His weight was delicious as it crushed her breasts, and his desire was rampant as it surged along her belly. Again his lips found her breasts, even as her hand closed over his hardness. With her free hand she cupped her breast and urged the nipple between his lips.

At the same time Elizabeth arched her hips, her body searching for his, desperately needing to feel his hard manhood filling her completely.

He entered her slowly, maddeningly, until they met and were one.

"Such a precious moment no man has ever known," he sighed.

She couldn't speak, but no words were needed. She saw and understood the glory in his words.

Minutes passed without sound or movement between them. And then the blood pounded to a roar in both their bodies, and they could hold back the tide of passion no more than the sea could be stilled in a storm.

He set himself hard against her and moved slowly. Elizabeth countered by matching his rhythm and motion with her hips. Tiny moans and little gasps from her throat let him know the pleasure he gave her.

Dimly she felt his weight lessen. Her eyes opened and

met his. She saw rapture and felt the triumph of his possession as they hurtled toward a peak.

The light from the window played around their moving thrusting bodies, giving the room and their place in it a sense of almost unreal proportions. Slowly the perspiration rose on their bodies from their mutual exertion, reflecting the moonlight and giving an otherworld quality to their passionate love-making.

Faster and faster Rory moved. Now and then he would pull himself away from her slightly, only to have her lock her legs ever more firmly around him and return him completely to her depths.

Her eyes were open, but they seemed to see nothing, finding their point of concentration in some dim vista far beyond her body. Her convulsive movements quickened and she arched her back even more to send her sensitivity harder against him.

"Oh, Rory, my darling, my love...my only love...."

"Elizabeth...Elizabeth...."

His voice was hollow, a disembodied roar in the silent room as the tempo of their blinding passion increased with their movements against each other.

"Rory...."

The one word, his name, told him everything. Again and again her body writhed spasmodically, until at last her whole being, her whole world, became a tornado of motion and she uttered a cry of triumphant delight.

Rory dropped his mouth to hers and drove his tongue hard between her lips. At no time in her life had she felt such total fulfillment. Her body, her mind, her very soul reached out to this wonderful being she had found to ravish and love her, to fill her with his love.

"Yes! Oh, yes, my dearest love!" she cried.

It began with a low roar in his chest and mounted to

a groaning shout as his whole being burst like a torrent inside of her.

And for the second time Elizabeth cried out in total joy, locking herself against him and driving herself to a frenzied fulfillment of passion that she had never before known.

THEY LAY SIDE BY SIDE, silent in the gray of the coming dawn. Now and then they would reach out to touch each other, their hands gently exploring as if the reality they had found were a myth and had already stolen away.

In this brief span of time Rory had whisked her to a different world. He had taught her what love, and love-making, could really be like. And she knew it would never be the same without him.

As her hand trailed over the damp skin of his thigh, she touched the jagged scar. She gasped but didn't pull away. Instead she traced its length, which brought a tiny cry to her lips.

"'Tis nothing," he said, moving her hand up to set-tle in the mat of hair at his chest.

"I love you."

"We've known it since the first moment so long ago in the carriage."

"My handsome rogue of the night."

"Who loves you more than life itself."

She felt a ripple of fear pass through her body, to be quickly calmed by his hand on her breast.

She knew the cause. "You love me, Rory, more than life itself. But do you love me more than Ireland?"

She felt his body tense and then move to roll against hers. "Does my schooled lady read the latest French romances, such as *Poleander* or *Cleopatre*?"

"Why so?"

"Then she would know that the love we have found cannot be compared to, or touched by, the world around us."

She was both surprised and elated when again he moved atop her. This time his entrance was harsh, almost rough but she didn't mind. In fact she reveled in it, letting his lack of inhibition stir her own senses to new heights. It made her forget all else but him, them, and what they had together at that moment.

And yet at the height of her ecstasy she heard her own voice cry out in desperation. "Oh, Rory, my darling, what will we do now?"

And his reply reached her along with his release. "We go on!"

CHAPTER TWENTY-FOUR

WEEKS PASSED, and the Queen's progress moved on from one wealthy lord's estate to another. Rory, much to his dismay, continued to make up part of the royal retinue. He was sure this was due more to the efforts of Robert Cecil than to the Queen's desire, but he could do nothing about it.

He guessed that the reason his presence underfoot suited Sir Robert so well was tied in with his brother's open aid to Maguire. The forays at Enniskillen were still being referred to as skirmishes but with the increase in Red Hugh's activities, open and outright war was on everyone's mind.

The word Rory received from O'Neill through Haskins was that the time was near. Red Hugh's open rebellion, combined with the bravado of his earlier escape from Dublin Castle and his subsequent survival of the forces of nature and of the English alike, had made him a hero. Kerns had flocked to his banner in hopes of gaining land. Scottish gallowglass mercenaries offered their support in order to join in on the capture of English plunder.

Through it all O'Neill continued to profess himself the peacemaker. He made trip after trip to Dublin Castle, urging restraint and conciliation, biding for time.

So astute had been his diplomacy that the Queen's lord deputy was leaning toward reprimanding Sir Richard Bingham for his actions, rather than admonishing Maguire and Red Hugh's retaliations.

But all this politicking merely served as an agile finger in a rupturing dike. Soon the fissure would expand until there was nothing that even O'Neill's genius could do to stop the floodtide of war from crashing through.

The O'Hara was wild with anger and seething with the desire for battle. His lust for blood and English heads was such that neither Deirdre nor The O'Neill could keep him at Ballylee much longer.

So O'Neill was preparing. Secret letters had been sent to Philip of Spain, promising a united uprising in all of Ireland if only the Spanish king would promise some degree of aid in men and arms.

Previously there had been either negative replies or none at all from Philip. But with the failure of the second Armada came a resolution of aid to O'Neill in his venture.

Emissaries had been sent into the south, urging the clans to cast aside their animosities and join together to rid their land of the common enemy, the English. Generally a wait-and-see attitude prevailed, but the O'Rourkes, the O'Sullivans, the O'Connors and the

O'Boyles had already formed a pact, and O'Neill was certain that others would follow suit.

With the aid of still more brigands-turned-stablehands and placed in the employ of lords hosting the Queen, Rory was able to slip away almost nightly.

He met often with Annie, and learned that Ned was almost recovered from his wound. Already the rogue was straining at the bit to sow more discord and bring his part in the rebellion to a head.

Rory was under no illusions. He knew that Ned Bull performed for coin. But he also knew that the man would stick to his word to the death.

The young O'Donnell's heart went out to little Annie, who unstintingly supported her man in the fervent hope that one day soon it would all be done with and they could flee England and find safety. She was well aware of Ned's oath to the Irishman to see it through to the end, and knew that he meant it. But that knowledge filled her heart with despair about losing the one thing she wanted in life, the one person who had brought her the only happiness she had ever known—Ned Bull.

But she was a strong-willed lass, a woman to match her man, and through her Rory constantly implored Ned to hold his lads under a hard hand. Few of the street rogues in London or other English towns knew the true reason behind the path down which Ned and his paid lieutenants led them. All they knew was that they were angry at crown and government and would soon have a way of venting their wrath.

With luck that wrath would culminate in a refusal to fight in any more Irish wars. This was the only way left for Rory to aid O'Neill. With his wings clipped by Cecil, he no longer had access to strategic information, nor did he have the means to feed it to Ireland.

He was determined that the internal insurrection he
planned for England should succeed.

"It will," little Annie mused, her thin lips set in a
hard line. "Me only hope is that we all see the day
after."

Rory had no reply. He, too, hoped with all his heart
that all of them—himself, Ned, Annie, the aging
Haskins, his own sweet Elizabeth, and even poor
Robert Southwell, whose tongue was holding well in
the Tower—would emerge alive and whole from the
gathering storm.

On the nights when there was no Annie nor any
emissary from Haskins to pass news and further his
plots, Rory rode like the wind to Holdenby and his
lady's bed.

The cottage had become a symbol of love and sanctuary for them both. For Elizabeth it was a wild escape
from boredom and a chance to discover the depths of
her passion. For Rory it was a place of safety where he
could forget the constant threat of betrayal that hung
over him. In Elizabeth's arms he found succor, and in
her body, release.

As August progressed and fall blossomed with radiant color, their love deepened more than they had
ever dreamed. There was no lessening of the ribbons of
fire their hands could ignite in one another's bodies, no
fading of the wild rapture once their bodies had joined.
Their physical need grew stronger, into a glory of love,
and they both knew it. So much so that many evenings
were taken up with merely touching, savoring the joy
of simply being together.

It was during these times that they began to talk.

Rory told her of his youth, and how little there had
been of it. He related the story of the long ugly scar she
had discovered on his body that first night, and went

on to tell her of the many others she had found since.

Only to one other woman, Deirdre O'Hara, had he confided his real self, the self that was so unlike his brother or The O'Hara, the self that would be a husband and father, a man of peace.

Elizabeth sensed how strong his love had grown, for him to bare his soul to her this way, and she responded by doing the same. She told him how hard she had fought her family over the matches they had chosen. She cursed the many nights she had wept herself to sleep because she was certain she would never find the love she so desperately wanted.

And then, because she had found that love in the tall lean man who lay naked beside her, she truthfully told him of her other dreams, her ambitious plans of one day gaining the kind of wealth and power at court that would make her independent of others.

"And on that day, my grandfather, my father... aye, even my Uncle Robert, who one day, I feel, will be the most powerful man in England... none will say me nay. I will bed and wed and do what I please, and be no man's churl."

"Not even mine?"

There was a long moment before she answered softly, "Nay, Rory O'Donnell, not even yours."

He raised his powerful body until he was hovering over her, his black eyes boring into hers even in the darkness of the room. "We shall see, sweet Elizabeth. We shall see."

Wildly he would tickle her body, bringing laughter and gaiety to replace the heaviness of their words. From one side of the bed to the other they would roll, as if they were two children inventing their play as an excuse to touch the mystery of each other.

And then he would enter her, smoothly and gently,

before she had even realized her own readiness. The instant arching of her body, the ready acceptance of his love and the spontaneous winding of her arms and legs around him told them both that there was a chance that her last words were only half-truths, that for this man she would be slave, concubine, mistress, and wife...if she could.

But she could not. And that they both knew also.

It didn't stop them from dreaming about some distant time in the future when things would not be as they were now. Wishful thinking, perhaps, but so deep had become their love that they couldn't help voicing it.

"Od's blood, I would that one day soon Ireland and England could be one...." Elizabeth murmured.

"Think you, my love, that that could make us any closer?"

"Aye, Rory, it could." She moved nearer to him and rolled to her side as if the heaviness of her naked breast against him could add to her words. "For I think it not a sin to say that one day, mayhap soon, a widow I'll be and my own woman again."

Rory said nothing. Sir William loomed like a silent specter between them always, but his name had never been mentioned. Now Rory searched Elizabeth's eyes to find the reason behind her words.

She voiced it. "My Irish lands in Munster are extensive. You don't need the O'Donnell lands in Donegal. Let your brother have them."

Rory frowned, biting his lip at the same time. How could he tell her that his feud with Red Hugh was but a ruse? How could he explain that one day he would have his own share of Donegal?

"You could make the Hatton lands in Ireland those of Rory O'Donnell," Elizabeth continued.

"And what if there is war? Your lands will no longer be yours to give."

She reared back, tiny lines forming in her forehead between flashing eyes. "How so?"

"Are you so sure, my sweet girl, that when war comes, 'tis the English who will be the victors?"

A flush suffused Elizabeth's face and made its way down to the dark tips of her breasts. She stammered for a moment, then squared her shoulders and flashed him the look he had come to know so well. The look said, *why shouldn't I know? Can't a woman be allowed to know anything?*

"Yes, they will... *we* will!" She squared her shoulders even more. The movement thrust her already jutting breasts forward. Rory leaned over and kissed her nipple.

"And how, my little military strategist, do you know with such certainty?"

She drew away, peeved by his seeming mockery. "I know because it has always been so." The quake in her voice and the truth of her words brought his eyes up again to meet hers and thinned his lips to a taut line. "Would God it needn't be so," she added, sighing.

"I'm afraid you are more wise than I thought. It is so."

Gently he reached up and pulled her back down to him. With a tiny sob she cradled her head to his neck and placed one of his hands on her breast.

"Then why must they fight? Why must there be war, only to lose... to die?"

When he spoke now there was no humor in Rory's voice, only a vague tiredness. "I fear, my darling, that your tutors schooled you only in English history. What do you know of Irish history?"

"The Norman conquest and—" her voice was tiny,

not wanting to anger him needlessly yet not wanting to cow before this new tone of his, either ''—and that the Irish were savages without laws or morals, who made sport of killing each other before the Normans came.''

Rory sensed the turmoil within her, and at the same time realized that her forthrightness was one of the things he admired in her. He lightly squeezed her breast and let a low mirthless chuckle rumble from his chest.

''At least that far they taught you well. From the first mention of an Irishman in history, faction fight and foray have been his chief occupations and the delight of his existence. And I'm afraid the Irishman of today hasn't changed a great deal.''

''You have.''

Rory let that comment pass and spoke again. ''The English have tried through the years to coerce the Irish, discredit them, conciliate them. They have tried compromise and even concession. It has all been met with a stubbornness that the greatest minds in England cannot understand.''

''Then we apologize!'' Elizabeth cried. ''I apologize, *we* apologize for past wrongs. Do you likewise and be done with it!''

''We accept,'' Rory said, smiling up into the darkness.

''And then. . .?''

''Then we would go back to the sword.''

Again she reared up, rolling over him until her breasts pillowed across his chest and her face was above his.

''Then what you're saying is you want to drive the English out so the Irish can start killing each other again, isn't it?''

''Perhaps.''

He curled his fingers playfully in the mist of her

auburn mane and tried to pull her lips down to his. She struggled until she was free.

"No, damme, don't trifle!"

"Trifle, m'lady?"

"You know of what I speak! Don't war at words with no meaning. You've not given reason enough to settle my mind. The Queen herself has said she wants no more than to bring civilization to Ireland. She would have temperance and tolerance in all matters, including religion."

"So she would."

"Well?"

"Well, what?"

"Rory O'Donnell...!"

"Lay beside me! Press your breasts against me, my sweet Elizabeth, and I'll try to explain...without trifling, though I doubt you'll see the jest of my words." Reluctantly she stretched herself beside him again. "'Tis the mind and will of the Irish people that cause the problem. Like you, Elizabeth, they would rule themselves."

"But they would bow to papist rule."

He laughed aloud then. "Nay, it only seems so. Know you of our early religion...our fairies, our elves, our many gods?"

"But that was heathenism."

"Aye, it would seem so. But 'twas England, remember, who first set the Roman yoke upon our necks. Then, when your good King Henry dispensed with the services of the Italian priest so that he could have more wives and an heir, he expected the Irish to comply and embrace his Protestantism."

"Is that so bad?" she wailed, more confused than ever. "You yourself have said that no Pope or Spanish Catholic could rule Ireland."

"True, but let me finish! Herein lies the Irish mind and its bent. Because of Henry's loves, the Pope claimed the right, in the true faith, to absolve the Irish from our allegiance to the English crown. Thus, to the Irish mind, rebellion becomes a sacred duty, does it not?"

Elizabeth was stunned. Through the morass of his words she realized his meaning. Nothing was logical. "Then there will be no end, ever, no matter what."

Rory was silent for many moments before speaking again.

"Human idiocy is the real original sin. It is endless and irredeemable."

CHAPTER TWENTY-FIVE

THE WIND WHIPPED through the trees, bending them until they nearly touched the upward side of the hill of Tullaghogue.

"We'll walk," O'Neill said, swinging from his horse with a groan. He held up a hand to those behind him and glanced at O'Hara.

The wide-shouldered, black-bearded O'Hara hesitated, looking sternly down at this man he had chosen as his mentor, this man the ballad singers said would be the savior of Ireland. He had half a mind to sit on his horse, with the wind blowing his beard, and wait out this foolishness with the others.

But the very command in the smoldering eyes, the sheer presence of The O'Neill, was enough to make O'Hara toss his rein aside and slip to the rocky ground. Burrowing into the lid of his mantle he stomped behind the taller man, who was climbing toward the stone.

Near the top a bolt of lightning made day of night and illuminated O'Neill's features. To O'Hara, the craggy red-bearded face looked worn and tired. Much of the long hair trailing to his shoulders was graying now, as was the jutting beard.

Only the pinpoints of light, like burning fire in the man's eyes, told O'Hara that the fierce desire was still there. And that was why O'Hara knew he would follow the man into hell if need be.

O'Neill paused for a moment to catch his breath. O'Hara reached his side. "Rain...soon."

"Aye," O'Neill nodded. "'Tis rain, O'Hara, that keeps the land green and the trees growing."

He climbed over the top and O'Hara flinched. Well he knew the meaning in those words, and the reason behind the harshness in the tone. From Dublin in the Pale they had ridden these two days, and always in the distance they had seen the English felling the trees, taking away the forests.

"'Tis Bagenal's idea," Lord Deputy Fitzwilliams had said. "And Bingham agreed. Scorch the forests and the rebels will have naught but stumps to hide behind."

O'Neill was speaking. "They desecrate the land now, Shane, as they've desecrated our souls. We lose the trees and we'll lose the game, and soon we'll lose the soil."

"Aye," O'Hara agreed, slowing his pace to match O'Neill's, whose breath now came in short gasps. "'Tis what I've said for two fortnights. Strike now while they're weak and we've something to strike them with!"

O'Neill smiled and nodded, squinting his eyes toward the clearing before them. "What would you do, Shane?"

"I'd join with O'Donnell and drive Bingham's arse back into the Pale, and the Pale into the sea!"

Again O'Neill nodded. They reached the wide clearing just as another jagged flash illuminated its center. A pile of stones confronted them. Carved into the center of the largest was a thronelike indentation three men high. Above it was the O'Neill lion, and the name crudely chiseled in the stone.

In front was a pure white rock, waist high and a man's height wide. It was to this that O'Neill moved and dropped to his knees.

He reached out and placed his hands flat against the stone.

"'Tis the O'Neill inauguration stone, Shane. My grandfather, Conn, and his fathers before him sat here to accept the O'Neill mantle. It was here they vowed to rid their lands of Englishmen."

"Aye, as mine did at Ballylee."

"Aye, as we've all done."

O'Neill stood up, painfully it seemed to O'Hara, and moved around the sacred stone to settle his huge body into the carved chair. His legs stretched before him in tight worsted trews as he shook the wide sleeves of his saffron shirt loose from the leather jerkin and settled them on the stone arms.

With the fiery mane on his leonine head blowing wildly in the wind and his chieftain's cloak falling in folds around him from its gold clasp he did indeed look like a king.

But king of what, O'Hara thought, the silence, broken only by the whistling wind, again making him impatient.

They had ridden hard for Dungannon, and at the last minute O'Neill had turned them aside. "I would have some council," he had said.

Council with what, O'Hara wondered. *The wind? A hard cold stone?*

O'Hara was a man of action. He cared little for philosophy or reverie. For O'Hara too much thinking took away from the joys of life: a full belly, the soft dampness between a woman's spread legs, and the cringing head of an enemy beneath his sword.

"The sun never shone on a lovelier land than nature made our Ireland, Shane. And witness what the English whore does now."

"The trees?"

"Aye, the trees, the children of the land." O'Neill's eyes looked through and beyond O'Hara, as if they could see every mountain, lake and glen from Ulster to Wicklow.

O'Hara shook his bearlike body inside his mantle. He reached for the goatskin bladder at his belt, thought better of it and dropped his hand back to the hilt of his sword.

"How grows your sprout, O'Hara?"

"Up like a weed and more like his mother every day."

"And the Lady Deirdre? She is again with child?" O'Hara nodded, and O'Neill chuckled. "That is one thing we do well, my friend. We create saplings as fast as the English can cut them down. How many bastards have ye had, O'Hara?"

The big man shrugged. "Six. . .eight."

"As do I, along with four stout lads by my wives. But 'tis all family, Shane, and 'tis family we all must turn back to in the end. What think ye of the O'Haras a hundred, two hundred years from now?"

O'Hara squirmed. He thought little beyond the present, and could see no reason to sit on a damp windswept hill contemplating what he would never see.

O'Neill saw the other man's discomfort and understood it. "No matter," he said, gesturing to the goatskin at O'Hara's belt. "Let us drink to young men and to now, rather than to what history will write about old men tomorrow!"

They both tipped the bladder, taking large gulps of the burning liquid, before O'Neill spoke again. "What think ye of the soldiers in Dublin?"

O'Hara answered at once. "I think their armor is older than ours, their horses underfed, their numbers slight, and they would gladly trade their muskets for fatter food rations and a good measure of this!" He held up the goatskin bladder.

"Aye, I see them as you do, O'Hara. And methinks they lack the leaders they need. Englishmen like Vere and Essex, who could lead and would fight, thankfully look upon Ireland as too inglorious a field for enterprise. The lad in England, O'Donnell, tells me they bicker more about the war that is no war with Spain than they care about Erin."

"Then we fight?"

O'Neill again got that faraway look in his eyes. He didn't mention to O'Hara the rest of Rory O'Donnell's terse message, for O'Hara wouldn't understand. The young O'Donnell had seen much and had matured during his bout with the English. His words proved it:

> . . . but no matter their bickering or their pettiness, they are strong. I see their great estates. They are vast, graced with beauty beyond my wildest dreams, and reeking of wealth. I have come to realize that war between us is not just Irish against English, but a clash of civilizations. One is hopelessly out-of-date and the other the most powerful and efficient in Europe.

O'Neill smiled and nodded, more to himself than to O'Hara, who had begun to pace with impatience. *Aye,* he mused, *the lad has gained much intelligence.*

"What's that, Shane? I fear my thoughts absorbed me."

O'Hara frowned and repeated himself. "Even now, on every scaffold in Ireland, martyrs are being born. Methinks 'tis time we give the English a few of their own to mourn over."

"Aye, O'Hara, I think 'tis time. We've stood by watching the English settlers move like land-ravishing ants from Munster north toward Ulster. We can stand by no more!"

O'Hara whooped and leaned across the stone toward O'Neill, his dark eyes wide and intense. "Long now I've played the neutral sop while Red Hugh danced the rebel's jig on the cutting edge. I can march in two days' time!"

O'Neill stood up. "So be it."

Although his mind was still troubled, he moved with a steady pace back down the hill toward the rest of his clan leaders. When he reached them he could see the lust for battle in their eyes. They knew him well enough to know his decision without words.

Once mounted, the group soon broke into two and parted company. Over his shoulder O'Neill could hear O'Hara's lusty shout. "On to Ballylee! And in two days' time, lads, Enniskillen and a bag of English heads!"

O'Neill murmured softly to himself, "Ah, there will be little wheat and rye sown this Michaelmas season, and even less barley and vetch seeds will find the ground come spring "

"You spoke, m'lord?"

"What? Oh, yes. I was just wondering aloud when we would all go a'booleying again."

ON A NORMAL SUMMER PROGRESS the court's departure from Whitehall and its subsequent return was determined by the onset of winter weather as well as by Her Majesty's desire to be present at Westminster for her own Accession Day celebration, November 17.

But in the year of 1593 internal and external pressures of state forced them to return much earlier, in August.

Gloriana had appointed Edward Coke as the attorney general over Essex's man, Francis Bacon. The earl was outraged, and openly railed against the Queen and Cecil. Normally little attention was paid to his injured pride and vanity. But his rantings now revealed his lust for power and his thirst for war, and they endangered Cecil's and even the Queen's already tenuous popularity with the common people.

It was becoming uncomfortably clear to the monarch that her headstrong favorite was paying more attention to cultivating his popularity with the people than with her.

Furthermore, Henry of France had been crowned at Chartres, and with his coronation he had declared his kingdom Catholic. This opened the door for a renewed war across the Channel. The rebellion in Ireland had taken on the aspects of a real war, and Spain still threatened.

As if this were not enough, the plague had barely diminished when a new kind of plague arose—the heaviest spring and summer rains in years had literally washed the crops away. Famine and disease were everywhere, and internal rebellion was in the air.

Even an outsider, an Irishman such as Rory O'Donnell, could sense it, smell it, feel it, as the royal party approached London's walls.

As usual the Queen left her carriage and entered the city on a litter. There were crowds who cheered her return, but not the shouting throngs of past years.

Even the lord mayor, when bidding her welcome, seemed subdued, and the London burgesses flanking him were red of face.

But once again Rory felt admiration for the aging monarch. Even though it was clear to all those present, and undoubtedly to Gloriana herself, that her people's tolerance was waning and that her own popularity was at a low ebb, she was regal in her speech to the lord mayor.

And when the crowds through the city proved even thinner, her chin jutted more proudly and her smiles became more gracious.

"Steel," he murmured to himself as he left the party at Cheapside and spurred his horse toward Newgate and Holborn beyond. "The woman is made of steel."

THE COURTYARD OF HASKINS HOUSE had about it an unseemly quiet. The groom, in taking Rory's horse, barely mumbled a welcome before scurrying toward the stables.

Inside the house the gloom was even thicker. Familiar faces of servants turned away from him, their eyes vacant and darting everywhere at once rather than meeting his.

He found Lord Haskins in his study. The man himself was a picture of gloom, and he passed Rory a glass of brandy without his usual embrace.

"Brr, 'tis an early winter chill I feel," Rory murmured.

Haskins placed a finger to his lips and moved to the

door. Cautiously he opened it a crack, satisfied himself that they weren't being overheard, and locked it with a click.

When he turned back, Rory was shocked at the acquired age in the man's face. The already deep wrinkles were made even deeper by hollowed cheeks and a pinching around the eyes. The eyelids themselves were swollen, and the upper lids drooped until he appeared almost ready to drift into sleep.

"Od's blood, m'lord, you appear as if I should be keening for a corpse."

"Very nearly, I fear," Haskins nodded. "Sit, lad." Even his voice had a coarse raspy quality not unlike the rattle of death.

Rory sat down, doing his utmost to ignore the gnawing hunger in his belly and to throw off the tremble that reached for his hands.

"Much news I have, and much of it bad."

"Southwell?"

"Nay. Though the man has less than half his body left and God knows how much of his brain, his tongue still holds."

"Garnet?"

"Is in the countryside, God knows where. The man is like a will-o'-the-wisp, and thanks for it. But his hunger for power and his wagging tongue will fell him, and I fear soon. He would have the Queen's head, and he preaches it at every turn."

The old man reached achingly for the decanter of brandy and refilled his glass. Rory stilled the beating in his chest and held his own tongue, waiting for Haskins to continue.

"O'Neill has sent word that both of us must flee England as soon as possible."

"Both of—" Rory had half risen. Now he dropped

back into the chair with a grunting sigh. "It's begun, then."

"Near. O'Hara marches to Enniskillen. He does it in small groups for secrecy, but Sir James Blake and Cecil's Irish spies know something is in the air. Sir Robert himself paid a call this morning."

"And. . .?"

"He discreetly advised me to contact my daughter and convince her, with whatever means possible, that she and my grandson should journey to England for their own safety."

"They would both be hostages in the Tower in less than an hour."

"I know. And I rather imagine Sir Robert knows as well. I fear I can no longer hide behind the ruse of pity that my children are rebels on their own and forsake me."

"And if Deirdre and little Rory stay in Ireland?"

"Then I rather imagine 'tis I who will inhabit their Tower cell."

"Damme," Rory hissed, slapping a fist to a palm. "Could not The O'Neill wait but one more week?"

"Methinks 'twould do no good anyway. They close in on us, lad. Sir Brian Russell was killed in Calais. A duel."

"Duel? With whom?"

"Blake."

"Then 'twas murder."

"Aye, probably. But even now I'm watched day and night. When word reaches Cecil that it is indeed O'Hara who reinforces your brother, I'll be arrested. When O'Neill comes into it, any Irishman of blood will be rounded up, no matter what pleas of fealty to the crown he makes."

Rory paused in his pacing to stare out the window.

Across Holborn there were double the number of idlers as would be found on a normal day.

"Aye, they now watch us both," he growled, and whirled to face Haskins. "Has Grace O'Malley's ship arrived?"

Haskins nodded. "'Tis anchored near Whitehall Gate."

"We'll go ahead then! The city—nay, the whole countryside—is ripe. I could feel it upon entering the city. The powder is there. All we need supply is the fuse! Can we send to Mile End for Ned?"

Haskins hoisted himself to his feet. "No need. Your rogue and his Annie have been in my cellar these past two days."

THE LITTLE WHERRY SLID DOWNSTREAM past the Whitehall Privy Stairs and the Queen's barge. Just beyond, near Whitehall Gate, the Irish longboat bobbed at anchor, its fore and aft lanterns gently rocking with the movement.

The sight of the O'Malley ship brought a smile to James Blake's lips. Somewhere in the darkness at the top of those stairs his man watched.

And then the smile faded as Blake lay further back in the wherry's stern. Even though it was a warm August night he was encased in a heavy black cloak. Now he burrowed deeper into it and furrowed his forehead in thought.

What if they didn't try to remove the propaganda? What if the two O'Malley kerns he had bribed in Clew Bay had been lying about the method and time of transfer? The penny sheets could already be off the ship and even now be passing around the country.

No. He'd had the ship watched twenty-four hours a day since its arrival. He was positive the packets were still on board, and he was sure the next night was to be the night of their removal.

"Mylford Stairs, was it, sar?"

"Aye," Blake replied, noticing that they were passing the Savoy Estate. The lighted windows of the gabled great houses cast dancing reflections in the water as the little boat heeled to port.

Minutes later Blake was slowly walking up the stairs, with one eye over his shoulder on the wherryman. When he was satisfied that the man had reached midstream and wasn't looking back himself, Blake retraced his steps to the wall.

One more quick look around told him that he was alone. He mounted the slight indentation halfway down the wall and gripped the blocks along the top with his fingers. Inches at a time he moved until he could drop down to the water steps that led into the gardens and house adjoining Mylford Stairs.

No one could have seen him traverse the distance in the darkness, but nevertheless he again scanned the river.

Blake's intentions this night needed such precautions. It wouldn't do for Sir Robert Cecil to know that his most trusted spy was paying a clandestine midnight visit to his arch foe at court, Robert Devereux, Earl of Essex.

The wrought-iron gate opened silently under his hand, and Blake stepped into the gardens behind Essex House. Not a light shone in the house, but lanterns pierced the night from Leicester House next door and Blake could see movement in the windows.

Keeping in the shadows of yew trees and behind tall hedges, he moved through the gardens to the side of the house. At the wicket entrance he disregarded the bell hanging from a gilded chain as well as the brass knocker, but rapped gently three times with his knuckles.

The door was opened instantly. "Come in!"

Blake stepped into the darkness and the door closed behind him. A lantern was lifted up to his face. "Ah, good, 'tis you. Od's blood, Blake, you're late. I've been by this bloody door fifteen minutes!"

Blake recognized the lisping speech of the profligate Earl of Southampton. Like all the other strutting wastrels Essex kept around him, Southampton thought himself a great patron of the arts, a genius at poetry writing and a fierce swordsman.

Blake thought of him—and the rest of Essex's entourage, save the Bacon brothers who were crafty—as opulent barnacles on society's butt.

But this night he needed them.

"I beg your consideration, m'lord, but secrecy being of the utmost, I traveled downstream to Winchester and wherried back up, rather than be followed directly to m'Lord Essex's door."

"No matter. But I've about wet my breeches in this damnable hall." He gestured waggishly with a kerchief. "That way, up the stairs and to the right."

"Thank you, m'lord."

They moved through the great rooms of the old bishop's palace like two specters in the light of the lantern that Southampton held. Even in its dim light Blake could ascertain the lushness of the furnishings and estimate the cost of the renovation.

He also guessed that very little of it was paid for. Essex was as adept at eluding his creditors as he was at coercing them into giving him credit.

Southampton swept into a lighted room and Blake followed, taking in everything at a glance. The Bacon brothers were hunched together at a table over a pile of papers. Essex lounged against an oaken mantle, in conversation with Sir Christopher Blount.

"Aye, m'lord, 'twas in St. John Street, at a puppet play. They say that when the roof fell five were killed outright...and, more's the pity, two were good handsome whores!"

Essex waved his glass. "No matter, the countryside will soon spawn two to take their place."

"He's here," Southampton declared, moving swiftly on across the room. "And now, by God, I'm to the water closet!"

"Ah, Blake."

Even in his den Essex looked dressed for battle, in a tangerine suit heavily embroidered with gold. He moved toward Blake as if ten squires and twenty trumpets were heralding him across the room.

"I must say, Blake, I was surprised and much intrigued with your missive. Don't tell me you've decided to abandon our little hunchback's ship of state?"

"Not quite, m'lord." Blake's eyes took in the aquiline nose, the full pursed lips, and the jutting red beard he knew hid a rounded weak chin, and then shifted his gaze to Blount.

When Essex had agreed to the meeting, he had also agreed on who would be present. Sir Christopher Blount wasn't one of the number.

Essex saw the smaller man's darting look and clamped him lightly by the shoulder. "Come, come, man. Sir Christopher is, after all, married to my mother. I trust him as I trust her."

Blake wasn't reassured, but he let himself be guided to a chair.

"Sit. Wind around, gentlemen, and let us hear what revelations Blake has for us."

Blake was conscious that Essex had not once used his

title of knighthood, nor had his host offered him wine. But he had expected the slight and cared little for it. He had lived with such slights since he could remember, and they only served to fuel his desire and his ambition.

With a last glance at Blount he launched into his tale. He spoke as much to Francis Bacon as he did to Essex, for he knew that the last word would come from that quarter.

His story was met with nods and occasional mutterings. When Lord Haskins's name was mentioned, however, Essex leaped to his feet and stomped around the room.

"I knew it, have known it for years! That old fool had treason in his heart long before his son's head found a pole on London Bridge!"

"Pray—pray go on, sir," Bacon said in a quiet stutter.

Blake did, even acquainting them with the sources of his information: the harper, a captured courier, and the two bribed seamen on Grace O'Malley's ship.

Other than Essex wringing his hands and declaring that uncovering Haskins's treachery would be a greater coup than bringing about the downfall of Doctor Lopez, Blake's last words were met with silence.

Months before, Essex and the Bacons had uncovered a supposed plot by the Queen's personal physician, Lopez, to poison Gloriana. As usual, hard evidence mattered little to Essex in his desire to win back the Queen's favor, to make a mockery of Cecil's intelligence-gathering forces, and to establish himself as a man to be reckoned with.

Both the Queen and Cecil had dismissed Essex's accusations as rash, but the man's ambition knew no bounds. At the time all London had been fanatic over a new play, *The Jew of Malta*, by Christopher Marlowe.

Essex played upon this frenzy until the people demanded the head of Lopez, who was a Portuguese Jew.

Reluctantly the Queen had signed Lopez's death warrant, and so Essex won out. In the people's eyes he was
firmly established as a hero. But at court the victory
was as hollow as the rest of Essex's undertakings.

The Lopez affair was the reason Blake now sought
the earl's aid. He could see how Essex would consider
arranging the downfall of a peer of such magnitude as
Haskins an opportunity to erase all doubts about his
ability to match—nay, outdo—Robert Cecil in affairs
of state.

Without even hearing Blake's plan, the earl was all
for it. As Blake expected, Francis Bacon proved a
cooler head.

"Tell me, Sir—Sir James," he said, his stutter more
pronounced by the deep thought of his words, "why
is—is it that—you come to m'Lord Essex with this—
this affair? Sir Robert Cecil, I'm sure, would reward
you greatly for un—uncovering such information."

"True enough," Blake replied, and paused to weigh
his words. "Know you the Irishman, Rory O'Donnell?"

"Aye."

"Aye, as do I, the churl. Were it not for the Queen's
wrath and Cecil's fear of angering the rest of the beggarly Irish, I would have skewered him long ago
myself," Essex interjected.

"Precisely my intention," Blake said, smiling.
"Should he be taken by the Queen's men, even with
such serious charges on his head, he would get no more
than the Tower."

"Why, sir, are—are you so interested in this—this
Irishman's death?"

Again Blake paused, scanning the faces around him

before speaking. He didn't want to tell them the truth of it, that he had designs on the Lady Elizabeth Hatton's hand and that he had discovered she and O'Donnell were lovers. He didn't want to admit that he suspected their love ran deep, and that O'Donnell might one day stand in Blake's way of acquiring Lady Elizabeth's lands and fortune.

"Suffice it to say that I think O'Donnell alive is more danger to the state than his countrymen's wrath at his demise."

"Bravo!" Essex said. "My sentiments exactly. Off with the serpents' heads and the bodies become wonderfully docile!"

"Then should I consider it a pact?" Blake asked. "With my only payment your silence as to my part in the affair?"

"And O'Donnell," Essex said.

"Aye, and O'Donnell."

Essex moved only his eyes as he glanced at Francis Bacon. There was a barely perceptible nod, and he again looked at Blake.

"'Tis a bargain," he said. "Would you like some wine, Sir James?"

CHAPTER TWENTY-SIX

ANNIE'S KNEES THREATENED to turn to water halfway up the gangway. She was sure she looked anything but a young Irish page in the employ of Grace O'Malley. Thus far she had been challenged but not stopped, however.

She had scurried like a rabbit through the darkness of St. James's Park, skirted the Queen's privy garden and tiltyard, and scrambled over a wall to a walkway that would take her out at the top of Whitehall Stairs.

All of this was to make it appear as if she was emerging from the Stone Gallery where the royal banquet was still taking place.

She had been challenged at the top and the bottom of the long stone stairs by the Queen's guard. Both times she had spouted gibberish that she hoped sounded like the lilting Gaelic tongue. That, and the style of her buckram clothes, plus the way Rory had styled her hair, brushing it forward over her head and most of her face like an Irish glib, was enough to convince the guards.

They waved her on with curses and a shake of their heads at her wild uncivilized appearance.

Now, as Annie neared the watching guard at the ship's rail, she hoped the O'Malley woman had not changed her mind. The occasion of the pirate queen of Connaught's visit to Gloriana was well-known. She wanted to make peace with England in return for her lands and the Queen's pledge that Sir Richard Bingham would henceforth leave her alone.

She had agreed, at O'Neill's urging, to perform this last service for the Irish cause, even as she begged leniency from England's Queen. The one stipulation Grace had made was that neither she nor her crew would know the nature of her illicit cargo. Only the two men placed on board by O'Donnell were to have any part in smuggling the penny sheets.

Annie hoped that the wild-looking man she now approached, with his glibbed hair covering much of his face, was one of the two. Panic gripped her when she realized she hadn't the slightest idea what he was saying as he held up a huge hairy arm and challenged her in Gaelic.

She replied haltingly in what she hoped was an understandable version of the Gaelic phrase Rory had drummed into her head. "I would to Seamus Burke for delivery of the Donegal hides."

"Aye, lad, ye'll find him amidships on the port side."

Again Annie understood not a word, but she got his meaning through gestures.

Compared to the large, many masted English galleys, O'Malley's ship was small. It carried only a foresail and one main mast. Most of its power was gleaned from forty or more oarsmen who lounged, lived, ate and slept where they worked when at sea—on the open wooden benches where they plied their oars.

Annie now made her way through several groups of these men as they idled their time away with drink, conversation and dice. Hardly one paid her any attention as she slipped around the main mast and hoisted herself up to the portside walkway that ran the length of the ship above the rowing well.

There was no need to find Seamus Burke. He found her by the red bunting on the collar of her buckram jacket.

"This way, lad, aft and below... follow me!"

Annie breathed a sigh of relief as she padded along behind his bare feet. Seamus Burke spoke English. It was barely understandable and the words were twisted as they came from his lips, but it was better than Gaelic.

They entered a hatchway and descended a ladder in near darkness to the bowels of the ship. At the foot of the ladder Burke lit a hooded lantern and again motioned Annie to follow him.

The passageway was narrow, lined with rough-cut timber and smelling of the caulking used to fill the seams and keep out the sea. The rocking of the ship against the ebbing Thames was more pronounced now. It brought a fluttering queasiness to Annie's stomach.

"They're here, under these sails," Burke said. "Give us a hand, lad!"

Between them they quickly unrolled the spare sail and uncovered two large bundles wrapped tightly in animal skins and tied with handwoven line.

"'Tis glad I am to be rid of these," the man growled. "We've O'Flahertys aboard and I trust not a one of them."

"How so?" Annie asked, tugging at the bundles until they pulled free.

"They shift with the wind and it takes little coin to buy their tongues. Over here, to the slops hole!"

They rolled the bundles to a latched opening in the side of the ship. Burke blew out the lantern and unhooked the narrow door. When it swung wide, Annie looked out into the night. They were standing about six feet above the waterline, and being on the riverside, they were well away from the streaming lights of Whitehall.

"Do ye see 'em?"

"Aye," Annie nodded. "There, midstream above the Queen's barge. The one with the red bunting on the canopy."

"Off we go then!"

Seamus hoisted both bundles through the slops hole. Silently they were lowered to the water by an attached line. When they were bobbing in the Thames he turned to Annie.

"Now you, lad!"

Before Annie knew it she was lifted in the air and her legs were through the opening. Seamus's strong arms handled her with ease. Then all of her dangled free of

the ship above the water, with Seamus's arms around
her middle. She felt his grip slacken, and she was
sliding through his arms.

"Damme," he suddenly hissed.

"What?"

" 'Tis a lass you are!"

Then she realized that he was grasping her around
the chest, with his hands literally on her breasts. Annie
was small, but there was no mistaking the fact that she
was a girl.

"Aye, Seamus Burke, but one who can swim like a
fish."

"Ye might be English," the big man chuckled, "but
methinks ye've got the spine of an Irishwoman. Godspeed, lass!"

Annie knifed the water beside the bundles and came
up between them, already swimming.

RORY HUDDLED BENEATH THE AWNING of the three-
oared pleasure boat while Ned and two of his lads held
the craft straight against the tide swirling by them.
Twice they had been cursed by passing wherrymen for
standing idle in midstream.

Ned had returned their oaths in kind, and now spoke
to Rory. "Methinks there's too much life upon the
river, even at this late hour."

"Perhaps, Ned," Rory nodded. "But mayhap that
will be a help once we get downstream."

"Aye, but first the lass must find us."

Rory cast a sidelong glance at the worried frown on
Ned's face. It was a risky thing Annie did, but
necessary. She would be the last one recognized if the
ship were being watched.

"She'll find us, Ned, and she'll make it to midstream. She's a plucky wench."

Ned grinned, his teeth shining in his dark face. "Aye, she's that."

"There!" said the lad on the bow oar. "I think 'tis she!"

They all strained their eyes into the rippling water until they saw the bobbing bundles and the tiny white face between them.

"Annie, lass, are ye all right?" Ned cried.

"Aye," she sputtered, kicking hard and maneuvering her burden around the stern of the boat.

One frail hand came up holding a line, and Rory gripped it. He pulled until the bundles were tight against the side, with Annie hanging on between them.

"How cold is it, Annie?" he asked.

"Like an early morning bath I once had," she chattered.

"Good lass," Rory said. "Hang on, it won't be long and we'll have you out of there. Let's go, lads!"

The three sets of oars lifted slightly and turned to act more as rudders than propellers as the current quickly carried them downstream toward the blazing lights of London Bridge.

JAMES BLAKE STOOD on one of the rear gables of Essex House, a glass at his eye.

"Can you make—make out the faces?" Francis Bacon said from his side.

"Nay," Blake replied, "the distance is too far."

"Then—then—then how can you be sure?"

"It has to be them," Blake said. "The boat stayed too long in midstream for no reason."

"But did—did you see them load—load the bundles over the—the side?"

"Nay, but 'tis them," Blake said, folding the glass

and turning to Bacon. "Give the signal to m'Lord Essex. I'm off to Haskins House."

THERE WAS A MOMENT OF SHEER TERROR as they shot the rapids beneath the bridge. One of the younger lads dipped an oar too deep and the stern began to shift around. The swift current nearly caught them amidships, then Ned applied his powerful arms to right them and they shot on through.

Their destination was Billingsgate, one of three wharfs used for the unloading of giant carracks from foreign ports. It lay halfway between London Bridge and the Tower, and was dark and deserted at this time of night.

"The small wharf, lads," Ned grunted, pulling hard at his oars to send the little boat scampering around its bigger sisters, like a mouse among a herd of elephants.

At last they reached the wharf and everyone moved at once. Rory grabbed the bundle of spare clothes, extinguished the lanterns, and scrambled from the boat to the water stairs. Ned gingerly pulled his Annie from the water while his lads rescued the two bundles of penny sheets.

"Ah, yer a brave one, my little wench," Ned said, kissing her matted hair. "When this evening's work is done, old Ned will give ye an extra ration of his night's happiness."

"Off with ye now," she giggled, unable to disguise the glee she felt in her accomplishment. "Give us some dry clothes before I shiver out of my skin!"

Rory passed the remains of his bundle to Ned. The two lads had already changed into the leather jerkins and broadcloth shirts of cartmen and had hurried away in the darkness. Annie quickly peeled to the flesh and sorted out her share of the clothes. She was pulling on hose when she heard a light chuckle from Rory as he stood watch at the top of the stairs.

"Damme, Annie, I think this intrigue suits you well. Methinks you're getting flesh on your bones!"

Her eyes found his and her face flushed. She looked at Ned, as naked as she, and saw him grinning also. "A pox on you both!" she said, but laughed as she turned away and finished dressing.

When they were ready, Ned was in the blue livery of a squire and Annie wore the white waistcoat and red sash of a linkboy. Quickly she stuffed her wet hair under a wide-brimmed hat sporting a white feather.

"Ready?" Rory said.

"Aye," they chorused.

"Good, they're here with the cart. Let's be off!"

"RUE THIS DAY YOU WILL, m'lord," Haskins sputtered, "for in England there is still some law against the invasion of a man's home!"

"Pray, don't bother me with your prattling tongue, old man," Essex replied, peering down into the courtyard and the gardens of Haskins House beyond. "When I show the proof of your perfidy to the Queen, she'll care little that it was obtained without her writ to search."

To add emphasis to his words Essex rippled the penny sheets in his hand and waved them in the other man's face.

Haskins chewed on his lower lip and eyed the two men guarding the door. How true were Essex's words, despite the fact that he knew the man hadn't found the traitorous penny sheets in Haskins House as he claimed. But that would matter little when Rory was caught on the grounds with thousands of them.

Essex left the window and moved to a table. Idly he

ran his fingers through the jewelry and coin he had found in the luggage that had just been removed from a coach that still stood ready in the courtyard.

"Traveling money, m'lord?" Essex said, grinning widely through the red of his beard. "Where would you flee? To France, Spain. . . mayhap heathen Ireland?"

"I would to the country."

"Od's blood, man, do you take me for that big a fool? No man would go abroad in the day, much less the night, among high-road rogues with this much wealth on his person! Nay, m'lord, you would flee the Queen's executioner. And I, Essex, have saved that hooded man his day."

Haskins had no reply. He sighed and let his weary body slip into a chair. It was over and there was nothing for it. The one thing that amazed him was the fact that they had been unmasked not by Cecil and the Queen's guard, but by Essex.

A third man appeared at the door. "M'lord."

"Aye."

"They approach, afoot with a cart."

"How many and how near?"

"Four, and they near the stables."

Rory and Ned secured the bundle in the boot of the carriage and strapped it down. The other was already on its way to a Bankside tavern, where it would be broken open and parceled for distribution by morning. The contents of the one they kept would find waiting hands on the road between London and Chester.

"Into the house with you, Annie, and fetch m'Lord Haskins."

She hurried away while Rory and Ned saw to the harness.

Minutes passed and she didn't return, nor did Ned's

lad emerge from the stables where he was changing into the livery of a Haskins footman.

"See to your lad, Ned. I'll find out what keeps m'Lord Haskins and Annie."

"Aye."

Rory mounted the steps and was about to cross the wide porch to the rear doors of the house when a window was flung open above him and Haskins's face appeared. "Flee, lad, we've been betrayed!"

Before the old man could say anything more he was yanked back inside. At the same instant the doors of the house opened and men, swords at the ready, poured through. Rory drew his own blade but could see at once it was useless. He whirled and sprinted for the stables, calling Ned's name as he ran.

To his left he saw a flash of white drop from a first-floor window. Before he could distinguish who or what it was, the stable doors were thrown open and he was confronted by four more men. On the ground behind them lay Ned, blood running from the side of his head.

Using the momentum of his charge, Rory bulled through them, sending the dagger in his left hand into the nearest body. There was a scream of shock and pain. The man went down and Rory was through, standing over Ned.

The man's head rolled around, and with a groan his eyes opened.

"I didn't see them, lad," Ned gasped.

"Can you stand?"

"Aye."

Rory reached down to offer his comrade a hand, but it was too late. The stable door was filled with leering faces and flashing blades. They came forward as one.

Suddenly sound and smoke filled the air. Ned had drawn both his pistols and fired them point-blank into the charging bodies. Two of them fell and the others stopped momentarily.

"Through them, lad!" Ned howled, lunging forward with his short sword. "We'll cleave a path through to the gardens!"

Rory followed in his wake, hacking with his dagger until they reached open ground where his longer rapier could be brought into play. Back to back they fought, with neither side gaining an advantage, until they found themselves with their backs to the garden wall.

"Over you go, lad," Ned roared, "and out the other side!"

"Not without you."

"Damme, go!" Ned cried. "They'll only have me in the Fleet. . . they'll hang you!"

So saying, the big highwayman bellowed from the depths of his huge chest and waded forward to scatter their attackers.

It was then that Rory saw Essex coming from their right, followed by more men.

His first thought was curiosity. Essex? How? *Why?*

But then he had no more time for thought. The new arrivals were cutting off Ned's flank.

Rory bolted forward to engage them. It was foregone. The battle, by sheer numbers, was lost. But perhaps he could take Essex with him.

The clang of steel on steel and the cries of wounded men were deafening in the otherwise still night air.

Rory couldn't see Ned to his left, and sounds of that half of the battle were fading. There was a break in the garden wall and Rory darted through into the darkness.

He paused, waited, but they didn't follow.

"What ho, Irishman, I see you've graduated to a gentleman's blade."

Rory spun to face the voice's owner, and came up

short. There beneath the trees, the moonlight playing on the rapier he flexed in both hands, was James Blake.

His presence quickly answered the curiosity in Rory's mind about Essex. "So, Blake, you've deserted Sir Robert. What manner of payment from m'Lord Essex could be large enough to make you so blind?"

"Your ears, Irishman. *En garde!*"

The man was like a cobra, his moves lightning, his blade a blur. Rory parried with his dagger at the last second and side-stepped to retaliate. But before he could do so Blake had spun around and again the blade was dancing before his eyes.

Strength and power were Rory's allies. For a few thrusts and parries they saved him. But it soon became apparent that Blake's superior skill and speed would take its effect.

And as the dancing blade drove him deeper and deeper into the garden, Rory also realized that, unlike their last meeting, Blake had no intention of toying with him this time. Gone was the finessed slashing that had torn his doublet to shreds. No longer did Blake use the tip of his blade like a scalpel merely to flick Rory's flesh.

This time each thrust, each lunge, was for the heart and a kill.

"Your skill has improved, Irishman, but your riposte is much too slow and done with your weight to the right."

He illustrated with an appel, three quick lunges, stomping his right foot on the ground and driving Rory a yard backward with each stomp.

"And your tierce and sixte are too open, making you depend upon your dagger too much for parry. Of course that can be rectified."

A sidestep. A whooshing sound. Rory's parry was

easily slapped aside and six inches of Blake's blade passed through his wrist. The dagger clattered to the stones around a fountain and Rory retreated, only to find the fountain itself against the back of his thighs.

"I'm afraid, Irishman, that you are still cloddish at a gentleman's sport. *Touche!*"

The lunge was true, and had not Rory tripped trying to avoid it, the other's sword would have been through his heart. As it was, the tip found a rib and bent upward as it entered.

Rory groaned more from the shock of watching the rapier disappear into his body than from the sting of the pain. It was a reflex action that made him drop his own blade and clutch Blake's to stop its progress.

"Ah, a pity. . . only a fair hit. But no matter." Blake released the hilt and took a step backward, drawing a dagger from the gold clasp at his sash. "This will do as well!"

The dagger came up in both hands, and Rory was powerless to stop its downward arc. Then, as if he were reliving past moments, a flash of white was at his shoulder, and the night was filled with sound.

Blake screamed, dropped the dagger and clutched both hands to the left side of his bloody head. He howled in pain as he spun in circles on the grass. Then he was on his knees, and with a last loud cry of agony, fell forward and was still.

Rory turned. Through the haze that had started to mist over his eyes, he saw Annie's ashen face. She still held the smoking dag in her hand.

"I was hiding in the hedges. I should have shot him earlier, but I was afraid I would miss unless I was very close."

"You were close enough. Where's Ned?"

"Alive, I think. They have him in the house. You

must away, Rory. There's a horse by the meadow gate. It must be his,'' she said, nodding her head to where Blake lay. "Can you ride?''

"Not with this.'' Rory rolled to his right so she could see the hilt and half the blade protruding from his chest.

"Oh, God. . .no. . . .''

Until then her composure had been heroic. But the sight before her, and the uncertainty of Ned Bull's fate, were more than enough to rend her frail armor.

She wailed as if she had been wounded and fell to her knees with her hands covering her face.

"Annie. . . .''

She brushed his hand from her shoulder and crawled away, still weeping hysterically.

"Annie, I'm supposed to be dead. Blake meant to murder me, I'm sure. They'll come to look, to discover my body soon. We must away.''

"No, no, I'll not leave my Ned!''

"You must. We'll find a way to free him.'' Rory lurched to his feet and immediately fell down again with a cry of pain.

She was by his side at once. "Your front. . .oh, my God, your whole front is blood!''

"I know, Annie,'' he gasped through gritted teeth, forcing one thought at a time through his mind to ward off the blackness that threatened to engulf him. "Annie—''

"Aye.''

"You've got to pull this out.''

"No. . . .''

"Yes.'' Rory grasped her hand and tugged it to the sword's hilt.

"I can't. . .I. . .by Christ's blood, I can't!''

"If you don't, we'll both die right where we sit,

little Annie. And if Ned lives, he'll rot in Fleet Prison."

Enough of his gasping words reached her to make her blink the tears from her eyes. "How. . . how do I do it?"

"Put your left hand here, flat against my chest by the blade. Aye, like that. Now take the hilt in your right and pull. . . straight and true, Annie, pull straight and true."

She placed her trembling hands as he instructed. She tried to focus, but it was as if she were underwater with the waves flowing over her eyes. She gave up, closed them, and pulled.

There was a muffled gasp and she was standing with the blade in her hand. Rory lay before her, blood seeping in a steady stream from his wound.

"Binding," she murmured aloud. "Bandage and binding. Stop the blood's flow!"

Finding strength she didn't know she had, she ripped up her white waistcoat and bandaged his chest and back. Tightly she wrapped the red linkboy's sash around and around his chest to hold the bandages in place. Then, somehow, she got him to his feet.

"Good lass, Annie, stout lass," Rory moaned, coming out of his stupor and realizing that he was upright.

"Can you walk?"

"Huh?"

"Walk, O'Donnell, can you walk?"

"Aye, I think."

"I'll get you to the horse, but 'tis a long ride to Chester."

"Nay," he said, a tiny slit of blood escaping from the corner of his lips and bringing another gasp from her throat. "Inside my shirt. . . a scarf. . . ."

The rest of what he said was lost as she staggered toward a path with most of his weight on her shoulder.

Together they stumbled the length of the garden. Twice he fell, taking her with him to the ground. Each time she thought she would never get him up again, but each time she gritted her teeth, cursed the English, cursed the Irish, cursed him, cursed herself, and managed.

Thankfully she found a lady's step near the gate. With its elevation and Rory's brief periods of consciousness to aid her, she managed to get him into the saddle, only to practically lose him over the other side.

Frantically she searched the ground nearby for something to tie him with, and found nothing. "Damme, damme, damme," she cried, tears of frustration again filling her eyes.

She sat on the lady's step, defeated. And then she saw that one of her white hose had slipped to her ankle. Quickly she stripped them both from her legs and tied them together. Then she bound Rory's ankles together under the horse.

As she stepped back, however, she could see there was no hope that he could ride alone. She would have to go with him. She quickly ran back to the fountain and found the black greatcoat she had seen the other man cast aside.

As she passed his body, she heard a groan. *He's alive,* she thought, *the sod is alive!* Her eye fell on the dagger near her feet.

But before she could make up her mind, she heard Rory's voice, faintly, in the distance. "Annie, lass... where are you...."

"Coming," she said, forgetting the man on the ground as she took a last look at Haskins House through her tears. "Oh, damme, I'm coming."

CHAPTER TWENTY-SEVEN

Rory lay for a week, awake and asleep in fitful starts. Three times his fever reached proportions that clutched at Elizabeth's heart and drove her to the chapel and prayer.

"Dear Lord, hear this sinful woman's cry, hear the pain in my heart. No matter what he has done, I pray you, don't let him die. For 'twas I, and not him, who created the sin.

"I...I would promise never again to commit this sin so great in your eyes, but such a lie would be an even greater sin. For I love him so much that there is no stilling my mind and heart, which cries out for him. I believe, oh, Lord, that he is a man among men and to his honor bound. What he has done I feel he had to do. But I think he speaks only truth when he speaks to me of his great love. Spare him, Lord, for should he die I fear I would want to join him of grief."

On the eighth day he awakened, seemed to realize where he was, and lapsed again into a fitful fever-laden sleep. On the morning of the ninth day he mumbled a few incoherent words, and soon afterward the fever broke. That evening, still slightly delirious, he was able to take soup from her hand, and then from Honor's when fatigue would no longer allow Elizabeth to hold the cup to his lips.

Sir William, along with his entourage, had returned to London with the Queen's departure, so his presence was no problem. Elizabeth pleaded for a few more weeks in the country, with the completion of the cottage as her excuse. She then stopped all work, saying that she needed silence and solitude, and moved into the partially finished bedroom beside Rory's.

The servants in the great house paid little attention and went on with their daily lives. Through the summer they had accustomed themselves to the capriciousness of their mistress.

Out of necessity, and at Elizabeth's urging, Honor had brought her beau, Charles, into the intrigue. He was a big strapping farm lad with a keen mind, an open face and a love for his Honor that knew no bounds. He inquired little about the strange visitor and accepted what Honor and the Lady Elizabeth told him.

Only he and Honor were allowed in the cottage to serve Holdenby's mistress.

In the middle of the afternoon of the tenth day Rory awakened completely. Elizabeth was standing by the window, brushing her unkempt curls from her hollowed eyes when he whispered her name.

She whirled around and rushed to the bed, where she fell to her knees. She grasped his hand and brought it to the dampness of her cheek. "My love...." she breathed.

"Elizabeth, I'm sorry."

"For what? For being a dastardly Irish spy? You practically told me you were more than once. Methinks I knew, but wanted nothing outside this cottage to mar what went on inside it."

"No, I'm sorry I came here like this, to endanger you."

She was determined not to cry, and set her mind and quivering jaw against the possibility. "A pox on your apology and your conceit. How can you endanger me? I am Lady Elizabeth Hatton. No one would dream I harbor a rebel."

Her attempt at humor brought a faint smile to Rory's pale lips. "Then you know of it. How much?"

"That you've led them a merry chase, most of all my Uncle Robert. But beneath Robert's seeming outrage, I think he admires you greatly."

"What say they in London?"

"At court they say you were an Irish rebel spy come to charm and lull them to sleep. In the streets, Essex would have your head, and he shouts it from the roof-tops."

"I must be gone," he groaned. "Should they find me here—"

"They won't."

"But Sir Robert, I fear, suspects that you and I—"

"Nay. My uncle doesn't suspect, he knows; and he would have you back in Ireland before the war there looms larger and drains his treasury more."

"How can you be sure?"

Elizabeth produced a letter from her bodice and read:

My dearest Elizabeth,

I fear you might not have heard the latest doings in London Town, so I take it upon myself to bring you up-to-date.

It would seem our jolly Irishman, Rory O'Don-nell, is truly a spy and in league with his brethren rebels. With Lord Haskins and several rogues of the town he did plan to sow the seeds of rebellion among the people. Indeed, I fear he has partially succeeded, for in the last few days sheets of pro-paganda screaming rebellion are in everyone's hands, and there is much talk of agreement. But like most such talk during our good Queen's reign, I doubt it will go beyond lip service.

But back to our Irishman and the means of his betrayal. It would seem that my own man, Blake, saw fit to go in league with Lord Essex rather than bring his discoveries before the Queen. If he should live, which is doubtful because he was seriously wounded in the confrontation, he will be stripped of his knighthood and made a captain in the Irish wars.

A just return, I think, on his investment in perfidy.

Lord Haskins doth slumber in the Tower, and O'Donnell has escaped. Though Blake could hardly speak, word has it that the Irishman suffered a sore wound that would make traveling far impossible. Even now Lord Essex turns the town and the nearby countryside upside down looking for him.

Essex would have his head, and this time, I fear, the Queen agrees with him. For myself, I am of a slightly different mind.

In Ireland the clans of Maguire and O'Hara have broken through the gap of Erne and overrun the plain of Roscommon. In so doing they have routed the forces of our Richard Bingham and captured Enniskillen. A counterattack was mounted, but Bingham was defeated soundly at the Ford of Biscuits across the Blackwater River, by Red Hugh O'Donnell.

I know, my dear niece, that you understand little of Irish geography, but I thought you might be interested since you had a mild acquaintance with O'Donnell. Unlike wild Essex, and now my Queen, I feel O'Donnell's head could serve us, and Ireland, better if it remains attached to the rest of his body long enough for him to return to his native land and convince O'Neill not to join with these rebels. I fear that a few battles won will convince them that the war is theirs.

Not true.

Our gracious Queen's temper runs shorter on the Irish problem by the day. Should O'Neill rise up in arms with O'Hara and O'Donnell, I fear even a vacant treasury will not stop her from sending into Ireland the biggest English army that that land has ever seen.

I know, dear Elizabeth, that you care little for these matters. I pass them along only for this reason: should you or yours, by some odd quirk of fate, hear of our wily Irishman, I urge you to inform him that I would have him safely back in Ireland with my blessing, in the hope that there is still some way to resolve our problems with conciliation rather than with war.

I remain your loving uncle and obedient servant,
Robert

She looked up to find Rory smiling.

"Your uncle is as complex as he is astute."

Elizabeth nodded. "I know. He is one of the two most complex men in my life."

"You'd best burn the letter," Rory said. "Should it fall into Essex's hands he would be shouting for Sir Robert's head as well as mine."

Elizabeth lighted a candle from the bedside stand, and together they watched the paper brown and curl.

Suddenly Rory's thoughts fell together. "Annie!"

"What?"

"The lass who brought me here."

"Oh, I knew not her name. She waited until you were safely abed, and then she was bound for London.

Between Honor and myself we convinced her to take food, but rest she would not.''

"Damme!"

Rory fell back into his own thoughts. He moved his shoulder and a jolt of pain shot through his body. It would be days before he could move with any reliability, much less ride or wield a sword.

He was sure that Ned would be lodged in Fleet Prison. His station was not great enough to warrant the Tower or Lambeth Gaol.

And what of Annie? Was she wily enough to engineer Ned's escape? Could she rally his fellow rogues to aid her? How could he aid her himself, and could he even get word to her? Surely she had gone deep underground.

All these questions and more were plaguing his mind when Elizabeth leaned forward and brushed her lips over his.

"I thought at first that you had taken that child as your mistress, the way she railed at Charles to carry you with care. I do believe she loves you well."

"Aye," Rory replied, "I imagine she does. And I love her in kind, but not the way I love you."

Gently Elizabeth slid into bed beside him and nestled her head in the crook of his arm. "Damn these clothes. I would have the styles change so that women could discover they had bodies again."

"And men discover it as well," Rory chuckled, sliding his hand into her bodice. "Why don't you remove it?"

"Careful, my O'Donnell, you've already ruined one pair of satin sheets. I'll not have your wound open again and ruin another!"

Reluctantly she removed his hand from her breast and held it with both of hers against her cheek.

For many moments they lay silently side by side, communicating their feelings for one another without words. When again he moved his hand, Elizabeth distracted him with Annie's tale of how she had brought him to Holdenby.

From the meadow gate of Haskins House she had ridden deep into Finchley Wood, propping him before her on the horse. There, at dawn, she had rebandaged his wound and buried him with leaves. After prying the silver trappings from the horse's saddle and bridle, Annie had ridden off bareback to forage for a more suitable means of transportation.

From a farmer she had bartered the silver for a cart and harness. Then for two days, with Rory lying in the back, she had traveled little-used roads until she reached Holdenby, where she had appeared with the scarf Elizabeth had used to bind Rory's wounds that night in the carriage so many months before.

"Two days on the road? Od's blood, how long have I lain abed?"

"This is the tenth day."

"Ned...." he whispered.

"Who?"

"A friend...a dear friend."

As if he needed to avoid his thoughts, his hand again slid to the rising swells of soft flesh above Elizabeth's bodice.

This time she didn't stop him, for she saw the tortured look of anguish on his face just before it disappeared into her hair. Deftly, even with his injured wrist, he managed to unlace her bodice. Then his hand was at her breasts, igniting the fire that had lain dormant within her for days.

Her lips found his and locked to them as she struggled out of her clothing with the least effort possible.

When there was nothing between them, his hand moved down between her thighs and his lips found her breast.

Waves of sweet desire swept through her body, swelling the nipple between his lips as she arched herself against his exploring fingers.

She felt his naked leg swing over hers. There was a groan and his body went taut. Reality returned, but didn't erase the need in her body any more than the sudden shock of pain took away the desire in Rory's eyes.

"No...no, my darling, let me."

Gently she pushed him back. Her body was already singing as she moved atop him and lowered herself to envelop his love.

IT WAS ONE HOUR AFTER DAWN on a gray morning threatening rain when the little ferry deposited the two prisoners from Bankside's Clink Prison onto Black-friars wharf.

"Stand tall, lad," Ned Bull told his young accomplice. "And don't let the bastards see anything but a smile."

Ned himself climbed into the cart with a roaring laugh. "Od's blood, I do believe this is the same one I was born in!"

He stood brazenly with his head high, his feet planted wide apart and his huge shoulders squared as the cart moved through the city toward Newgate.

As they passed Paternoster Row and neared East-cheap, the crowd that had come for the hanging grew in size.

Ned set the tone by glowering down at the two Queen's guards who led the horse pulling his cart and shouting, "Damme, lads, can yer legs and that old nag go no faster? At this pace Ned Bull will be late for his own hanging!"

The crowd roared its approval of Ned's bravado, and he answered them with a wave and a wide grin.

The procession passed through Newgate in the west wall, and prisoners pressed to the barred windows of the Old Bailey and cheered. Ned looked up and shouted to those faces familiar to him.

"Dan Clybourne, you fox, how is it your neck has beat the ax so long! And you, Ryder, 'twas not true what I said about your mother. Forgive me, I was drunk!"

And then they were on Holborn Road. By squinting his eyes Ned could see in the distance the gallows of Tyburn Tree.

"Me life's been a long road, lads. By God's will I hope I don't die of boredom these last three miles."

Again the crowd, which had tripled in size, roared its approval. As they moved along, grand carriages pulled into the procession from Holborn's great houses and those of Farringdon Without. Highborn ladies blinked at Ned from behind their fans, and the lords who sat beside them had a glazed look in their eyes born of anticipation of the coming show.

Ned began scanning the crowd that flocked around the cart. He saw a few faces he recognized, those of his mates. They weren't smiling. Ned gave them brief nods that were returned in kind. To a man they told him with their eyes that they would respect his wishes.

Word had reached him in his Clink cell days before that they were planning to attack the gallows in hopes of freeing him at the last minute. Ned had sent out several messages, ordering them not to try. Now he was glad he had done so. The size of the well-armed guard was overwhelming. A try would have meant failure and sure death for at least half of them.

The cart's wheels rumbled over the stone bridge at Fleet Street and began the climb.

Ned's lads outside the Clink had served him well in his request for a proper suit to take his last ride. His breeches were of scarlet taffeta, and his doublet matched. The shirt beneath was of fine linen, with heavy gold thread embroidered into the ruff and the lace front. The black, knee-length velvet cloak was banded with gold lace, and was as fine as any worn by the titled carriage riders behind.

The cloak went first.

"Here, lad," Ned roared, tossing the garment to a young man dancing alongside the cart, "dream yourself a fine gentleman in that!"

The crowd shouted with glee at Ned's action, for they well knew his reason for doing it. A good portion of the hangman's fee was garnered from the sale of his victim's clothing and possessions after the deed was done. This day the hangman would drink no sack on Ned Bull.

The sound of the crowd's roar grew frantic as Ned's gaudy doublet, his shirt, and his Spanish-leather boots joined the cloak.

Then the cart was drawn up at the foot of Tyburn Steps.

Ned cast his eyes up at the black-hooded figure and flashed him a wide smile. "I'll go first, if ye don't mind...before the lad? It truly looks like rain!"

As a last defiant gesture while stepping from the cart, Ned ripped the costly breeches, rendering them worthless.

Three steps up, he halted, a wrenching in his chest

for the first time that day. Annie's elfin white face, dry-eyed, her chin set firmly, stared up at him.

He turned slightly and waved to the crowd over Annie's head. "Ah, there's one thing I'll miss from this world that I hope to find in the next...and that's the love of a fine woman."

Again he looked down. A single tear rolled from each of Annie's wide eyes.

"Ah, lass, I know ye not, but have one kiss for old Ned Bull."

He bent and effortlessly swept her into his arms. The guards in front and behind didn't interfere. It was a fairly common thing Ned did.

He squeezed her tightly, and as his lips brushed her ear he whispered, "Promise...don't watch!"

"I promise."

"Goodbye, lass."

And then she was back on the ground and Ned's broad bare back was climbing the last few steps.

True to her promise, Annie turned away. She didn't watch, but she listened to every sound. She heard Ned beg forgiveness of his Maker and beg the Queen's pardon, as many condemned before him had done.

She heard the pastor's mumbled prayers as the noose was put in place, and then the dull thud of the dropped trap, which silenced the crowd.

She listened as Ned was cut down and put to the knife. Every scream of pain he uttered she forced into her memory. She listened through it all, to the pawing horses with their breath whistling through their nostrils as the manacles were attached to Ned's wrists and ankles, to the crack of the whip that sent the horses straining in opposite directions.

She listened until there was silence. And then she began walking through the crowd and turned north toward Hampstead Road.

There were no tears now as she looked up at the sky and felt the first drops of the day's rain dampen her face.

"Goodbye, Ned."

Part III
Spring 1596

A BRIGHT WARMING SUN bathed Ballylee. From where he stood on the roof of the castle's great tower, Rory O'Donnell basked in the sun's gentle rays. He looked down across the moat to a wide heath stretching to a stand of sturdy oaks at the foot of the hill. These Ballylee oaks, so far, had escaped the English ax.

How much longer would they, he wondered.

The heath was wild with spring heather, and halfway between the moat and the trees Annie romped with little Rory. She was good with him, and she had lifted many cares from Deirdre's shoulders.

How odd it was that these two women should become so close in the two years and more since Annie had first returned with Rory to Ireland. One was high-born, the daughter of an English lord and the husband of an Irish prince, while the other was a waif of the London streets.

But then, not so odd, he thought, for they both had grit and they were both English, traits Rory had come to respect.

Annie looked up, saw him and waved. Her face beamed and her mouth curved with laughter just before little Rory tumbled like a tiny bull into the back of her legs and she rolled in the heather.

How different she looks now than she did that night so many months ago at Holdenby, he said to himself.

She had walked almost all the way from London,

and had appeared near midnight at the cottage door. Elizabeth and Honor had hustled her inside immediately before she was seen by the other servants. She was bedraggled, soaking wet, and obviously asleep on her feet, but she insisted on seeing Rory before anything else.

He remembered how like an apparition she had looked, standing pale and forlorn in the bedroom doorway with the candlelight accenting the dark hollows of her eyes and sunken cheeks.

"If ye be for Ireland, O'Donnell, I'll be goin' with ye...if ye'll have me."

"Aye, we'll go, lass, as soon as we've seen to Ned."

"He's been seen to." Rory had already guessed from her look and the tone in her voice, but she confirmed it. "He died well, O'Donnell, my Ned died well."

"As he lived, Annie. Aye, we'll be for Ireland."

Urgent messages were sent to Cecil. Like the politician he was, one exchange wasn't enough, for he wanted assurances from Rory that he would do all in his power to avert the catastrophe of all-out war in Ireland. Rory had given him those assurances, because he too looked upon such a war as the beginning of the end.

At last Cecil's promise of a safe passage came, and it was the last night in the cottage. Until then, even through hours of touching and the near violent joining of their bodies, Elizabeth had held up well.

She had even managed to banter, "You would bed me like a whore and run back to your naked Irish wenches?"

"I would bed you and run, m'lady, or stay and lose my head," he replied in kind. "But I prefer to act like an Englishman and run, to bed you another day."

And then she had broken, wildly winding her arms

around him and weeping against his chest. "Oh, God, will there be another day?"

"There will, my love, I swear there will."

"Do you? Do you swear that all we have isn't a useless dream? How can you?"

"Because I will it. Because no woman have I loved before you, and I'll have no love but you from this day on. There will be a way and I will find it. On this I swear!"

And then they had made love again, a soft gentle love that lasted till dawn, and he was gone.

With Annie dressed as a boy and Rory carrying false papers supplied by Cecil, they sailed from Chester the following day.

Before docking at Dublin Bay the ship made a brief stop up the Irish coast at Drogheda. It was there that the two of them left the boat. The papers given them by Cecil would be useless in Ireland, so from Drogheda they traveled north by night, constantly evading English patrols. With the need for such stealth, the trip into Armagh and westward to Tyrone took two days.

They spent the day in a deserted booley house. It was here, shortly after they had crawled into blankets on two pallets before a small peat fire, that Annie had shown the depth of her anguish.

Until that moment she had not mentioned Ned's name again, nor had she shed a tear. Now, from across the room, Rory heard the barely perceptible choking sobs.

And then she started talking. She'd never known her mother nor her father, she told him, but had been brought up in the taverns of Bankside. The details of her childhood shocked Rory even though with his own eyes he had seen similar things while in London.

She had met Ned when she was ten, while trying to

steal his purse. He'd cuffed her, then found a home for her and taken care of her. When she was twelve she paid him back the only way she knew: she seduced him. By the time she was thirteen she was in love with the big highwayman.

There was more, much more, but Rory could hardly make it out through the sobs until she said, "Aye, I was a woman at thirteen, but I wonder if I'll be a wife at thirty."

"You're in Ireland now, lass. Some fine lad will take a fancy to your pretty face and carry you off."

For several moments there was silence from the other pallet, and then she spoke again in a halting voice. "I think, O'Donnell, that after Tyburn an Englishman I could never marry. Think ye that I could ever become an Irish wife?"

He thought for a moment and then answered truthfully, "Nay, not as an Irishman knows her, but methinks for every good man there is a good woman, no matter where their birthing took place. Indeed, good marriages between Irish and English have been known to happen."

"Mabel Bagenal, wife to The O'Neill?"

This brought an involuntary chuckle to Rory's lips. "Nay, not that unfortunate wench, for O'Neill has made her life the same hell that she has his."

"Then this Lady O'Hara you tell me of?"

"Deirdre? Aye, she's a fine wife and a good woman. But she is gentle and kindly, and I fear one day she will regret that part of her personality. It is another I think of now. What do you know of the Desmond wars, lass?"

"Only what Ned told me of his service—that it was bloody, with much slaughter; that the earth was scorched; and that the rebel Desmond took three years to capture."

"Aye, 'tis true. Desmond started his rebellion in Munster with five thousand good men. Five years later his force was down to one. And that one was his wife, the Lady Elinor. After the first two years they were forced from their castles. They lived off the land in booleys like this one, or caves, or even in the open. For three years Lady Elinor left her husband's side only to journey to Dublin Castle and plead for his pardon. All the rest of the time she ate berries and what meat they could steal, and fought by his side."

"And that's the mettle of an Irish wife?"

"Aye, and Lady Elinor was an Englishwoman."

There was a long silence between them, with the only sound a faint breeze outside and the hiss of the peat in the hearth.

"And Lady Desmond? Where is she now?"

"She lies dying in London Tower."

"And Desmond?"

Once again Rory could tell only the truth. "He became a worn-out old man before his time, and was killed by one of his own kern who was tired of the long war."

This was met by another silence, and then Rory realized that she had risen and was standing by his pallet.

"You love the Lady Hatton, do you not, O'Donnell?"

"Aye, that I do. I love her as Ned loved you."

Then, in the firelight, he saw the chemise slip to the floor. Before he knew it her naked body was in the blankets, pressed against his.

"Annie...."

"Nay, 'tis not that I want. 'Tis your arms around me and your warmth to drive away the cold of loneliness."

She had wriggled her soft backside against his hard belly and they had slept.

Now, eighteen months later, little Annie had grown into a pretty gentlewoman of Ireland. No more were the eyes hollow and the cheeks sunken. And her body, moving lithely under the close-fitting leine, had fleshed out with a womanly fullness.

She made a good nanny to Rory, the future O'Hara, and because of what she had gone through in her own life, a mature confidante and companion to the Lady Deirdre.

There was little doubt that Annie had grown happy in Ireland, and the fact made Rory glad because in part he had fulfilled his promise to Ned Bull.

Not so his assurances to Robert Cecil, however, for by the time he reached Tyrone O'Neill was already in the field. Besides Enniskillen and Newry, many other forts and towns had fallen to the Irish, and Ballyshannon was under seige by O'Hara.

Then came the battle of Clontibret and it was too late. The O'Neill was at the head of his men when the better part of an English company led by Bagenal was wiped out. All Ireland and England now knew that O'Neill had joined with O'Donnell and O'Hara.

The Queen's lord general, Sir John Norris, and the new lord deputy in Dublin, Sir William Russell, saw only too well the strength O'Neill had kept hidden for so long. He outnumbered Bagenal four to one, and for the first time the Irish possessed artillery.

The rest of the year became one long battle, and, seeing no alternative, Rory had thrown himself into the thick of it. One month he was at O'Neill's side, and the next with his brother. And when there was a lull in the O'Neill and O'Donnell camps, he would go foraging with The O'Hara.

He put his Elizabeth, as he had come to call her, in the back of his mind, as he did everything about London. He pushed away thoughts of old Lord Haskins in a Tower cell. He barely flinched when word came that poor Robert Southwell had become another martyr for the Jesuit cause.

The expression in Rory's eyes had changed. No longer did he look upon the world with taunting amusement. Now it was with brooding intensity.

He thought only of war, of fighting the English that seemed to roll toward him over every hill in unending waves. He gained a reputation nearly as large as his brother's as a fearless leader who neither took nor gave quarter. He had been wounded twice more, and even now, after a month's lull in the fighting, his voice was still hoarse from shouting over the din of battle.

No more did he appear the London dandy with balloon breeches. Now his muscular legs were tightly encased in worsted trews. The gaudy doublet had been cast aside and replaced by a tanned-leather jerkin. And through the half sleeves of the jerkin bloused full saffron-colored sleeves. The shirt, with no ruff or lace, was open, and his chest had turned a burnished mahogany in the sun.

He had let his hair grow long again, and cut it in the Irish fashion—to his shoulders in the back and in an even glib across his forehead.

Elizabeth the Queen had issued a special proclamation concerning the Irish rebels, something she had never done before. It declared that they were all traitors to the crown of the highest magnitude, and as such were deemed outlaws worthy of a high head price. It had even slyly stated that the reward could be claimed by anyone, Irish and English alike.

Rory's name was high on the list.

"Come along, lad. The O'Neill has need of your keen mind!"

Shane O'Hara's booming voice and the man's heavy hand, falling like a gallowglass ax on his shoulder, brought Rory from his reverie. He turned, looked down at the slightly shorter man, and matched the grin that beamed at him through the heavy black beard.

A strong bond had grown between Rory and O'Hara. They shared the kind of closeness that frequently happens between comrades-in-arms who almost daily face death shoulder to shoulder. But the tie between these two had grown even deeper than usual.

"How so?" Rory asked, letting O'Hara guide him by the elbow to an oaken table where the others sat. "What new caprice has O'Neill decided upon?"

The question was met by a booming laugh from O'Hara's barrel chest. "Why, he would sue for a truce and draft our peace demands of the English bitch while we use the time we gain to plan the summer campaigns!"

"I'VE GOT YOU... I've got you!"

Annie tottered a moment with the boy's arms locked around her knees and then fell into the heather. In a second his strong little body was astride her, his knees at her shoulders and his face straining as his hands pinned her wrists to the ground above her head.

"Do ye give up, Annie, do ye give up?"

"Aye, ye're too strong fer me, little warrior!"

Giggling and panting, he rolled to the side and came up in a sitting position facing her. "That's what I'll do one day to the English so'jers!"

"Aye, that you will, and more, little Rory. Once ye have yer own long sword, ye'll cleave 'em good."

"Tell me a story, Annie. Tell me again how you killed the Englishman and saved Rory's life!"

"Nay, 'tis an old dog now, that story."

"Then tell me of Clontibret and how the English blood ran cold!"

"Aye," Annie laughed, "that I'll do."

"Annie . . . no!"

Annie rolled over, her eyes squinting at the sun over Deirdre's shoulder. The older woman held the young girl child, Shanna, in her arms.

" 'Tis the only story he ever wants, m'lady."

"I know, but. . . ." Deirdre's face softened and she slipped to the ground. "He grows with too much war around him as it is. When he's not with the men I would have him hear words of a gentler nature. Rory, take the basket and fetch me some berries."

The boy stared for a moment at his mother, and then looked at Annie.

"Do as yer mother says, lad. An' don't stray into the woods too far or it's after ye for a whackin' I'll be!"

Reluctantly the boy took the basket from his mother's side and trotted on down the hill. Both women watched him go.

His body was already taking on the solid well-muscled shape of his father, and his face, with its high cheekbones, its doe-soft black eyes and long lashes, was forming much like his mother's. The thick black hair that fell to his shoulders had a sheen that was deeper than either Shane's or Deirdre's.

"Ah," Annie sighed, "he grows into a fine lad."

"That he does." The baby began to whimper in Deirdre's arms. Deftly she pulled aside the bodice of her smock and shrugged her breast clear. When Shanna was happily nursing she returned her eyes to Annie. "I didn't mean to be short with you."

"I know."

"It's just that his mind has been so filled with tales of Irish glory and English treachery. At times I am actually afraid that when he grows older and realizes that I was born English, he will hate me."

"Nay, m'lady, no more than he would meself, fer we're both Irishwomen now."

Deirdre smiled.

It was true, perhaps for Annie even more than for herself. Since the first day of her arrival the girl had refused to think good of any Englishman and had forsworn everything English in herself. She had adapted much faster than Deirdre had to the Irish and their ways.

Annie saw the thoughtful, almost pained look on Deirdre's face and decided to change the subject. She rolled to her back and opened the top of her own smock to let the sun reach her breasts.

"Ah, the sun feels good after so long a rain."

"That it does," Deirdre replied wistfully. "It will seem odd to not go abooleying two summers in a row."

Annie's Gaelic was coming swiftly, but she still hadn't mastered all the Irish terms and phrases. "Booleying" she did know, and she thought that she, too, would like to spend the summer in the uplands, grazing the cattle. One reason for her interest was that the clans usually grazed their cattle together. Lately Annie had felt again the need for a man, and in a booley in the mountains she knew she would probably meet one.

But a booley couldn't be defended like the huge fortress of Ballylee that loomed above her. So she knew, as Deirdre did, that there would be no booleying this year.

"Annie?"

"Aye."

"We've grown so close, you and I, near like sisters...."

"Aye, we have," Annie replied, a smile spreading across her face as she rolled to her side to face Deirdre. "And I thank ye fer it."

"There's but one thing that seems to hang between us—"

"Between us?"

Deirdre nodded, trying to find the right words. Rory had told her so little about this girl, and Annie herself had said not a word about her past.

"It's the hate you bear. It pains me when I see it in your eyes and hear it from your lips. I love you, dear girl, and I feel I must help you, or one day it will consume you."

The smile faded from Annie's lips and a cloud seemed to pass across her face. "Aye, mayhap one day it will."

"It needn't, believe me."

"How would you know, m'lady?"

A flush burned Deirdre's cheeks, and suddenly she felt the younger of the two of them. "Because it's what I believe."

"Aye," Annie said, a sudden hardness coating her eyes, "I know you do."

"Annie," Deirdre said, averting her eyes from the girl's hard stare, "perhaps if you prayed with me...."

"I've never done that, m'lady."

"You've never prayed?" Deirdre exclaimed in shock.

"Oh, I might have said some words when I was a wee lass, but I never understood them nor to whom I was speaking."

"Are you Catholic, Annie, or New Church?"

"I don't think I'm either, m'lady."

"But you . . . you must believe in God."

"I believed, my lady . . . in Ned Bull."

"Ned Bull?"

Suddenly Annie was on her feet. Back and forth she paced in front of Deirdre, who sat still, cradling the child to her breast with a puzzled frown on her face.

"I don't mean to anger you, Annie, I only—"

"Nay," the girl said, dropping in front of her. "I could feel no anger toward ye, m'lady, ever. Indeed, sometimes I think I give ye a heavy heart and that's why I'm for telling ye."

"Telling me?"

"About Ned Bull."

" 'TIS TRUE, m'Lord Russell fears our strength greatly, but methinks he fears a return to England with a less-than-full purse more."

Heads nodded in agreement at O'Neill's statement. They all knew that Lord Russell, since his arrival months before, was bent only on a course of personal gain. O'Neill was trying to make the point that such a man, with greed as his only God, was hard to combat. At no time could it be predicted what he would do next.

"Ah, but in his bed, safe behind the walls and army of Dublin Castle, I hear he does shake," O'Hara offered. "So much does he fear O'Byrne in the south that 'tis said around eleven of the clock some nights ago he raised the whole garrison when some cows of Kilmainham broke out of a bourne!"

There was a general round of laughter, and Red Hugh added, "Mayhap he had reason. The way m'Lord Russell pillages the countryside, they were probably our cows!"

There was a second peal of laughter before O'Neill

stopped it with a groan and brought the conversation back to the matters at hand.

"What think ye, Rory, of taking Dublin itself?" he asked.

Rory left off scratching one of O'Hara's wolfhounds which had been lolling by his chair, and settled his elbows on the table. He looked at each face in turn before speaking.

"Because of Clontibret the English are humiliated. They dare not show themselves in the field without more strength. Right now we have firepower. Thanks to O'Neill, the southern clans, as well, have matchlocks. On rivers and roads and in every field English settlers and soldiers keep a constant watch over their shoulders in fear of a ball."

"All the more reason to strike now!" Red Hugh blared, slamming his fist to the table.

"Aye, perhaps," Rory replied. "But I wonder about Dublin."

"Damme, man, why not Dublin?" Rory's brother roared again.

Rory and O'Neill exchanged quick looks. They had talked much on this point the previous night. More and more often, The O'Neill found himself going to Rory rather than to Red Hugh or Shane when the political and strategic aspects of the war were in question. O'Neill had discovered that the younger O'Donnell, since his return from England, had a cooler head when it came to appraising the enemy.

"Fiach O'Byrne has already burned the Pale all the way to the Boyne, and 'tis true Dublin is now a fragile city which the O'Byrnes, from their Wicklow glens, could reach between sunset and dawn. But I fear for it," Rory went on.

"Why so?" O'Hara asked, his own enthusiasm for

the project slightly subdued due to the ominous tone, which he had come to respect, in Rory's voice.

"Because till now we've fought armies lame to a man, soldiers who would rather sell their muskets than fight with them, and armies whose leaders place greed above loyalty. Our victories have angered the Queen, but not enough to make her spend the money it would take to send a thundering herd of well-trained and well-equipped troops north. If we strike at the heart of her little Ireland, the Pale, we might see that wrath."

There was a thoughtful silence before O'Neill spoke. "Rory is right. Such an army would overwhelm us now, without reinforcements and more aid. The Spanish have laid siege to Calais. Should it fall, Philip of Spain will rush to send us troops."

"Why?" Red Hugh barked. "He hasn't yet!"

"Aye, I know. But with one of England's flanks under Spanish guns, Philip will see the worth of putting the other flank under the gun as well."

O'Neill now turned his attention to the fifth man at the table, the one who as yet had tendered no thought or word.

"What think you, O'Byrne?"

McTeague O'Byrne, cousin and underclan leader to the fox of the Wicklow Mountains, Fiach, The O'Byrne, turned his weatherbeaten face and slitted eyes toward O'Neill. He shifted a bulge of moss from one cheek to the other and spat before he replied.

"I got to agree with the O'Donnell lad. The English whore would come down on us right ready if we attacked her pets in Dublin. Right now, meself and The O'Byrne have all we can do to hold Glenmalure and keep Ballinacor under siege. Ye can be sure we'll keep the war flag flying over Wicklow to the full of our pledge—to fight to the last and not give up while there's a man of the clan left alive. But to take on more now would be a possible disaster.'' He spat again and a lopsided grin curled back over crooked yellow teeth. ''Now, if ye've a mind to send men south as reinforcements, I might change me mind.''

The other four exchanged looks. They all knew the answer. Red Hugh was stretched as far as he dared, holding Sligo Castle and keeping Ballyshannon under siege. O'Neill was backing Maguire and holding all of Armagh. O'Hara would be the only possible one to go, and he didn't dare let Ballyshannon fall lest an English wedge be driven between himself and O'Donnell in Donegal.

'''Tis impossible now. We'll wait for word, and in the meantime these shall be on the way to England to keep Whitehall tilted,'' O'Neill said.

He gathered the papers upon which were written the nine demands they had all agreed to and stood up, signaling the end of the meeting.

''There's yet one more thing,'' Red Hugh said.

''Aye?''

''This new captain of Russell's, the one with no name who runs with Tom Lee. I've seen him.''

''Aye, as have I,'' O'Hara said. ''Gray hair, with a nasty scar and a patch over his left eye.''

''The very one,'' Red Hugh nodded. ''We thought Captain Thomas Lee was bad. This one has no mercy, and he preys as much on the peasants as he does on us. The man's like a phantom. He's everywhere at once, stealing more of our cattle than he does our heads.''

''Aye,'' said O'Hara. ''And worse, he promises the kern big land parcels and cash money to betray us.''

''Then we have a man who fights a different kind of war,'' said O'Neill. ''Rory, know you of this man?''

''Nay, but mayhap there's a way to learn.''

"Find out what you can," O'Neill replied. "There are two chinks in our armor: lack of cavalry in the field and the tendency of our own people to betray us for profit. We can do little about the one, but we can try to stop the other."

RORY AND O'HARA DESCENDED from the barbican stairs and stepped out onto the drawbridge.

"If 'tis my clan that goes south when the time comes, lad, I would like you in the field with me. Would you go?"

"Aye, O'Hara, you have my word on it."

They stepped from the drawbridge to the heath and turned to where Annie and Deirdre sat in the grass.

"What think you of McTeague O'Byrne, O'Hara?"

"Methinks the man's eyes shift too much and too swiftly."

"My thoughts exactly."

The words were barely out of Rory's mouth when their attention was arrested by Deirdre, who was running toward them as hard as she could, shouting O'Hara's name.

She came to a sudden stop just in front of her husband and paused, her eyes wide and wild, devouring his face as if she were seeing it for the last time.

"What is it, lass?"

"Shane...."

"What is it?" O'Hara repeated.

Suddenly she was in his arms, with her stark-white face buried in his tunic and her body trembling like a fragile leaf in a storm's high wind.

The two men exchanged puzzled frowns, and then Rory sensed Annie at his elbow.

"What is it?"

"I told her of Ned," the girl replied, stone-faced.

"What of Ned?"
"How he died."

CHAPTER TWENTY-NINE

ELIZABETH MADE SURE that everything at Hatton House
was done as tradition dictated. The main rooms and
staircase were draped in black cloth. A black mourning
bed was purchased for her to lie in as she received the
visits of condolence.

The pall over Sir William's casket was of purple velvet
trimmed with gold, and an even larger one serving as a
canopy over the bier was entirely of costly gold cloth.

Later this would be affixed to the horse litter that
would carry Sir William to his last resting place.

"'Tis near time, m'lady. Your cloak."

"A second, Honor," Elizabeth said, gazing at her
reflection in the mirror.

In her own way she had tried to honor him in life.
There had been indiscretions, but Elizabeth had been
discreet. Sir William had never been hurt with the
knowledge that his beautiful young wife had put horns
on his head with the Irishman, Rory O'Donnell.

For that she was thankful.

But because of the affair with O'Donnell and the
nagging guilt she felt about it, Elizabeth planned to
give her late husband all the honors due him in death.

She had used no belladonna to make her eyes
sparkle. She rarely needed a great deal of purpurice to
redden her lips, anyway. And under the conservative
black hat with its heavy veil she had forgone her usual
elaborate coiffure. Instead her thick hair was curled
tightly to her head and pinned with bodkins.

The upper part of her body was squeezed into a long stiff-pointed doublet with a much-higher-than-usual bodice, which hid her breasts above the nipples. The doublet was jet black, as was the shirtwaist beneath it, with sleeves slitted but set off with no other color than black.

The satin skirt over her wide farthingale was also black, but Elizabeth had acceded to a little lace trim—again in black. Her pumps, nearly obscured by the skirt, were black lace over soft black leather, as were the accessories she carried—her fan, her gloves, and the purse hanging from her girdle.

All black.

"Black, black, black," she mumbled.

"M'lady?"

"Nothing, Honor," she said, but thought, *Oh, God, a whole year of black!*

"On you 'tis fashionable, m'lady."

"A pox, Honor," Elizabeth said. "Even you with your bulging belly look better than I do in this drabness!" She shrugged into the black velvet cloak and patted the girl's hard belly. "Your lying-in comes soon?"

"Aye, in less than two weeks, m'lady."

"And I'm sure it'll be a bonny lad as handsome as your Charles."

"We hope, m'lady."

Elizabeth watched the girl waddle toward the door. A cold chill passed through her body with the long-ago memory of those fretful weeks after O'Donnell's departure. Not a moment had she thought about it during those wonderful nights abed in the Holdenby cottage.

But later fear had stalked every moment of every day. A slight ache in her belly or the merest hint of a throb in her head would send her into fits of worry and depression.

What if O'Donnell had left her with child? What would she do? For months Sir William had not spent an hour in her bed.

Would she be able to seduce her own husband at the last minute and make him believe he was the father? Would he be able?

Rather than gain, she had lost weight. Then she had missed the following month, and in desperation she had gone to Sir Robert.

"Marvelous," he uncle had replied. "I'm sure Sir William will be elated."

"But, uncle, if 'tis true, Sir William will know full well 'tis not his seed."

"Ah. O'Donnell?"

"Aye," Elizabeth had replied, averting her eyes.

Her uncle had paused for many moments, and then that tight-lipped grin she knew so well had creased his lips. "Perhaps such an occurrence will be to our advantage, dear niece. Given the fact that O'Donnell is not like other Irishmen—and assuming he doth care something for his offspring—mayhap he will strive harder with the charges I've given him once I tell him he has a sprout in my family's house."

It was then that Elizabeth realized how changed her uncle had become, how much power had wooed him, how far from her her favorite relative had drawn.

She was furious. Politics, the court, his intrigues, his wealth and position—these were all he cared about. She had stormed from his presence that day, and had not spoken of him or to him ever since.

And two weeks later her cycle had come and her fears had abated.

She had been thankful, elated, and relieved. For months she had floated in a euphoria, realizing that not a whit of her own prestige or position at court would be damaged.

And then the memories of O'Donnell and of their love overcame the aftermath of his leaving, and a new melancholy had set in, one that had remained with her ever since.

She still loved the wild Irishman, and there wasn't a thing she could do about it.

Honor opened the door for her and stepped aside.

"M'lady?"

"Yes."

"Sir William was a good man, a kind man who treated one and all with grace and much heart."

"Yes, he was."

"As are you, m'lady. You should feel no guilt about that time these months past, for during those days I saw the same happiness and love in your eyes that I see every morning when I look in my mirror. 'Tis little enough for a woman to have, I think—love."

Elizabeth felt tears well up in her eyes as she leaned forward and kissed Honor on the cheek. "Thank you, girl. Would that the world could see me through your kind eyes."

Then Elizabeth draped the veil over her face, straightened her shoulders and descended the stairs of Hatton House to bury her husband.

SIR ROBERT CECIL SLIT THE SEAL on the letter that had just been handed him and unfolded it with misgivings. With his usual unerring instincts he could almost guess its contents.

He read quickly through the first paragraph containing the usual complaints about troop morale, lack of munitions and food and then slowed down to assess every word:

...and I daresay, Sir Robert, that at no time since the first Norman set foot on the soil of this God-forsaken land has the situation been more dire. Everywhere I look, Munster is full of treachery. The north is a powder keg, and Connaught is a rebel's playground.

The state of the English realm in Ireland, sir, has never been in so dangerous a way within memory. This I say in regards to the uniting of O'Hara, O'Donnell and all the chieftains of Ulster and Connaught with Tyrone, and the great combinations, peasant and kern alike, that they have drawn to their bosom.

'Tis frightening indeed. Nay, bone-chilling it is how they stretch themselves into all parts of this kingdom with the strength of Tyrone's wealth. Even now they are better furnished with the habiliments of war than are we. They have so trained their men that we seem to be facing an entirely different enemy. Where before they were wont never to attempt Her Majesty's forces in the field, they now strike with impudence.

I say, nay, *stress*, Sir Robert, that Ireland never stood in greater danger of being lost. Should Philip end his vacillating ways and come to O'Neill's aid, this monster of the north will be able to march to Dublin's gates with no force to resist him.

Cecil refolded the letter, stood up and walked around the huge desk to where its bearer sat. He dropped it to the man's lap and, without pausing, continued on to the window. From where he stood he could see the high curved arches at either end of Whitehall Palace. Directly across from him were the tall latticed windows of the privy chamber, where Cecil could imagine his aging wrinkled Queen just calling her handmaidens to her as she awoke. Her face would be worn and haggard without cosmetics, and would show the ravages of the past two weeks' worries. Her hair, what there was left of it, would be straggly and chalk gray until she donned one of the garish red wigs she now habitually wore.

Her ailments were many, and like those of his father, the Lord Burghley, they came one upon the other.

Cecil knew the old lord, his father, was near death. But when would the Queen die? And who would be her successor?

The topic was on everyone's lips, but of course was never mentioned in front of Gloriana herself. The problem of succession, like the Queen's age, was a taboo subject at court if one valued one's head.

Cecil knew that the question of the next monarch was also uppermost in his rival's mind. Essex had been sending feelers north to James VI of Scotland. He knew this because some of Essex's courtiers were in his employ.

It tweaked him that Essex had made vague accusations that he, Cecil, had made overtures toward Spain to place the Infanta, the King of Spain's daughter, on the English throne at Elizabeth's death.

Devereux was a fool, as were all those around him. But then, looking further than one day ahead was not Essex's strong suit. He, Cecil, was already looking years ahead, and many of his future plans included paving an easy ascension for King James.

Robert smiled. A gaggle of geese had just lifted off the river beyond Whitehall and now soared gracefully over the recently completed Swan Theatre on Bankside.

His smile broadened as he thought of a few words he had lately heard on a Bankside stage:

> Well, whiles I am a beggar, I will rail
> And say there is no sin but to be rich;
> And being rich, my virtue then shall be
> To say there is no vice but beggary!

Unlike Essex, Cecil had been far from highborn, but Sir Robert planned in the months to come to become principal secretary to the Queen and the most powerful man in England.

He should, perhaps, attend the theater more often, he thought. This Will Shakespeare exhibited a good mind and could form a well-wrought phrase to Cecil's liking.

Behind him he heard the faint rustle of the letter being returned to the desk.

"What think you of our lord general's predictions?"

"I think, Sir Robert, that he has not stated the situation gravely enough."

Robert turned, eased his rear against the window seat, and studied the man sitting before him. He disliked his guest intensely, and distrusted him even more. But the man had a genius and a ruthlessness that few men possessed. And Sir Robert was not so small nor unwise that he couldn't forgive past transgressions in lieu of future services.

"Tell me the thoughts you've gleaned in these past months," he suggested.

"Ireland is truly the devil's own land, and the Irish his henchmen," his visitor quickly replied, and went on without pause. "They wisely shy from battle in the open plain and skirmish in passes, bogs, woods, fords, and in all places to their advantage. And they hold it no dishonor to run away should the battle not go their way."

Cecil chuckled as he moved across the room and

once again seated himself behind his desk. "What you're saying is that these Irishmen do not fight like English gentlemen."

"Nay, they do not," came the reply, accompanied by a lopsided grin. "And that's why they win. They outlast us because they need but scant food and, if need be, can go months without house or clothes. With their savage way of life they can wear down any army that seeks to conquer them. It is no more possible to defeat them at once than it would be to destroy a pack of free-running wolves.

" 'Tis a land of few roads, and those that there are can be blocked with a few felled trees, behind which will always lurk a nest of rebels. They will swoop in for a quick kill and be gone before an English shot is fired, leaving our soldiers littering the ground behind them. In the narrow entrances of their northern glens, on the stony paths through Tyrone and Armagh—and Donegal where O'Neill and the O'Donnells lurk—there is naught to be faced but annihilation from ambush."

"You paint a gloomy picture indeed. How would you combat this plague, should you have its charge?"

Now the lopsided grin widened, and the single dark eye gleamed with a vibration of evil that chilled even Cecil's bones until he was hard put not to let it show in his face.

"Two ways, Sir Robert. First, I would lure as many of them into the south as I could. The land there is bared of woods, denying them cover. There are more open plains where our cavalry can harass them. And in the south the clans are not as well united as they are in the north. Ten times as many men in the south are willing to gain by treachery."

"You know this for a fact?"

"I do."

Cecil believed him, for the man was a master of treachery himself. "And what else? Go on!"

"Secondly, I would assassinate the rebel leaders... each and every one."

Cecil wasn't shocked. He himself had thought of such a solution in the past year. But he was dismayed when he considered the possible aftermath. Ruling Ireland without Irish rulers would be as difficult as maintaining a treasury without taxes.

And the Queen herself was loathe to entertain such a solution. She wanted to have O'Neill and the rest brought to their knees, but kept alive for crown use, just as she used her own barons and earls in England.

As yet the situation in Ireland was dangerous, but it wasn't quite hopeless. But should Calais fall. . . .

Cecil leaned forward and trained both his eyes on the other man's one. "I think the former a better solution for now. Should any of their leaders fall in battle, then so be it. What we need is to stall the war, as we always have, until some peace can be made with Spain."

The head, with its chalk-white hair, wagged in agreement, but Cecil could see frustration and anger in the gleaming eye.

"But think ye on this," Cecil continued. "Your second solution is not without merit, and will be given some thought. And bear this in mind as well. Should your service continue as fruitfully as it has in this last year, I do believe that once again we should call you Sir James Blake."

THE PROCESSION WAS LARGE, for while Sir William had gained little attention in life, Elizabeth meant to give it to him in death.

In front of the litter walked two hundred mourners in long black cloaks. Cloaks and mourners alike had been paid for by Elizabeth. In their hands they carried branches of bay and rosemary, emblems of the deceased soul's immortality, which would soon be thrown into the churchyard grave on top of Sir William's remains.

Immediately behind the litter walked Elizabeth, and behind her came about a hundred lords and ladies. Most of these had gathered out of curiosity rather than out of friendship for Sir William. Elizabeth had long been considered a beautiful woman, perhaps one of the most beautiful in England, and now she was also one of the wealthiest. Almost everyone in London hankered to pick up gossip about what this rich and beautiful widow would do now that Sir William was dead.

The procession passed Shropes and Castleyard and neared St. Andrew's. It was here that Sir Robert joined the entourage and walked beside his niece.

"My condolences, dear niece, on your loss."

"The bereaved thanks you, Sir Robert," Elizabeth replied coldly.

They walked a while in silence, neither of them realizing that their appearance together was rather strange and, were it not for the occasion, even humorous. Robert, shuffling slightly, the hump beneath his cloak pronounced, was a full head shorter than Elizabeth, who walked with her back straight and her body swaying with a movement that could almost be termed jaunty.

"We must repair the breach in our friendship, Elizabeth," Robert said at last.

"Oh? And why so, uncle?"

"Because you are family," he replied with a smile. "I would aid you in your future decisions. Let us face the fact, you come now into vast lands and estates that will draw every courtier from far and wide to your feet."

"And think you, uncle, that I cannot handle the courting popinjays that I know will flock around me?"

"Aye," Cecil chuckled, low in his throat, "I know you can, for I've seen you do it. But money is a flighty thing, and not unlike power, Elizabeth. It must be handled wisely. I stand able to give you what sage advice I've gleaned. Surely during Sir William's illness you have contemplated the possible pitfalls."

It was true. Elizabeth had fretted over Sir William's impending demise not just because of his passing, but also because she had become fully aware of the realities of her position. She had been handling the bulk of the Hatton businesses and estates for a long time already, it was true. But she had done it with Sir William's stamp of approval. Had anyone disagreed with her judgments in the past, they found themselves disagreeing with Sir William, a man.

Henceforth it would be with a woman—herself—and Elizabeth knew all too well how devious a man could be in love and in business when he knew the scales of trade were balanced in his favor.

"What, uncle? My thoughts were there in the litter with my poor husband."

"I'm sure they were, m'lady." Robert's barely perceptible snicker was clearly one of sarcasm, and Elizabeth didn't miss it. "But I was just reminding you of the fact that my father, your grandfather, is failing. I pray you, Elizabeth, think of the power and influence I will soon have, and what aid I can give you with it."

"But not for nothing, I am sure," she replied wisely, allowing a hint of sarcasm to creep into her own voice.

"Nay, my dear niece, even in blood nothing is got for nothing. I think, even in your widow's weeds, it would be wise if you would make yourself available again at court."

There it was. She could sense it in his manner and see it in his eyes. Even walking behind her husband's bier, on the day of his funeral, her uncle was planning her next match.

For the third time he would use her as a pawn.

The realization infuriated her, and no matter how unseemly it was at such a time, she couldn't hold her tongue. "And whose favor does the powerful Cecil covet now that I'm free to be traded?"

"Calm yourself, Elizabeth," Robert hissed, quickly realizing his error. Too well he remembered the spark of his niece's anger, which could erupt at any time, no matter its consequences to her or anyone around her. "I only thought, as a man—"

"Men! Oh, you men! God, what hell it is to be a woman around you! You barter with our hellish lives, our heavenly souls, and even with our earthly bodies. I think at times that even my breasts are not my own, the way your eyes paw them! And this device I have between my thighs is thought of by you only as good cheer. God, in this age one would indeed have to be a Queen to remain a virgin! Aye, I'll to court, uncle, even in my widow's weeds, but mark this and mark it well...this time your pawn is older and much wiser, and she knows just how to twist the situation to *her* advantage."

"I only meant—"

"I care not what you meant."

"Elizabeth...."

"Pray you, *dear* Sir Robert, shut up! Indeed you do grieve the bereaved with your cunning male ways and wily words."

CHAPTER THIRTY

"OD'S BLOOD," the Queen ranted, "with all that we do shoulder in these dire times, this damnable bush-kern, this monster of the north, this viper in the bosom of our realm doth make these churlish demands on our royal personage?"

Sir Robert stood in silence, listening to his Queen and nodding now and then.

The situation that Gloriana referred to was indeed precarious. Intelligence from Spain told of a third Armada being readied by the stubborn Philip to invade England. Calais had fallen, giving Spanish ships access to English shores a mere twenty-two miles away.

And now O'Neill had given England his price for peace.

In his mind Cecil reviewed the terms on the paper that the Queen now waved in anger. The Catholic religion would be openly preached and taught throughout Ireland. All church lands would be returned to Catholic churchmen. All officers of state in Ireland would be Irish. The Queen would not press Irishmen to serve against their will. O'Neill, O'Donnell, O'Hara, Maguire and their kinsmen would enjoy all their lands and privileges without crown interference. All Irishmen would travel freely and traffic in merchandise in England as Englishmen, and would pay the same rights and tributes as Englishmen. And finally, the Irish would arm at their pleasure.

Upon reading these demands, even before passing them on to the Queen, Sir Robert had taken pen in hand and scrawled across the paper, "utopia."

And it would be. For should Elizabeth accede,

O'Neill would virtually supplant the Queen as ruler of Ireland.

Now, even though she railed in the manner of old, Cecil could see doubt and indecision in her eyes. Gone was the absolute sense of control he had seen in years past. Elizabeth at sixty-three wasn't a mockery of herself, but Sir Robert felt that it could happen soon.

Her personal vanity had grown worse in the past few months. Her face, caked with inch-thick makeup like her neck and her bare breasts, was aged and wrinkled. Her teeth were yellowed, and many were missing so that her speech was getting more and more difficult to understand.

Her dress was more suited to a woman less than half her age. Instead of dark sedate colors that would befit her age and stature she wore gowns even gaudier than she had in years past. Today her dress was of silver and crimson and the slashed sleeves, which were lined with red taffeta, hung nearly to the floor when she wasn't twisting them in her wrinkled hands.

Essex alone among her courtiers was still able to bow before her and go through the pretense that Gloriana still retained her youth.

And now Essex was off to attack Cadiz in hopes of forestalling another Spanish Armada, and the Queen was without anyone to play her game.

"What say you of this, Sir Robert?"

"I think, Your Majesty, that O'Neill presses for far more than he expects to achieve."

She accepted this with a nod and wrung the sleeves of her dress harder as her eyes narrowed in thought. "Like your father before you, Sir Robert, you are a wise man and a balm to our cares."

"I would draft a reply to the demands, Your Majesty, couched in obtuse language that will take weeks to unravel. In the course of those weeks I would sue for a truce with O'Neill to buy time.''

"And during that truce he would lick what little wounds we've given him and build up his men and arms.''

"Aye, I do believe he will. . . but then, so will we.''

LADY ELIZABETH HATTON, even in her widow's weeds, returned to court. For several weeks she played the grieving widow, but soon her free spirit could stand it no longer. She felt the need to taste life and society again.

She began to attend the masques. On warm days she took to the fields and meadows north of London to join in the hunting and hawking. Afternoons were spent again at the Bankside bearbaitings and at the theater.

True to Sir Robert's predictions, she was surrounded by suitors. The Lords Pembroke and Greville seemed constantly at her side. Other admirers paid her court at Hatton House as if she were a queen.

Even Francis Bacon saw the advantage of a liaison with such a wealthy influential woman. Elizabeth saw through Bacon all too quickly. He was a man without means, although he showed promise. The Lady Hatton had no need to marry promise, but she saw uses for Bacon as she did for all her suitors. So he, like the rest, was allowed to pay his respects at her pleasure.

As the year wound down and Christmas approached, Elizabeth and her widowhood became the gossip of fashionable London. She seemed to do everything contrary to established ways.

Since most wealthy widows were much sought after, they usually married soon after their husbands' demise. Elizabeth not only refused to make a choice, she also refused to give evidence of a primary suitor.

By January of the new year all London was making wagers on who would win her hand.

Had they only known.

Elizabeth followed the news from Ireland as if she herself were a general, plotting the wars. She hung on every scrap of information, and in so doing was able to piece together the movements of the man she still loved, Rory O'Donnell.

She couldn't and wouldn't forget their time together. And now that she was a free and a rich woman, she plotted and planned for the day when the Irish wars would be over and they could be together. For she had no doubts that they would be, as long as O'Donnell survived the battles.

To that end she trekked almost daily to St. Andrew's, her tiny Bible in hand, to pray for him.

And with the passing of each day the courtiers and gallants around her paled even more in comparison. She longed for the excitement of Rory's presence and the thrill of his passion.

Until that time came she determined to further her power and her influence through the acquisition of more and more wealth. She acquired land through mortgages, and ventured capital in the building of arms and war machines.

She played down her role as a woman of business, but a few men, Sir Robert Cecil being one of them, kept a watchful eye on her transactions and knew what she was about.

"I think, my dear Elizabeth, you aspire to be an empire builder."

"And is that so wrong, uncle?" Elizabeth replied, serving brandy in an upstairs sitting room of Hatton House.

"Nay. Both your father, Sir Thomas, and myself have watched your astuteness with much approval. You have purchased lands cheaply from the wastrel heirs of extravagant families. Your moneylending is contrived to bring you vast returns, and your industrial concerns reap you handsome receipts.''

"And the taxes I pay are astronomical but promptly paid, so that cannot be the reason for this visit. What is, uncle? Do you wish a loan?''

Sir Robert chuckled and drew a paper from his sleeve. "Nay, dear niece, although I am sure your present funds could well provide one.''

"Your spies should be able to tell you that," she replied caustically.

His mouth bent down in a scowl then, and the sternness she knew so well covered his face. "I know you, Elizabeth, as an independent and self-willed woman. So be it. I know you to play with half the suitors in London as if they were puppets on a string. 'Tis your fancy and I care not how you do it. But beyond that I must interfere.''

"If you mean interfere in my life—''

"I do.''

"Then I'll have none of it! I've told you, Sir Robert, I will brook—''

"You will, if you value your prestige and your wealth, Elizabeth.''

His tone was so commanding and so harsh that she was taken aback. His eyes as they bored into hers were devoid of any semblance of humor or warmth.

She blinked, averting her gaze, and began a new tack. "Uncle, you have used me, and I admit that through the years I have profited greatly. But now I would live my life as I see it, without being drawn into your intrigues.''

"Believe me, could that be so I would not be here now. But you have overstepped the bounds and threaten now to hurt, nay, perhaps ruin, what we Cecils have fought so long to attain.''

"How so?" she replied haughtily, unable to read his reasoning in those cold eyes.

"My position is strong at the moment," Cecil said, playing idly with the paper in his hand. "But Essex's position also strengthens. 'Tis naturally so. War is all around us, and in wars the position of warriors is always strong. Should m'Lord Burghley die soon, Elizabeth, my position at court could be in question."

"My, uncle, how the winds do shift."

"Aye, that they do. And that is why your affair with the Irishman must cease."

Both hands went to her throat and the color drained from her face. Somehow she knew words were futile, but something had to be said. "Affair? Uncle, you jest! That was two years—"

"I have intercepted your letters these last few weeks, Elizabeth," Cecil replied calmly. "I know your thoughts and plans."

Now Elizabeth's color returned and, with a vengeance, her anger, as well. "*My letters?* How dare you do such a thing!"

"I dare," he hissed, "because you conspire with an enemy of the crown."

"Conspire? Is that what you call it? Conspire? I speak of love with the one man I've ever known who is a true man, and you call it conspiracy?"

"Aye, I do. For that man is a rebel and an outlaw with a price on his head."

"I care not!"

"I do. Sit down!" The usually calm tone was completely gone from Sir Robert's voice. In its place was the bark of command. "Have you no idea, woman, what this would do to our family's position if word of what you do were to fall into our enemy's hands?"

"Damned if I care."

"Damned if you don't care!" he threw back at her. "You would lose all, Elizabeth, and I know you well enough to know that you couldn't stand such a thing."

She hated to bend, even slightly, before him, but she knew he spoke the truth.

"Uncle, this cannot go on forever. You yourself have said that Ireland one day must lose, and when they do the Queen, as she has always done, will grant them amnesty in return for future fealty. When that time comes O'Donnell and I—"

"Nay, it cannot be. . .because of your position!"

She was openly weeping now, but no sound came from her throat. The tears made rivulets in the makeup on her cheeks, and she could barely see him through the mist before her eyes.

It's not fair, she told herself, *nothing is fair!* If she were a man it would matter little whom she chose.

"I have here a list of eligible suitors." He laid the paper he had been holding on the table between them. "I care not whom you choose, but choose you shall. And I beg of you to not think too badly of me, Elizabeth. It is the nature of a man to survive, and survive I will."

"Of a man?" she cried. "And what of a woman!"

He held up a hand, palm turned toward her. "I've heard enough of your railing on women, Elizabeth."

"No!"

"What?" The strength of her reply startled even him.

"No, you haven't. You've heard little enough, only what you wanted to hear."

"I am a man, you are a woman and, by God, you will do as I say!"

"By God, I will do as I please." Her voice started low, barely a whisper, but it rose in volume and momentum as the words tumbled from her lips. "What I have done you have been well aware of, and you have condoned it because at the time it served your purpose."

"And now it serves my purpose—"

"To listen to me, uncle. Men rail on about bad women because they are intrigued by bad women. No one rails about bad men because men are expected to be bad. We, indeed, have rolling eyes while men have railing tongues. Our eyes, they say, cause men to look upon us lasciviously. Why? Because all men are given to lechery, that's why. But that is only one of their faults. They are also deceitful, lustful and malicious. And so, if women bring woe to men, men bring care, poverty and grief to women!"

"Don't be a difficult shrew, Elizabeth."

"Difficult? Shrew? The difficulties women have with men come not from shrewishness but from the very kindness of a woman's nature. And because of this they open themselves to slander. If men thought that women would stand up to them, then the male sex would instantly feel weaker. But they have been so used to the good nature of women that they take advantage of feminine goodness. The greatest faults women have are that they are too kind and honest, for could we flatter as men can dissemble, or use our wits as well as they can use their tongues ill, then never would we be under their thumbs as well as under their bodies!

"In all ways I would love a man better if he would love me like. But I fear in most cases the ways of love run parallel, and never meet. For while a woman wants gentleness, caring and companionship as well as satisfaction, a man has other thoughts on love. For him it is good enough to get himself up, in, off, and back to business as usual. And that business is usually railing at his fellow man or his besieged wife!"

At the end of her tirade Elizabeth whipped the paper from the table, balled it with her fist, and flung it defiantly into the fire.

"And that, uncle, is that! And if you do not see fit to agree, I will shout everything I have said, as well as what I have done, from the gables of Hatton House for all of Holborn and London to hear!"

"My God, you would."

"Aye, I would, uncle. And then you would see what a bloody scandal it would be for the Cecils."

CHAPTER THIRTY-ONE

O'HARA FITTED HIS CHIEFTAIN'S CLOAK around his shoulders and snapped the gold clasp across his broad chest. Then he turned and smiled down at his dark-eyed son, so much a miniature of himself.

Little Rory's arms ached from holding the sword up to his father, but he wouldn't let it fall.

"Thank ye, me lad," O'Hara told him, lifting blade and scabbard from the boy's hands and attaching them to his belt.

"Where is Glenmalure, father?"

"In the south, lad, in the Wicklow Mountains, where the boulders are as big as a castle room and the waterfalls roll down from the heavens above."

"When you've killed all the English, may we go there one day?"

"Aye, lad, when the English are gone ye'll see every bit of yer Ireland from the back of a good horse. Now fetch Annie, I'd say goodbye to the lass."

The boy ran from the great room, and O'Hara clomped across the stone floor and out onto the parapet. A chill ran up his spine as he stepped to Deirdre's side and looked down.

The drawbridge was lowered and men poured from the lower bailey over it to spill into the meadow beyond. In all there were a hundred good horse and three hundred foot. A hundred of the foot were Scottish gallowglass axmen, looking wild and ferocious in their highlander robes.

Horses pawed the ground and filled the air with the breath from their nostrils. Here and there in the vast field below steel clanged against steel as swordsmen warmed their early morning muscles in mock combat.

"A sight it is, lass."

Deirdre turned her clear eyes up to her husband and nodded as she looked back at the mingling soldiers. "Yes, a sight."

"You did not sleep well." He slipped an arm around her narrow waist and hugged her against him.

"Nor did you." She let her head bend until she could feel the reassuring roughness of his woolen cloak against her cheek.

O'Hara sighed. As much as he hated to admit it, she didn't have the stuff of a warrior-wife. Where he, O'Hara, gave lip service to religion, his Deirdre lived it. Where battle and the sound of steel on steel awakened him, it drugged her with fear.

But it was that gentleness in her that he loved.

"And soon, lass, it will be over. Every day more Scottish galleys land at the mouth of the glens of Antrim with reinforcements. More gallowglass flood Ireland to fight on our side. Mark me, lass, England will quit soon."

Still Deirdre didn't speak. She had no more words to say. She had said them all, and only Rory O'Donnell understood them. England would not quit, and each battle the Irish chieftains won would only drive the Queen closer to a full commitment.

She turned into him and slid her arms beneath his cloak to hold him. "Go with God, my Shane."

He tilted her head upward and kissed her lips, at once with gentleness and savagery. Deirdre returned the kiss in kind, and then felt life itself being drained from her as he disengaged her arms and stepped away.

"You've a hundred men and a year's provisions inside the walls, lass. Don't leave Ballylee!"

And then he was gone, down the narrow stone steps to the lower bailey. Rory O'Donnell awaited him along with Annie and little Rory.

"Guard yer Annie and yer mother with yer life, lad, fer I leave Ballylee in yer care."

"Aye, I will, Father," the little boy replied, fighting to hold back his tears and prove himself a man.

The O'Hara kissed his son and hugged Annie. "Keep a quick eye on the lad and stay near the walls."

"Aye."

The big warrior vaulted into the saddle and spurred his horse. Rory leaned down and brushed Annie's lips with his own. "If there's another letter, send it by courier."

Annie nodded.

With a salute to his namesake, Rory spurred his horse toward the drawbridge. He pulled abreast of O'Hara just as they reached the open meadow.

"'Twas an ill dream that kept me awake this last night," O'Hara blurted, without turning to Rory.

"A dream of what?"

"I dreamed I heard a keening, and in its midst I heard Paoveen."

A chill, twice the one caused by the morning cold, passed through Rory's body.

Paoveen was the banshee of the O'Haras, and her keening foretold a death in the clan.

JAMES BLAKE URGED HIS LATHERED HORSE into the glen and took his bearings from the sound of falling water.

His head ached like the pounding of a hammer on an anvil. It felt as though his left eye had taken the ball just short of an hour before, rather than weeks shy of two years. But the throbbing beneath the black patch was good. It was a constant reminder of what he had lost, and of what it would take to get it back.

Money he had accumulated in great quantities. The Lord Deputy Russell's own greed knew no bounds, so he was more than glad to look away when his captains carried out their own rapes of Ireland and the Irish.

But more than money, Blake still lusted after status and prestige. The Lady Hatton was now a widow. Blake planned to place himself in such a position that when he sued Cecil for her hand it would be impossible for the man to refuse.

But first he must rid himself of Rory O'Donnell.

The letters he had intercepted for Sir Robert told the tale only too well. The Lady Hatton was an even bigger fool than Blake had first thought when he had discovered her dalliance with the Irish rebel. To carry it on now that O'Donnell had a price on his head, and to make matters worse by claiming her infatuation to be love, was suicidal.

But with O'Donnell out of the way, Blake would bring a fire to the lady's bed that would quickly make her forget the brash Irishman.

He found the waterfall with ease, and reined up in a mossy clearing near its base. He had barely stepped from his horse when a sound made him whirl around, his hand to his sword.

But there was no need. The tall man in the drab mantle who stepped from the concealment of a heavy whortle-berry bush was well-known to Blake. They had done much business together in the past.

"I thought you might be too late to do us any good, Captain Blake."

"What you require, and the way you require it, takes a great deal of planning," Blake replied.

"Aye, that it does." The tall man spat, and a stream of greenish saliva shot into the pool beneath the water-fall. "Is it done?"

"First, what news?" Blake replied, casting a wary eye into the tree-dappled sunlight beyond the clearing. True, he had done much business with this man, but the fellow was still an Irishman, and not a one of them could be trusted.

"They come with nearly four hundred men by sea to Arklow. From there they can easily enter Glenmalure."

"And you know which pass they will use?"

"Aye." A roar of laughter came from his lips. "An' well I should, for 'tis I and one of my sons that'll lead 'em! They'll come hard nigh for the fort at Ballinacor. Half will attack the fort there, and the other half will split off for Rathdrum."

Blake nodded. The plan was set. Only a skeleton force would be in the fort at Ballinacor. The rest would be in the woods around it. When O'Hara marched his troops to the walls to lay siege he would be surrounded on all four sides. Outnumbered two to one and unable to maneuver, his men would be slaughtered.

"Who will lead the second force to Rathdrum?"

"Rory O'Donnell."

Blake barely managed to keep the elation from his face. "Are you sure?"

"As sure as there's a sun. Now, about the other part of our bargain."

"You know that your cousin holds a truce now," Blake replied. "It needs be a ticklish business to do him in."

"Damn yer excuses, man. Will it be done?"

Blake looked up through the trees until he found the sun. "I would say that by now Fiach O'Byrne's head has left his body."

Another booming laugh met Blake's words. "Sure, an' that means that by sundown I'll be McTeague, The O'Byrne!"

RORY DIDN'T LIKE THE SMELL of it. The Irish won battles by tracking the English as they marched through the country and harassing them at every turn. To skirmish with the enemy on his flanks was to win, giving battle only when opportunity was favorable.

Openly attacking an English fort, even if it was ill-manned and short of provisions, was not their way.

And where was Fiach O'Byrne?

McTeague had said Fiach would meet them at Rathdrum. But that hadn't been the original plan. They were all supposed to meet at Glenmalure, where Fiach had a defensible fortress, before venturing out to meet the English.

Rory had been against this change of plan, but McTeague had insisted. "Would you leave my cousin without reinforcements? He had to attack both Ballinacor and Rathdrum, or lose the advantage of numbers."

O'Hara had been thirsty for battle, so Rory had stilled his fears. And now he followed McTeague through a narrow pass that led to the plain outside the fort of Rathdrum.

"It is here that I'll leave you," O'Byrne said, reining his horse in front of Rory. "I'll take the high path . . . there, and meet Fiach. We'll be on their flanks with scaling ladders while they hold you at the front gates."

Rory nodded and watched the man ride off through the trees.

A feeling like prickly heat was attacking the back of his neck when he gave the signal, and the long narrow column moved forward again.

THE FORT AT BALLINACOR stood on a low promontory, with the narrow plain before it ending at a river. The plain was wooded on both sides and behind the fort.

O'Hara led his men across the narrow bridge and fanned them out into two'wings of shot. Swordsmen and pikemen took the center, with the gallowglass bringing up the rear, already caterwauling their eerie chants for blood.

"Start the drums!"

Slowly the cadence rolled along the line, and then they were moving forward down the avenue made by the open plain.

They reached the halfway point, with about fifty yards to go, when a tall figure mounted the holding wall waving a white flag.

"Glory, would ye look at that?"

"Nary a shot!"

"I am Captain Thomas Lee, in the service of the Queen," shouted the man from atop the wall.

"And I be The O'Hara, Shane, an' ye're a dead man."

"As commander of the fort at Ballinacor," came the reply, "I would plead leniency. We are but twenty in strength and would surrender."

"Damme," O'Hara hissed, "there'll be no battle here today." He turned to one of his lieutenants. "Pass the word down the line. We'll secure Ballinacor, and I'll take half the men to reinforce O'Donnell at Rathdrum."

"What say you?" Lee yelled from the wall.

"Aye. Line up yer men, with their muskets on the ground, and open the gates!"

The line moved forward. They had barely started when the two wide gates of the fort's entrance swung open. When they were twenty yards from the entrance the gates swung shut again, and a barrage of musket rained down on them.

"Back! Fall back!" O'Hara cried, reining his horse around.

But, too late, he realized that they couldn't fall back. Streaming across the river were horsemen, and pouring from the trees on both sides of the plain were English pikemen.

Too late Rory realized that the English had taken a page from the Irish book of war. He had dispersed his whole company along a line fifty yards short of where they would break through the trees.

They were moving forward cautiously when the roll of English drums met them. Within seconds the three men Rory had sent forward to scout the hill ahead were crashing toward him through the undergrowth.

"They wait just over the hill!"

"'Tis a trap, O'Donnell!"

"At least fifty horse and a hundred foot!"

Rory's mind whirled. Fifty horse and a hundred foot—he outnumbered them slightly. But how many were behind this force, in the fort?

And then he heard the drums behind them.

"What say you, captain?"

"Cut their line," Blake replied. "Force half of them from the woods onto the plain. Let the other half run wild. They'll find themselves in a bog where they can be cut down easily."

"Aye."

The man moved away and Blake put the glass back to his one good eye. Within minutes he saw the first rebels flushed into the open. The English horsemen charged. Foreseeing their fate the rebels tried to scatter back into the trees, only to be met by marching pikemen.

Blake smiled. Long months had he studied the Irish fighting methods, and he found them well worth copying.

Another group of Irish and Scots broke free and massed to meet the oncoming horsemen. For a while, because of the ferocity and fearlessness of the gallowglass and their swinging axes, the charge was withstood.

But then another of Blake's innovations was brought into play when the horsemen broke under a rebel charge. Like the prow of a ship the enemy advanced through the sea of sword-wielding cavalry, only to find themselves facing a wall of musketeers.

From a kneeling position the twenty musketeers loosed their shot and were quickly replaced by a second line. The rebels fell to a man.

Blake lifted his glass and focused behind the woods. The Irish who had retreated through the trees were hopelessly mired in a bog and being cut to ribbons.

The he saw the wall of horsemen, and at their head Rory O'Donnell.

Blake was just mounting his own horse when a mud-soaked courier pounded up the hill behind him.

"How goes Ballinacor?"

"A rout, captain," the courier breathlessly replied. "All dead save thirty prisoners, including Shane O'Hara."

Blake nodded and thought for a moment. "Tell Lee

to hang the prisoners, but save O'Hara. Hie him to Dublin Castle.''

THE PIKEMEN FELL LIKE SO MUCH WHEAT before Rory and his fellow horsemen's swords. But beyond them came the English horsemen, swords at the ready. And if they should fail, line after line of musketeers waited to take their place.

The field was lost, and Rory knew it. And in his heart he knew the cause of it. McTeague O'Byrne, proud and ambitious, had long coveted his cousin's lands and title. McTeague would rather be The O'Byrne in his little corner of Ireland, under the English thumb, than ride with the winds of change and be an Irishman instead of a clansman.

McTeague was one of the many O'Neill had feared, one of the many driving a sword through the armor of a united Ireland. And if McTeague succeeded there would be others, widening the chink in the armor so delicately designed but as yet not totally forged.

"At them!" Rory cried. "When we go down I would have English bodies to cushion our fall!"

They charged as one, and the fighting was furious. It wasn't for nothing that Rory's reputation in the field had risen to the point where it nearly matched Shane O'Hara's.

The air was filled with sounds of battle: the shouting cries of men, the thundering of horses' hooves and the clanging of steel interspersed now and again with the dull thud of steel finding flesh.

And then they were through the horsemen and charging the musketeers. Smoke filled Rory's eyes, and the scent of burning powder stung his nostrils. There was a shudder beneath him and a whinny of agony, and then his horse went down. He rolled in the meadow's soft grass and came to his feet like a cat.

Miraculously, their charge had shattered the line. The musketeers were in chaos. But he quickly calculated how his own numbers were depleted.

"O'Donnell!"

Rory looked up, blinking into the setting sun. Thirty yards away were ten or more horsemen, and in their center was the gray-haired man with the patch; the phantom who seemed to be all over Ireland, in ten places at once, wooing the Irish to fight the Irish.

"Surrender, O'Donnell. The field is ours."

The man's appearance had changed, but Rory recognized the voice.

"So you lived, Blake!"

"Aye, worse the wear for your treachery, but alive."

"Then come, let me finish what the ball didn't accomplish!" Rory shouted, raising his sword and filling his left fist with the hilt of his dagger.

Blake threw back his head and roared with laughter. "Nay, O'Donnell, you know my rapier won't match your sword in the field. I am not the fool to fight you on your terms. Surrender or we'll cut you down with numbers!"

Rory said nothing. He planted his feet and awaited the charge.

But it didn't come.

Instead, Irishmen by the hundreds came swarming from the trees.

Blake saw the shift in numbers all too quickly and flashed a lopsided grin in Rory's direction.

"I've missed you again, O'Donnell, but O'Hara is mine. Another day!"

He reined around and, flanked by his protectors, rode into the woods toward Ballinacor.

CHAPTER THIRTY-TWO

" 'Twas Fiach's sons, Felim and Redmond, who came to my aid. Blake's forces had shattered my company, but fifty men were saved by the O'Byrnes' arrival. They had discovered their kinsman's treachery too late to save O'Hara, but they managed in the nick of time to rout Blake."

Rory paused. There were tears in his eyes as he rolled a tankard back and forth between his palms.

" 'Twas my fault, for I smelled McTeague's treachery and should have cautioned Shane with greater vigor."

Rory finished his tale along with the last drop of *uisce beathadh* in his tankard, and motioned for more.

Deirdre came around the long oaken table and laid her hands upon his shoulders with a sigh. "Nay, Rory O'Donnell, 'tis not your fault, this deed. My Shane was rash."

She then turned to O'Neill. He sat motionless as he stared into the fire in the great hall of Dungannon Castle, his craggy features showing all too clearly the anguish in his mind and heart.

"And you do think 'twas McTeague who betrayed you?" he said at last. "The O'Byrnes were sure?"

"Aye," Rory replied. "I've no doubt of it. It was all too plain when I discovered O'Hara's fate."

"I'll have his heart," O'Neill hissed, "to feed my swine."

"What good this!"

Both men looked up in shock. Not once in their memory had they heard a harsh word from Deirdre's lips, much less a shout.

"How can my man be ransomed?" she stormed. "Is there any way we can cause his escape? What talk is this of revenge, or a swine's heart for a swine? I want my husband back at my hearth, back in my bed. What good is revenge to a widow on a cold winter's night!"

"None, I daresay," O'Neill replied, rising and pacing before the fire, his boots echoing hollowly on the stone floor. "But Shane is a great catch for Russell and the crown. Methinks the only ransom they'll ask is for the clans to lay down and give up their arms."

Suddenly Deirdre's composure shattered. With a moan she sank to her knees and covered her face with trembling hands. Her shoulders and breasts shook with silent weeping, for she knew O'Neill would never order the Irish to lay down their arms because of one man's capture, or even his death. He had said as much of himself should he fall into English hands.

"But we can take heart, girl," O'Neill added. "For they'll keep him alive. A prize such as O'Hara would be worthless to them dead."

Her eyes came up to O'Neill's great height, flashing fear and anger through her tears. "But can you be sure? You yourself have said that m'Lord Russell is slightly crazed. How can you be sure what he will do?"

Rory and O'Neill exchanged glances. They both knew that she spoke the truth. Russell had a hatred of the Irish like no English official before him had had. He had declared many times from Dublin Castle that should any rebel leaders fall into his hands, they would be hung at once as an example.

"Well?" Deirdre said.

"'Tis true, lass, there is chaos now at Dublin Castle like we've never seen before, and methinks at Whitehall as well. But hear this. We make a mockery of the English army and of English rule. Kings and princes all over Europe are heralding our victories. They say now that the English are not gods after all. Philip of Spain, aye, even Henry of France, have secretly sent their well-wishes and what aid they can spare from their own wars. Even James of Scotland has hinted that, should the crown of England be his at Elizabeth's death, he would treaty well with us. Do ye think, lass, he would do that if we were weak?''

Deirdre bit her lip to hold back more tears. She folded her hands and dropped them to her lap. ''I confess, 'tis only Shane I care about. I fear I am all woman when it comes to my man, for I would have him safe by my side and in my bed. And should he die, I would have him do it near me and peacefully, without the agonies attending an execution.''

Rory's head came up, and he looked with narrowed eyes across the table at her. He knew the meaning of her words. She was thinking of Annie's tale of Ned Bull.

''Here, lass,'' O'Neill said, raising her with gentle hands. ''I would you think on this. O'Hara is a rebel and a warrior, as are we all. You knew this when you mixed your vows. Think now of how your husband thinks. Think now of his own words, 'I would live free, or die for it!' Anything less, and he wouldn't be the man you love.''

''M'lord.''

They all turned. A courier stood in the door, his glib matted wetly against his face and his clothing dripping.

''Aye?''

The courier stepped forward. He eyed Deirdre and then turned toward O'Neill. They spoke in hushed tones.

Deirdre began to sway. Her face drained of color. Rory quickly moved around the table to her side. As he

wrapped an arm around her shoulders her hands,
balled into fists, came up to his chest. Against these she
rested her forehead and whispered, "No, oh, pray
God, no."

The courier's shuffling footsteps receded, and they
both turned as one to face O'Neill.

"Nay," he said, " 'tis not The O'Hara."

"Oh, thank God," Deirdre gasped, letting her
weight sink against Rory.

"He's celled in the same cell he's seen before in
Dublin Castle, and he's well. Now it's to bed with you,
lass, for O'Donnell and I have much work to do this
night. Rory."

Rory lifted Deirdre into his arms and carried her
from the room. "Annie?"

The girl appeared at once in the hallway. Rory set
Deirdre on her feet and Annie immediately saw the
need.

"To bed with her. She's had enough for one night."

"Aye. And The O'Hara?"

"A prisoner, but alive."

Annie, like the mother hen she had become, cradled
the older woman in her arms and led her toward the
stairwell. When Rory could no longer hear the padding
of their feet he returned to the room and O'Neill.

"Well?"

"If I know the Queen, how she thinks and reacts, I
think the fools in Dublin have done us a grisly favor."

"How so?" Rory asked.

"Thomas Lee was so proud of his victory that he car-
toned his prize and sent it off to Whitehall. The Queen
is outraged, and rants that she has barbarians in
Ireland fighting the barbaric Irish."

Suddenly Rory's eyes grew wide. He somehow
sensed what had occurred.

"Aye," O'Neill nodded, reading the other's thoughts. "The fool, Lee, has sent Elizabeth Fiach O'Byrne's head."

IN THE THIRD-FLOOR BEDCHAMBERS Deirdre slipped from beneath the heavy quilts and crossed to the hearth. She stoked the peat into a brighter glow and then turned to little Shanna's bed. Satisfied that the child slept soundly, she padded to young Rory's side.

In his sleep he had kicked the covers from his body, and now he shivered. Deirdre shivered as well as she looked down at his naked form. Already his legs and arms, as well as his shoulders and chest, were taking on the strong definitions of his father's body.

Like his father he wouldn't be overly tall, but he would be wide and powerful. His legs would be girded like two posts, and his arms would be muscled steel.

She pulled the covers to his chin and tucked them in around his body. At once the quivering stopped, and in his sleep he smiled his thanks at the warmth.

Lightly she brushed her lips across his forehead and then dropped to her knees. She tugged silently at the huge chest that had accompanied them to Dungannon from Ballylee. When it was free of the bed she opened it and searched by the fire's dim light.

"M'lady?"

"Shh, Annie, whisper or you'll wake the child."

"Is something wrong, m'lady?"

"I couldn't sleep."

And then Annie was kneeling by her side, and Deirdre had found what she was searching for.

"Annie, tomorrow we're to the woods, you and I."

"The woods, m'lady?"

"Aye," Deirdre replied, opening the case. "I would have you teach me how to use these."

Annie looked down, and her eyes fell on a brace of pistols.

"THE FOOL! The bloody damn fool!" Sir William Russell roared, slamming his fist to the table. His ample belly jiggled with the effort. "I just obtain writs from Whitehall to do as we please in this devil's country, and that fool Lee struts his arrogance before the Queen in such a manner!"

Across the desk James Blake sat with his legs stretched out and crossed before him. His face was a mask of calm, not showing the inferno that boiled inside him. For Blake would never rant and rave and show his emotions, either to friend or foe, as Sir William was wont to do.

But he agreed with the man. Lee's actions had been stupid. They had brought the Queen's wrath and disgust down upon their heads. There was even talk that Sir William would be recalled, and Blake wanted none of that. His successor, whomever he might be, would probably be much stiffer with his captains' actions. And Blake, as long as he had to serve in Ireland, wanted to do it his way; his way was the only profitable way.

"I have followed Cecil's order, Sir William, and placed Lee in a cell."

"Good, damn good. The fool."

"Aye, Sir William, the man is a fool. But you know as well as I do that we dare not keep him jailed too long, nor can we let him come to trial, should Cecil insist."

"Aye, damme, I know."

Lee, as well as Russell and Blake, had profited well in Ireland, and they had done it with each other's cooperation. Should Cecil order Lee's return to London and the Tower for his insult to the Queen, his tongue might loosen.

"Methinks, Sir William, that we must devise a way to shift Whitehall's concentration away from our dear captain."

Sir William searched the other man's single eye, trying without success to fathom his meaning. But then he never could. The man was an enigma, and a frightening one at that.

"How so, Blake? Speak not in riddles, it only adds to my vexation!"

"We have the means, in O'Hara...twofold for our purpose, in fact."

"How so?" Russell asked, smiling now. He could almost see the other man's brain at work.

"We both agree that the war, to this point, is a stalemate."

"Aye."

"We'll gain no glory, you and I, without a huge commitment from Whitehall to end it. At the same time we have milked it as much as we can under these conditions."

Russell's smile broadened. "So you would force the Queen's hand, as well as O'Neill's?"

"Exactly. Bagenal paws the ground for a fight. Given enough reason he will invade the north, forcing O'Neill into the field. There is no way on earth O'Neill can be defeated on his home ground."

"And such a defeat would throw the fear of God into Whitehall."

"Aye, it would," Blake said, the severed nerves in the left side of his face drawing his lips down instead of up when he smiled.

"But how do we provide Bagenal with a reason?"

"If O'Hara is executed, Sir William, the whole of the

Pale is open to the revenge of the O'Donnells and O'Neill. It shouldn't be too hard to convince Bagenal of that.''

"Aye, it wouldn't, for the man thinks himself invincible. But I heed a warning in my brain. Cecil's orders were to do nothing with O'Hara. What happens if I get orders to dispatch *him* to London?''

"That knotty problem, Sir William, we shall have to solve when the time comes.''

James Blake sighed, stood up and stretched. He also yawned but not from tiredness. Sir William bored him.

Blake was anything but tired. Such intrigue as they had devised always made him keenly alert.

" 'TIS FOOLISHNESS,'' O'Neill snapped.

"Aye, perhaps, but a necessity,'' Rory replied. "With Russell in Dublin Castle we have no way of knowing if Cecil receives our words as we pronounce them or as Russell changes them to suit his purposes.''

"Aye, true,'' O'Neill nodded.

"And what better way to inform Cecil of what his lord deputy does than face-to-face?''

O'Neill stalked to the fireplace with his head bowed. Putting up his long arms he leaned against the mantel stone and groaned. "But what if you take yourself to England for a face-to-face meeting with Cecil, and he proves as treacherous as the rest? Then they'll have *two* pawns, you and The O'Hara.''

" 'Tis a risk I think worth taking.'' Rory moved over to stand beside him. "I think I know Cecil. He is devious and cunning, yes. But he is also a man of honor, and he wants peace in Ireland. The battles we win or the battles they win mean nothing as long as we keep negotiating. He wants full-scale war no more than we do, and for the same reasons.''

O'Neill nodded and sighed deeply again. "Because neither of us now is strong enough to defeat the other."

"Aye."

"Damme," O'Neill hissed, slapping a fist into the opposite palm. "How many years have we played the waiting game with this war and with our lives? And now with O'Hara...."

His words trailed off as he began to pace again.

"I would do anything to save O'Hara," Rory said. "Once before I was helpless when such a friend needed me, as Shane needs me now. 'Tis worth the effort, no matter what. If we can get O'Hara away from Russell's clutches and to London, the worst he'll suffer is imprisonment."

"You have that much faith in Cecil?"

"Aye, and more. And in the Queen as well. She is loathe to use the executioner's block unless all else fails. An instance: these many months, nay, years, she has stayed her hand rather than sign the execution order for Deirdre's father, m'Lord Haskins. Why? Because of his age, partly. But also because she shies away from bloodshed, particularly when it comes at her own hand."

Rory would have spoken more, but O'Neill held up his hand for silence. He poured a glass of wine and moved to a shuttered window. A chill blast, strong enough to lift his long hair, blew in when it was opened.

"How would you get word to this woman?"

"Annie. The lass is known by her."

"How long would it take?"

"A month, six weeks at the most," Rory replied, keeping his voice barely under control as he sensed victory.

Slowly O'Neill's head began to nod. "It would be

enough time, for Dublin will do little more than we before the spring.'' Then he turned to face Rory. The wind now blew from his back, scattering his fiery gray-flecked mane across his shoulders and face. ''How come you, Rory, to trust this Englishwoman...this Elizabeth Hatton?''

Rory started to speak, couldn't, and turned to the fire.

''Oh, God,'' O'Neill moaned. ''Are we all destined to be star-crossed with English wenches?''

CHAPTER THIRTY-THREE

ELIZABETH BOUNCED LITTLE CHRISTOPHER, Honor's baby, on her lap as the mother stood nearby, beaming. ''He is indeed a hearty lad, Honor, with your looks and his father's fine even disposition.''

''Thank you, m'lady. And see how he smiles? He does adore you.''

''As I adore him,'' Elizabeth said, taking in every line of the cherubic little face and still-toothless mouth that smiled winningly back at her. ''You are so lucky, Honor.''

''Aye, I know that,'' the girl replied, looking away. ''As you will be too, m'lady, one day.''

''Ah, if only I could be sure. If only, in all these months, he had answered a single letter to those I wrote before my cunning uncle—''

''Be careful, m'lady...oh, I'm sorry.''

''Whoops!''

The child had grasped an emerald necklace where it rested between Elizabeth's breasts. Before Honor could stop him he had yanked it with amazing strength, breaking the clasp. Now he clutched it roguishly to his little chest.

"Naughty. Give me that, Christopher!"

At last Honor successfully pried his tiny fingers from the stone. The instant she had succeeded, the child in no uncertain terms let her know that he wanted it back.

"I'm so sorry, m'lady. I'll have it repaired."

Elizabeth only laughed with glee and dropped the necklace into her jewelry box. "No matter. But I will say, he has lungs to match his taste in stones!"

"To bed with you now, darling," Honor said, moving toward the door. She turned and executed a brief curtsy. "Excuse us, m'lady."

"Good night, little one," Elizabeth said, wriggling her fingers at the tiny face that was once again smiling.

When they were gone, Elizabeth moved to the window and looked across Holborn to Covent Garden and the Strand beyond. Here and there in the gardens of the great houses she could see daffodils and the beginnings of cherry blossoms. Her own glorious garden behind Hatton House was also starting to bloom, and she made a mental note to take a few days during the week to oversee the work of her gardeners.

Spring was coming slowly this year and it was just as well; she had no taste for sunshine, or for a summer progress if the Queen should take one in this hellish year of 1598.

It seemed that Elizabeth's world had come to a standstill while everything around her raged in chaos. Being at court was no longer a joy, for the lords and ladies formed a brooding, unsmiling assemblage seemingly locked in a fear of their own making.

The only saving grace was that her uncle now had more important matters weighing upon his shoulders than her prolonged widowhood.

Essex had been made earl marshal of England. It was
not as powerful as Sir Robert's office as first secretary
to the Queen, but it was powerful enough to increase
the enmity between the two men to intense proportions.

Even the court gossip held little interest for Elizabeth
lately. Only that morning she had heard that Mistress
Bridges had been banished from the Queen's coffer
chamber. It seemed that she and Mistress Russell had
been caught in the privy gallery where they had been
observing Lord Essex at exercise. He was bare to the
waist, playing at balloon, when the Queen had entered
in a tirade.

Elizabeth had dismissed this bit of gossip offhanded-
ly. Years before she wouldn't have been able to wait an
hour before passing it on. But no longer. The jealousies
of an aging, near-toothless Queen over a much younger
and irresponsible man suddenly seemed so trivial in
Elizabeth's eyes that it bored her.

There was only one thought in her mind, only one
image that didn't bore her—Rory O'Donnell.

"M'lady!"

"My God, Honor, what is it?"

Honor stood in the doorway, her face white, her
shoulders trembling as her hands twisted and wrung the
apron she was wearing. Suddenly she stepped aside,
and Elizabeth realized that there was someone smaller
standing behind her.

"Who? What is...Annie!"

RORY DISMOUNTED and tethered his horse near a stand
of stump wood overlooking a stream. He had been
seeking fresh game when, from a far hill, he had
spotted Deirdre and the children going into the wood
with a picnic basket.

Straying so far from the walls of Dungannon Castle

was dangerous. He had said so to Deirdre repeatedly and now he meant to bring the point home to her. Crouching, he silently entered the wood and made his way through the dense underbrush toward the tiny knoll where they sat.

As he reached the clearing and caught sight of them he stopped. A picture they made. Deirdre's long leine of bright purple was covered with a sleeveless dress of azure blue. Her long black hair hung down the middle of her back from under a rolled linen headcloth. Little Rory sat raptly before her. When O'Donnell got closer he could see that Deirdre had unlaced the low bodice of her dress and had freed her breasts. Shanna contentedly suckled as her mother rocked her.

He was about to step into the clearing and surprise them, as if he were a whole regiment of the Queen's men, when Deirdre's words stopped him.

"Nay, little one, I'll not tell you a story of war, but I'll tell you one of love."

"Love?" the boy replied with a grimace.

Deirdre chuckled. "Oh, lad, I hope one day you will think about love, and perhaps grow to honor it more than you do battle. I'll tell you the story of Deirdre."

"That's your name, momma."

"I know, darling, but this story is about another Deirdre, one who lived long ago. She was called Deirdre of the Sorrows."

"How long ago?"

"A great long time ago, during the time of Our Lord, Jesus. A great king ruled over our Ulster then. His name was Conchobar."

"Was he a king like The O'Neill?" the boy asked, warming to the story at the mention of kings.

"Aye, he was, lad. But you must know that The O'Neill—like all men, kings or those who would be kings—is human. And because they are human, they are prey to human frailties.''

Young Rory furrowed his brow in concentration and moved closer to his mother. Lovingly she reached out and tousled his dark hair, then traced her fingertips along the line of his strong young jaw that was so like his father's.

"But on with our story. Conchobar was a handsome man, with eyes as blue as the sea and hair as black and curly as yours. He was so handsome that sometimes he was vain. One day his chiefs brought to him a tale of a young girl. They said that she was called Deirdre, and that she was so beautiful, with such an angelic face, that once they had set eyes upon her they could not look away.''

"Just like you, momma!'' the young boy cried.

Deirdre threw back her head and laughed gaily. "Ah, Rory, my son, methinks you will go far in this world with your brave Irish heart and your glib Irish tongue! But shush you now, let me finish my story!

"The great king, Conchobar, was so taken with their tale that he needs must see this magnificent creature himself. So with all his retinue he set off for the far end of Ulster, where the beautiful girl child, Deirdre, lived. And when he came upon her, indeed he could not believe his eyes. She was so beautiful that Conchobar decided he would spirit her away until she was of marriageable age, and then he would have her for his wife. He placed her in a great castle, and around her only those servants he trusted.

"Deirdre grew up to be an even more beautiful woman than Conchobar had expected. He named their wedding day and eagerly awaited it. But love, working in its strange ways, denied Conchobar his bride.''

"She ran away!" Rory interjected, momentarily awakening his sleeping sister.

"Shh, darling, not so loud. Now see what you've done?" Deirdre quieted the child with her breast and then frowned. "Now, where was I...? Oh, yes. One bright spring day, Deirdre wandered much farther than usual from her castle. Near some woods, by a stream much like this one, she met a boy. His name was Naoise, and he was as darkly handsome as Deirdre was beautiful.

"Neither could resist. They fell in love with one another on the spot. And in the days that followed they kept meeting. Their love grew and grew until they knew they could never live without each other. And then Deirdre one day began to cry. She told Naoise of her betrothal to Conchobar.

"'Never!' said Naoise. 'We will flee!' And they did, to Alba, which is now called Scotland. But the King of Alba learned of Deirdre's beauty and would have had her for himself. The lovers were again forced to flee, this time to the place we now call England."

Again the boy interrupted, clapping his hands. "And the English king did take her for himself, just like the English take everything belonging to the Irish!"

"No, not quite, darling," Deirdre said, laughing. "Now don't interrupt. We're coming to the most important part of the story!"

"All right. Go on, go on!"

"Back in Ireland all the nobles felt sorry for the wandering couple who were so much in love. They begged Conchobar to swallow his pride and let them return to their homeland. For the longest time he wouldn't relent, but finally he agreed.

"The lover rejoiced and set sail for Ireland's shores. But Conchobar had an evil plan in his heart. For when the ocean wave swept them to shore, the king raised his sword and struck Naoise with a death blow.

"With his last breath Naoise shouted his love for Deirdre. Again Conchobar raised his sword. But this time when it fell, Deirdre had covered Naoise's body with her own. The sword struck her, and Conchobar fell to his knees and cried out, 'What have I done? What have I done?'

"And Deirdre, with her dying words, said this lament over her lover's body:

> The lion of the hill is gone
> And I won't be left to weep alone.
> Without my love I can't abide,
> So dig the grave both deep and wide.

"And so she became known as Deirdre of the Sorrows."

Huge tears filled little Rory's eyes, and his words, when he spoke, could barely be heard. "'Tis sad. 'Tis very sad, momma."

"Aye, it is, darling. But then, sometimes love can be very sad."

O'Donnell, hidden in the trees, also thought it was sad. No matter how he tried he couldn't stop the tears from stinging his own eyes. Deirdre's tale had struck close to his heart.

As silently as he had come he left, winding his way through the trees to his horse. Then he mounted and rode toward Dungannon with a heavy heart.

Did he long to see Elizabeth for Ireland's sake, or for his own? Would she, after so long a time, even agree to see him? Had she found another lover? Worse yet, had she remarried?

All these questions and a hundred more gnawed at

his belly and riddled his brain as he topped a hill and saw a lone rider on a lathered horse pass below him.

Then all else dissolved as he recognized the tiny body and the elfin features.

"Annie!" he cried, putting spurs to his own horse. "What ho, Annie, what news?"

CHAPTER THIRTY-FOUR

IT WAS AS IF THE FLOODGATES OF HELL had opened and let loose the devil's wrath on the tiny Isle of Purbeck off the southwest coast of England.

Oblivious to the lightning, the thunder and the crashing waves pounding the rocky shore beneath her, Elizabeth stood on the bulwark of the second ward of Corfe Castle. Before her the foreboding sea churned, its towering whitecaps illuminated and made more frightening with each jagged flash of light.

The sky above the sea, when she could see it, seemed low enough to reach out and touch. The air against her face was bitterly cold, and driving rain pelted her in chilling drizzles.

Nay, she thought, *he'll not come tonight.*

Seven nights she had stood just like this, waiting hour after hour. And for seven nights the storm had raged so fiercely that no vessel—nor man, no matter how daring—could brave the churning waters.

The Isle of Purbeck was slightly protected from the full anger of the sea by St. Alban's Head. Elizabeth could imagine what it must be like in the darkness out there, somewhere beyond the point in the open sea.

No, 'tis past hoping, he'll not come this night.

But still she stood, not yet willing to enter the keep

and climb the gigantic stone stairwell to the third ward and her chambers.

Twice already that night Honor had called to her from atop one of the castle's hulking towers to come inside.

"Nay, Honor, not yet. I'll stay a bit longer."

"But, m'lady, you'll catch your death! Your cloak is already heavy with rain!"

"I know, but not yet. To bed with you, Honor, to bed."

Suddenly she threw back her head, and a long pealing laugh bubbled from the white column of her throat. If only her many suitors could see her now, what would they think? The rich, beautiful, and oh, so desirable widow, Lady Elizabeth Hatton, standing before an ancient Norman keep, soaked through to her shivering skin as she waited for a wild Irish outlaw with the Queen's price upon his head.

Waiting?

Nay, yearning.

Yearning so much that her breasts were swollen with desire, and the quivering in her body came more from the aching void between her thighs than from the chilling rain.

What would her suitors think of such abandon? Would the stuttering Francis Bacon blurt out were his rodent's eyes to find her in the lightning's flash?

And Fulke Greville, so calm and self-assured. What reasons would his nimble mind conjure up as to the cause for her actions? For he could never—or would never—believe the true ones.

And Pembroke. Dear sweet Pembroke, who would have her for companionship only, who was too shy to admit that there could actually be a coupling after their vows. Shy Pembroke, who spoke one thing and thought another, evidenced by the need to place his hat over his lap whenever he was around her.

And the latest addition to the list, the attorney general himself, Sir Edward Coke, who had buried his first wife, Bridget, only this fortnight past. Coke who hinted rather than asked, and in his hinting gave Elizabeth the impression that he would have her just so that his arch foe, Francis Bacon, couldn't have her.

What would they all think if they could see her now?

Elizabeth wished they could. She wished they were all standing right there on the sea wall below her, so they could see how she would greet her true lover, with her pelvis thrusting and her breasts jutting to meet his embrace.

If the passion of their affair had been exciting and satisfying the first time, the anticipation of it now was even more wildly thrilling.

And it held a much deeper meaning—because she was free.

"Oh, Rory, my love, my darling!" she cried, the wind throwing the words back in her face. "I'm free, free, free! I'm a woman with no bonds, no fetters...a woman who can love as she pleases!"

Only too well did she know the dual game she played. But she didn't care. Damn the disastrous effects, and damn those who would cause them. For the first time in her life the ambitions and the intrigues with which she had always lived meant nothing.

To the winds with them! They paled beside her love for the Irishman, Rory O'Donnell.

"Elizabeth."

She whirled around, her eyes searching. The wind had played tricks with the voice and she couldn't find its source.

And then again, "Elizabeth."

She looked up just as a bolt of jagged lightning, and then a second one, sliced across the storm-swept sky.

It was he, and the first shock of seeing him made Elizabeth gasp and step back. His figure, outlined against the sky, was almost frightening as it stood between the keep's parapet, glowering down at her.

He was draped in a huge black cloak, its cut strange to her. He had allowed his beard to grow, as well as his hair, which reached to his shoulders now. Even wet, it blew wildly in the gusting wind.

My God, she thought momentarily, *were it not for the voice I would be hard put to recognize him!*

And then he was gone, and above the rain she could hear his boots pounding down the keep's stone stairs.

She was rooted, unable to speak or move, her eyes fastened to the keep's arched doorway.

"Elizabeth, my love."

He stood for a second in the grayness and then lurched toward her, a gliding black bulk of immense proportions, his strong white teeth gleaming in the darkness of his bearded face.

And then she was running, stumbling to meet him. A bolt of lightning seemed to halo them with eerie yellow light as she glided under his opened cloak and into his powerful arms.

His hands found the small of her back, and only the tips of her slippered toes touched the stones as his wet and heated lips found the hollow at the side of her throat.

"Elizabeth, my own Elizabeth," he moaned, whispering her name over and over as his kisses moved up her throat, over her rain- and tear-soaked cheek, until his lips fastened on hers.

The thunder that shook the foot-thick walls of Corfe Castle was nothing compared to the roaring in her body as his lips spoke his love. His arms tightened, threatening to squeeze the life from her, while his tongue plundered her mouth.

She welcomed his kiss with aching desire, thankful that he held her as tightly as he did because her legs had turned to jelly. There was nothing now except the feel of his lean, hard-muscled body against hers, his hotly probing tongue, and the maleness she could feel already rising against her belly.

They were alone in a sea of each other, their only companions the searing lightning and the rumbling thunder that crashed around them.

And then his lips lifted from hers and again found her soft throat. "The touch of your body, the sweetness of your scent, aye, your very being has filled my every waking hour."

"As your face has filled my every dream, my love," she moaned, wrapping her arms tightly around his neck and pressing her body even harder against his in surrender.

Again he kissed her, this time with gentle deliberation. And then he released her, his hands holding her face before his eyes. "Beautiful, even more beautiful than I remembered."

His dark eyes, slightly hooded in his shadowed face, examined her as though she were an apparition that would suddenly fade. "Your lips, your eyes, your hair...every part of you has haunted my every thought."

"Like a witch or an angel, my darling?"

"At times, I think, like a little of both. Whenever I thought of you, whenever your face would appear before my eyes like a vision, I would feel such an ache that sleep, food, yea, even movement was sometimes impossible."

"There are no words to say what hell these months have been," she murmured, leaning forward again.

He moaned and seemed to sway as his hands moved up to cradle and knead her breasts. "So much to say, so much to tell you."

"Shh." She placed a finger to his lips. "Not now, not yet. Love me, my Rory. Let nothing exist except our love."

Effortlessly he swung her into his arms. "Where?"

"There, up the stairs," she said, burying her face in the thick damp darkness of his hair. "My chambers are in the third ward, to the right."

Wordlessly he entered the keep and ascended the stairs. His boots barely sounded now as he tread lightly on the stone floor of the narrow corridor. With a gesture, Elizabeth stopped him at the proper door.

It opened at the touch of his foot. He stood her on her feet near the huge canopied bed and returned to the door. Once it was closed, with the latchstring pulled inside, he threw off his cloak and moved toward her.

She shivered with anticipation, her head thrown back, her eyes squeezed tightly shut as his fingers worked at the laces of her bodice. And then her overdress was gone, a sea of wet cloth at her feet. Quickly the farthingale joined it, and his fingers were peeling her chemise down to her waist.

When his lips found the soft valley between her full breasts, Elizabeth gasped with the thrill that coursed through her body, and she opened her eyes. She curled the fingers of one hand in the dampness of his hair, and with her other hand she cupped her breast, offering the hard nipple to his searching lips.

Gone was the chill of the storm as his lips caressed, teased, and then enveloped the jutting point of her breast. No longer could she hear the thunder beyond the shuttered windows, because of the passionate thunder raging in her ears from his touch.

"You're mine," he moaned, curling his fingers in the chemise that hugged her hips.

"Always," she whispered, as cool air bathed her trembling thighs and the heated petals of her womanhood.

His lips moved to her other breast and she felt the darkness between her thighs blossom and open with yearning.

"Now, my darling, please! Hurry!"

He stepped back, his fingers opening the leather thongs of his jerkin. Then it and the plain cambric shirt were cast aside. His chest and broad shoulders were like rippling mahogany as he threw off the rest of his clothes to reveal his readiness.

Elizabeth didn't bother to slip the bed's rich brocade coverlet aside. Instead she lay down on top of it, her thighs spread slightly in invitation, her arms wide in welcome.

In the firelight's glow Rory's eyes savored the curves and planes of her perfect body. They drank in the flow of her pink-tipped breasts as they rose and fell with her breathing. They traveled in awe and wonder over the gentle swell of her belly and jutting hipbones to her full tapering thighs and the soft treasured valley between them.

"You are like a painting of all that is woman come to life."

"But I am real, and here, and yours. Come, my darling! Take me, take me!"

He melded his nakedness to hers and claimed her with his arms and then his lips. Languidly she stretched, unable to keep her lower body still as she searched for him. And then his lips left hers, lightly brushed her breast, and continued on.

"No...no, Rory!" she cried, but only once before she was transported.

She was floating, gliding toward a bliss she had never known before. She lifted her hips to meet the caress of his lips and hands, which seemed to be everywhere at once. It started as a tingle and roared to a rapturous end that left her panting with her own exertion and crying out her joy.

And then his body was over hers, his weight pressing her down, down into the many mattresses beneath them.

"There...there...oh, now, my darling! Ohhhhh!"

He paused a moment, panting.

"No, don't stop! It's...it's just been so long, there is bound to be a little pain. But I want it! I want to know that you're there!"

Again he moved, and like steel he entered her. There was pain, but it quickly faded in the joy of her surrender. Her fingers moved across his back until she found the corded tautness of his buttocks. She gripped him with all her strength, urging him on to seek fulfillment with her.

"Yes, yes!"

"Elizabeth...my Elizabeth."

The smooth rhythm of his thrusts gave way to a savage frenzy as the passion mounted in both their bodies. The darkness of his skin and the lightness of hers seemed to merge rather than contrast in the dancing firelight.

Waves, great waves of smoldering fulfillment rushed over them like the ocean sea that slammed against the rocks outside; never stopping, always building, until the winds of the storm subsided.

Elizabeth shuddered, her legs, her arms, her very soul clasping him in her release.

A hoarse cry of exaltátion burst from Rory's throat to shatter the room's stillness as his body went as taut as an arrow and his warmth filled her.

As his weight settled gently over her, Elizabeth remained entwined around him, her hands lovingly stroking his neck and shoulders. Outside she could hear the storm still raging, but inside there was peace.

THE STORM CONTINUED for three more weeks, making any travel, no matter what the distance, impossible. Locked together in isolation, Rory and Elizabeth plunged more deeply into their love for each other. During their quiet times Rory explained his plan to Elizabeth in detail. She understood O'Neill's demands, and thought the reasoning behind them, once Rory had explained it, was sensible.

The old warrior wanted a treaty for all the clans throughout Ulster, from Ballylee northward to the sea. Included in this agreement would be a clause insuring self-rule, as well as self-determination in religion. In return O'Neill would promise to stop seeding rebellion in Connaught, the Pale and southern Ireland. But only so long as the treaty was kept. Another stipulation was that a new lord deputy should replace Sir William Russell in the Pale, so that there would be some degree of fairness in the treatment of the southern Irish— chieftains and peasants alike.

Elizabeth understood what O'Neill wanted, but in the time Rory had been gone she had studied Irish politics thoroughly and had listened avidly to every word when Ireland was discussed at court.

"Methinks that my uncle, and most importantly the Queen, will not agree to a tenth of these demands."

"Perhaps not," Rory nodded. "But the lines of negotiation must be opened, and kept open, or there will be full-scale war."

Timorously she asked the next question. "And who would win that full-scale war?"

"England," he quickly replied, "without a doubt. But not without annihilating the Irish, and not without spilling staggering amounts of English blood."

It was after several days of their blissful confinement that Rory told her of O'Hara, and of what he, Rory, planned to do.

"No, no!" she cried, clutching him to her. "I won't be a party to that!"

"'Tis only as a last resort, my love," he said, gently cradling her in his arms. "I would trade myself for O'Hara and serve as a pledge that O'Neill would keep his faith."

"They'll kill you!"

"Nay, there would be no reason for it."

"But why you?" Elizabeth cried, angry now and frustrated that she might be thwarted in her plans for them to remain together.

"'Tis Ireland and the clans you'll have to understand, Elizabeth, in order to comprehend this. O'Hara is a chief. I am not."

"You are!"

"Nay," he chuckled. "'Tis my brother, Red Hugh, who is The O'Donnell and chieftain of the clan. 'Tis to him the people owe their allegiance, and his commands they obey. 'Tis the same with The O'Hara. While he lies in Dublin Castle with the shadow of the hangman over him, no one, not even O'Neill, can be sure what his underchiefs will do. Nay, Elizabeth, the leader of each clan must be free, and in power, or any treaty could unravel in a moment's notice."

But such reassurance didn't restore the color to her face. "Prison. You'd be in prison!"

"You should be thankful," he said, chuckling.

"Thankful? How so? You jest!"

"Nay, for surely I would be lodged in the Tower, and that way would be much nearer to you. In fact, I'd be but a stone's throw from Holborn and Hatton House."

Her small fist lashed out, and he caught it barely in time. "Od's blood, woman, would you strike a naked, defenseless man?"

"Aye, I would!" she laughed, the tension caused by their weighty problems broken for the moment. "Would you rape a naked, defenseless woman?"

"Only if she were as beautiful as you," he replied, covering her body with his.

Elizabeth clasped him to her with all her strength, and once more surrendered herself totally, passionately, to his love.

THE SKY ABOVE WHITEHALL was gray, matching the Queen's mood. She stood at her window looking down at the foreboding darkness of the Thames, her thoughts masked in silence and the only sign of wakefulness an occasional shiver that shook the wide ruff at her neck.

Suddenly she spoke. "And you think this rebel, O'Donnell, whom we once succored in our court, speaks the truth?"

"I do, Your Grace," Sir Robert replied from across the room. "I believe Rory O'Donnell to be the voice of O'Neill, and perhaps of others, too. He would sue for peace."

"At times I think there will never be a peace in Ireland. For 'tis man against man, and you men know naught but the sword. Witness such an insult as lately we have received from our own soldiers."

Sir Robert winced. For weeks he had lived with the embarrassment of Captain Thomas Lee's rash act.

Before he could reply the Queen spoke again. "What think they, these noble swordsmen I have in the field, to send such a grisly token?"

The aging Burghley, seated near the fire, exchanged looks with his son. Sir Robert turned away. Sir John Clapham, Lord Burghley's secretary, coughed nervously.

"Well?" the Queen rasped, whirling to face them. "Do they think their sovereign has placed so many heads on yonder London Bridge that she now needs such tokens in her *chamber*?"

"Nay, Your Majesty," Sir Robert offered. " 'Twas the foolish act of a stupid man."

"Was it?" Their eyes jerked up at the sudden plaintive tone in her voice. "Mayhap not. Perhaps a sign it was that we enlightened people still need sword and ax to convince our people to follow our laws."

Sir Robert averted his eyes so that his Queen wouldn't see the startled look he knew they betrayed. Like his father and his Queen, he believed in peace and justice. He also believed in the forgiving nature his Queen had so often used in the wielding of her power.

But the words he heard now from her quivering lips conveyed a strange sense of foreboding. It was as if she knew her armor had cracked, and she could find no way to stop the rent from widening.

Elizabeth the Queen moved slowly across the room to stand behind the seated man who had served her so long and so well. Gently she put her hands on the elder Cecil's shoulders and rolled her eyes toward the ceiling.

"How many years, m'lord, has it been since I was a young girl called to the throne to make our England merrie once again?"

Clapham coughed in embarrassment.

Sir Robert dropped his eyes to the floor. He almost wished his enemy Essex were there to bring a smile to the old woman's haggard face.

Without turning, Burghley reached up and found her bejeweled hand with his trembling fingers. "Your Majesty has given our land years of plenty, and has made us strong in peace and war."

"And how many more years, I wonder...."

Her voice trailed off. Sir Robert cast a wary eye toward her and felt his breath catch in his throat. Tears flowed from the Queen's eyes, making tiny rivers in the thick makeup covering her cheeks.

"I would that, before our reign should end, we could remove from our side this thorn called Ireland." She paused, and a heavy sigh echoed throughout the room. "And would that it could be done without any more English or Irish babies made orphans."

Suddenly she whirled around and, her behavior very unlike the Queen of England, ran weeping from the room.

When the door had closed behind her Lord Burghley painfully pulled himself to his feet and faced his son. "I do believe that in the meantime your rebel O'Hara has been granted a reprieve."

"Aye," Sir Robert nodded, "it would seem so. I'll have a courier to horse and Dublin within the hour."

ELIZABETH HATTON LIVED A LIFETIME of joy and sorrow in those few weeks. To have Rory again beside her, to feel his savage strength within her, was all she had dreamed of.

To think that she might lose him again was hell.

The storm abated enough to make travel possible. Together they composed the letter that sturdy and always faithful Charles, Honor's beloved, would deliver to Cecil. The afternoon of his departure left them both with an agonized empty feeling.

They knew that in less than two weeks of hard riding Charles would return. And no matter Cecil's answer—agree to the one-to-one meeting or not—the lovers' lives would change again.

And it was that change, that unknown, that caused them both such trepidation.

They found solace in the quiet darkness of Elizabeth's bedchamber, wrapped in each other's arms.

Elizabeth treated each hour she had alone with him as a lifetime. She could get enough of neither his love nor his lust. Every touch of his lips on hers, every tender caress of his hands on her breasts was like the first.

And each time he plunged himself into the depths of her body she feared, down deep in her heart, that it would be the last. For this reason there was no letup, no stopping, in the outpouring of her passion. And she found that Rory felt the same way. Day blurred into night, and vice versa, and each time she called upon him he was ready.

"You make me feel...so much a woman," she murmured softly into his hair during a moment of respite from their all-consuming passion. "Years ago I wondered if I would ever feel this way."

"Your desire matches your love, my darling. Few men are as lucky as I."

She was silent for a moment and then rolled to her side. She studied his face, the now full beard, the many new wrinkles etched by battle, wind, weather, and worry, and the long cut of his silky black hair.

"What are you thinking about?"

"Your hair. It's so long now, and I had forgotten how black it was."

"Aye, 'twas my father who gave me my hair. That's why he was called Black Hugh. Some think it was because he was so fierce and scowling in battle, but 'twas because of his hair."

"It couldn't have been darker than this," she said, spreading a portion of his heavy mane across the whiteness of the pillow. "It's. . . it's like. . . ."

"A raven's feather?"

"Aye, that's it!" she exclaimed. "It has the ebony sheen of a raven's wing!"

"My father once told me that had I dropped female from my mother's womb I would have been christened Brenna."

"Why so?"

" 'Tis Gaelic for raven."

"Brenna," Elizabeth said, letting the syllables roll from her tongue as he had done. "An odd but beautiful name. . . Brenna."

With the rains over they escaped from the castle and on horseback toured the tiny Isle of Purbeck. The only industry was a huge marble quarry, and the only signs of civilization a few thatched cottages for its workers. Some of the isle was green, but much of it was stark and barren.

" 'Tis like your Castle Corfe, this land," Rory said once.

"Oh? How so?"

"Rocky, bare, a challenge to life. Have you given any thought to how much different your castle here on Purbeck is to your glorious Holdenby or your vast London house?"

Elizabeth thought for a moment and then returned his brooding stare with a puzzled frown. "No, why should I?"

He shrugged. "No reason, really. Just a random thought that flicked across my mind."

"No, tell me! You've piqued my curiosity. Why do you speak and frown thus?"

"Because you would have me always."

"Aye."

"You would wife me and mother my brood."

"I would. And I tell you, you're the only man whose brats I would have."

He turned then, and took her almost roughly by the shoulders. "Would you do all that . . . here?"

"Here?" Suddenly she laughed. "Here, in this god-forsaken pile of stone? Do you not remember the manor house at Holdenby? Nay, even my quaint cottage—*our* cottage—where we spent so much time, and our love became love?"

"Aye, I remember."

"Then," she laughed, "how can you ask such a question?"

"Because, dear Elizabeth," Rory answered slowly, "your Purbeck is not unlike my Ireland."

CHAPTER THIRTY-FIVE

"I'LL TAKE THE MESSAGE," Blake said, holding out his hand to the young blond courier from Whitehall.

"But 'tis to be delivered to Sir William Russell only. I am to see it delivered. That is m'Lord Cecil's orders."

"And so you shall. Now here."

Reluctantly the youth handed over his charge. James Blake broke the seal and read. Then he looked up and nodded. "So be it. Come along, lad."

"Come along? Where?"

"Why, to Sir William's Wicklow encampment. Did you not say you would see the message delivered?"

"Aye, but I thought Sir William was here, in Dublin Castle."

"Nay, lad, he inspects the Queen's troops in Wicklow. Come along!"

They rode four abreast through Dublin's gates; the courier, James Blake, and two Queen's men who owed their souls to Blake.

Two hours found them deep in the Wicklow forests. Another hour brought near-darkness and found them descending into a shadowed glen.

It was here that James Blake took the gallowglass ax from the bag at his horse's side. Even in the fading light the blond head made a perfect target. Without a sound the boy fell from his horse like a stone.

"Bury him, and deeply," Blake said.

He then reined around and spurred his horse back toward Dublin Castle, knowing full well that if the boy's body was ever found, his murder would be blamed on the Irish.

There was no mistaking the blow made by a gallowglass ax.

SIR WILLIAM RUSSELL WAS SWEATING as he held the paper in his trembling hand. "Do we dare? I mean, Cecil's message is explicit. 'Deliver The O'Hara, Shane, posthaste to London.' I mean, with his present power, Cecil literally speaks as the Queen."

"We must dare," James Blake replied evenly, exchanging quick looks with a leering Thomas Lee. "There is nothing for it. The machine is in motion. Captain Lee has been freed with a fine of five hundred pounds. 'Tis his testimony of O'Hara's atrocities we've used to condemn the man. We know O'Donnell is in England. Damme, man, Bagenal is ready to march. Would you turn squeamish now and lose all?"

Sir William tried to pour a glass of brandy with his trembling hand. He couldn't. At last he gave up and brought the mouth of the bottle to his lips.

"Enough," Blake hissed, wresting it from him.

"Here, here, sir!" Sir William cried.

Blake struck him soundly across the face. It was a stunning blow, one that sent Sir William reeling backward against the wall.

"Blake—" Lee said, grabbing the man by the arm.

"Be off!" Blake shouted, shaking himself free. There was a hissing sound as his rapier left its scabbard and its point found Sir William's throat.

"Hold, James!" Sir William cried, half in fear, half in anger. "How dare you...?"

"I dare anything, you groveling bag of pus. For months we've done the dirty work in the glens, Lee and I, while you've sat on your blubbered arse in Dublin Castle. For months we've dodged swords and balls from heathen rebels while you've tried to be a man with Dublin whores! And we'll have no more of it."

"Please, Blake...please."

"Please be damned, I'll skewer you like the pig you are unless you sign that warrant!"

"But Cecil—"

"Damn Cecil and damn the Queen!"

"Blake!" Lee gasped.

"Shut up, you fool. Don't you see we must bring this war to a head? If we don't we're all lost. Even now might be too late, with O'Donnell prattling to Cecil. Well?"

"Sign...yes, I'll sign. My God, I'll sign."

Blake removed the blade from his throat, and Sir William staggered to the desk. Gasping, he took pen in hand and scrawled his name on the paper.

"But the burden of guilt will lay upon me," Russell

whimpered, dropping the pen and melting into his chair.

"Nay," Blake replied, folding the paper and placing it inside his doublet. "For I'll see to it that it is McTeague, The O'Byrne himself, who will open the trapdoor on the gallows that O'Hara will fall to hell through."

"God help us," Russell choked.

"God be damned as well," Blake growled. "For it's only myself that can help us now."

THE CROWD WAS LARGE. But unlike the raucous cheering throngs that had jammed the hill of Tyburn Tree in London, the crowd at Dublin Castle's gallows green was sullen.

They were for the most part Irish at heart even though they lived in the English Pale, and today an Irishman, a chieftain, a lion of the hill, was to die.

"Hail Mary, full of grace...."

The prayers echoed around Deirdre as she moved with the rest of the hooded women through the stone archways of Dublin Castle.

Between the tall decaying Bermingham Tower and the squat round Black Tower the gallows stood on a grassy incline. It was toward this spot that the crowd moved.

English soldiers held the bulk of the crowd back with their raised pikes, but the hooded, keening women were allowed closer to the scaffold.

Deirdre maneuvered herself nearer the steps and, like the rest of the women, dropped to her knees. Her eyes darted from beneath the dark cowl, and she shuddered as they fell on the four snorting horses standing nearby.

The sight of the horses strengthened her resolve. For The O'Hara to die in battle was a possibility she had lived with for a long time. She had come to accept it. She could even accept her gallant husband's death at the end of a noose.

But the degradation beyond the hanging—the knife, and the quartering by horses—she could not accept.

That was no way for a chieftain to die.

There was a roar and a surge from the crowd behind her and then she saw him. His face was battered, his eyes held a haunted look and he walked with a slight limp; all no doubt due to torture.

But he walked upright, with the point of his dark beard thrust forward.

As the procession passed her, Deirdre pulled the cowl closer around her face. Among those already assembled on the platform she saw the traitor, McTeague.

"And you call *us* heathens and savages!" came a voice from the crowd.

"All Ireland will avenge you, O'Hara!" came another.

Through Deirdre's mind went Annie's words: "My Ned was still alive when they manacled his wrists and ankles to the horses. . . ."

O'Hara mounted the platform without a stumble, and shook off the hands that tried to guide him. By himself he stepped under the noose. As he passed McTeague O'Byrne he spat in the man's face.

"That's the only vengeance you'll get today, you sod!" O'Byrne cursed.

An English Protestant rector began mumbling prayers, and O'Hara stopped him. "Nay, whether it's heaven or hell I'm bound for this day, I'll not be sent off with your hypocrisy. Now let's be on with it."

A steward began reading the list of charges, but eventually gave up as the crowd drowned out his voice.

Deirdre murmured a prayer and eased to her feet. All

eyes were on O'Hara as the noose was being fitted around his neck. No one even noticed Deirdre until she had gained the top step of the scaffold.

"Here, girl, stay back," a soldier said, reaching for her arm.

She brushed his hand away and moved to the center of the platform, directly in front of O'Hara.

"Stand aside!" she cried, throwing the cowl back with a flick of her hand.

Surprised, the two men stepped away from O'Hara and turned to scowl at her.

She raised the pistol in her right hand and aimed. "For love, Shane," she whispered.

The bullet hit him squarely in the left side of his chest. But just before it hit, O'Hara saw, and realized. Even the stopping of his heart didn't erase the smile from his face.

Deirdre dropped the pistol and whirled, pulling the second one from a pocket beneath her cloak. The range to McTeague was even shorter. She couldn't miss.

"For Ireland, McTeague!" she cried, and fired again.

Through the smoke she saw the traitor's face freeze in disbelief, and then he was sprawled at her feet.

A musket cracked behind her, and she staggered from the impact of the ball. The stunned crowd roared and surged forward to the very points of the soldiers' pikes.

Deirdre held the pistol aloft and coughed out the cry, "A Dhia save Erin, my people! God save Ireland!"

Another roar answered her words, and another surge.

But then a horrified hush fell over the people as she turned and staggered toward the fallen O'Hara. The cloak had slipped from her body, and the back of her dress was stained bright crimson with blood.

Almost as one the now silent crowd moved to make the sign of the cross.

Deirdre dropped to her knees. Her lips moved, but only the last few words could be understood before she tumbled forward over her husband's body.

"So dig the grave both deep and wide...."

CHAPTER THIRTY-SIX

RORY O'DONNELL FELT ILL. His stomach churned and his mind whirled with a dizziness that made him place a hand against the stone wall for support.

"'Tis amazing what you Irishmen do to our English-women," Robert Cecil said from nearby. "I knew the Lady Deirdre only slightly, but I would never have suspected such a depth."

"She would have O'Hara die quickly, like a man," Rory replied, gazing with misted eyes toward the sea.

"I have recalled Russell, of course, and to show good faith the Queen has pardoned Lord Haskins. He will retain only a portion of his lands, but at least he has his life."

"The fools," Rory said.

"Aye, it was stupid what they did, but not entirely their fault. My courier never arrived. More than likely he was ambushed by your people. Ironic, that it caused O'Hara's death."

Rory groaned. "There can be no truce now. All Ireland will be in flames."

Cecil moved to the teeth of the parapet and sighed as he looked out at the churning waters. "The Queen wants most of all in these, her declining years, to make peace with Spain and to settle the problems in Ireland."

"Then, damme, why does she not let us rule ourselves?"

"It has gone too far for that now, O'Donnell, and you know it. For Her Majesty to bend at all on the Irish question would be a sign of weakness to Spain and to the other rulers of Europe. No, I fear that all means of conciliation are gone."

He turned, and Rory met his stare.

"You're sending an army?"

"Nay," Cecil replied, "not yet, but soon, I fear. Bagenal marches on Armagh and Tyrone."

"But he can't win. . . . O'Neill will annihilate him."

"I fear so," Cecil nodded.

"My God, you want it to happen!"

"No, not really. But our Queen vacillates greatly these days. Calais was lost because of it. I find it more and more difficult now to move the ship of state without her resolve on questions that must be answered."

Rory's voice sounded eerie even to himself when he spoke. "A drastic English defeat will move her to send whole armies into Ireland."

"Aye, methinks it will." Again Cecil sighed. He crossed over and laid his hand on Rory's shoulder. "We have done, you and I, whatever we could to stop the bloodletting these past years. But 'tis now foregone, I think. You do what you feel you must do for your Ireland, and I will do for Queen and country what I must do."

Rory looked down at the smaller man and saw genuine sadness in his eyes. "At least, Sir Robert, the two of us have been friends as well as foes. I believe you when you plead ignorance of O'Hara."

"And I thank you for it." Cecil dropped his hand, and the two of them walked to the parapet together. "You know, of course, that I should lodge you in the Tower until all this is over."

"Aye, I would expect it."

"But I shan't. I think it would serve no purpose but only make you bitter. You see, O'Donnell, I do admire you as a warrior, even as I admire O'Neill as a clever leader. For that reason I would have you die in the field instead of rot in prison."

"I think, Sir Robert, that I shall fool you and live."

Cecil forced a smile. "For that reason I must ask one thing of you."

"This in exchange for my freedom?"

"Aye, it must be."

Cecil turned and surveyed the stone battlements of Corfe Castle where they towered against the sky behind them. "I would have your word, Rory O'Donnell, never to see Elizabeth again."

Rory whirled around. "It is a great deal you ask, Sir Robert."

"I know. I've seen the look in her eyes when she thinks of you, or when you're near. And I sense your love for her. Believe it or not, O'Donnell, there is a side of me that feels for both you and Elizabeth. But like two moths you hover too near the flame, and it will do nothing but destroy you both."

There was an interminable silence before Rory's strong shoulders heaved in a shuddering sigh.

"'Tis a sad choice you force upon me, but one you know my answer to," he replied in a low voice. At the same time he felt such an emptiness overcome him that he had a mind to throw himself from the parapet into the sea.

RORY STOOD WITH HIS BACK against the stone of the keep's walls. A few paces away the sea air blew Elizabeth's unfettered hair around her head like a golden halo tinged with blue by the moon.

It was a stalemate, their last night together. Both had

wanted it to be a night of love, but it had quickly degenerated into a tumultuous travesty filled with bickering and revelation.

Now, more from desperation than from any hope of succeeding, Elizabeth begged him to give up his useless rebellion and make peace with the Queen. Couldn't he then openly live in England? And wouldn't that eventually allow them to be together?

Rory had sworn to Cecil that he wouldn't reveal their agreement, and no matter how much pain it caused both himself and Elizabeth, he knew he had to adhere to his promise.

But it was difficult, for he wanted to end their arguing and take her in his arms.

"My darling, you ask the impossible," he said quietly. "Could you give up everything and come rule my Ireland with me?"

"Would you have me do such a thing? Would you have me step down from wheat bread at my table to rye or barley? Would you have my nostrils assaulted by tallow candles instead of scented wax? In short, would you have me a savage in your Ireland?"

Rory ran a finger along the path of a tear on her cheek. "Nay, I would not. Elizabeth, you speak often of our nights at Holdenby, those wonderful nights of loving and touching in the safety of our cottage."

"Aye, they are burned into my soul and body."

"Then remember, too, those long conversations. You knew what I was from the beginning. Do you realize how often I've thought about leaving everything to be with you? How tempted I am even now? So much so it terrifies me. That's what you've done, my darling, my love. That's how you've shaken and changed me."

"Then stay! Stay and live!"

She was weeping openly, her hands like talons entwined in his cloak.

Slowly his head moved from side to side. "Nay, that too would be a kind of death—a living death. For an English country gentleman I could never be while Ireland is at war."

"But Ireland won't be at war! You yourself have said there is no winning for the Irish. Rory, oh, God...."

His hands went to her shoulders, and he shook her gently. "Elizabeth, you must understand...'tis not to win or lose. That makes no difference. I see now that Ireland will always be at war with England. 'Tis beyond us, my love...far beyond us."

With a gasping cry she buried her head against his chest. "Fools! All men are vainglorious fools!"

"Aye, perhaps. But what think you of a woman who would kill, and die herself, for love?"

His reference to Deirdre's act on the gallows green in Dublin made Elizabeth's body go taut. She had been shocked and aghast when he had first told her. And then, after a great deal of thought, she had come to the conclusion that the act had been useless and barbaric. But she hadn't told Rory so.

Now she wanted to.

"You are like all your countrymen, after all!" she cried instead.

"How so, dear Elizabeth?"

"I think the method of death not so important as the result. For once dead, the corpse knows little and cares less."

"You are true to yourself," he said, able to summon a slight smile. "And for that I am thankful."

Something in his tone made her pull back and look up into his face. His smiling lips added to the rising wave of anger and frustration she had started to feel since his mention of O'Hara and Deirdre.

"Do you doubt my love, Rory O'Donnell?"

"Nay, not a whit, and I hope you do not doubt mine. But beyond our love there is, I fear, very little understanding."

She started to speak, to object, but he placed a finger on her lips. "You comprehend little of what drives me, Elizabeth, nor at times do you care. And I am guilty as well. For to me your ambitions of having wealth and vast estates are petty compared to mine. I would have a whole land."

"Then beyond my bed you think of me as a spoiled child?" Her eyes were flashing now, and the curls of her auburn hair danced as much from the quivering in her body as from the chill wind that blew around them.

"Perhaps we've both been spoiled by so much love."

A gust of cold sea air enveloped them. Rory looked deeply into the eyes of the woman he loved as if to blaze her face forever into his memory. Then with an aching heart he moved down the keep's outside stair to the bailey and his waiting horse. Elizabeth followed, her face ravaged with anguish and passion.

Without another word, Rory vaulted into the saddle and turned to face her. "But for all that, know, Elizabeth, that I will remember you as a woman."

"Aye, I am that, Rory O'Donnell, and methinks I've just discovered it. More a woman than any man can match! Now, go!"

He wheeled and spurred his mount into a canter. At the gatehouse he looked back once. It was then, with the moonlight dancing on the darkness of his raven mane and his body so tall and straight in the saddle, that the full brunt of this parting struck Elizabeth like an arrow to the chest.

With a gasp she stretched her arms toward him. She wanted to take back her words and cry out, "No! Come back!"

But he was gone, only a dim shadow on a far hill.

It was then that she folded her arms over the budding life growing in her belly and wept again. There was no doubt of it this time.

Would it have done any good to tell him?

She thought not.

Part IV
Fall 1598

"THEY APPROACH, M'LORD, six regiments; two in the vanguard, led by Bagenal himself, two in the main body, and two in the rear."

"How spaced?"

The rider smiled, his eyes flicking to Rory O'Donnell and back to his chief. "Just as you said, m'lord, the whole column is stretched out for miles, and the gap between regiments is more than ample enough to cut them off from one another."

Now it was O'Neill's turn to smile. He had seen to every detail himself, and had based his preparations on Sir Henry Bagenal's rashness. Henry of the Battle-axes, as his troops called him, was a fearless fighter and a commander of supreme confidence. He was not, however, attentive to drill or formation, and O'Neill was intending to use this carelessness to his own advantage.

He waved the rider on and turned to Rory. "We stand on the brink of history, lad. What will happen here today has never happened before in Ireland."

Rory knew what he meant. They had spent long hours with Red Hugh and Maguire planning this battle, preguessing what Bagenal would do. And now the fool was doing it, marching to his death and unknowingly setting off the spark that would ignite all Ireland.

"And what comes after?" Rory asked.

"Only God and the Queen can decide that," O'Neill replied. "We have done all we can."

And he had. Days before, O'Neill, Earl of Tyrone, had proclaimed Ireland an independent Catholic state. Such a declaration would give the Queen but two choices: bow to it, or commit all her armies to stop it.

He had provided for a united national rising by sending couriers all over Ireland in the name of the Church. Religion was the one factor that would unite the clans, and O'Neill had used it.

In the far distance they could see dust rising from the approaching column. O'Neill put a glass to his eye. "I'd say some four thousand foot and nearly three hundred horse."

Rory's eye swept the horizon. It was an awesome sight indeed. Six regiments moved like a human wave along the road from Armagh to the Blackwater Fort, their numbers extending for what seemed five or six miles in the distance. The terrain was firm and flat, giving room on either side of the road for deployment of regiments of pikemen, artillery and cavalry. The terrain was precisely suited to the English style of fighting; particularly since the Irish were known to avoid open-field warfare, preferring instead to ambush from the cover of hills and woods.

But this day the English were in for a surprise. What Sir Henry Bagenal and his English forces were not prepared for was the revolution in Irish arms and the tactics O'Neill had devised.

Rory O'Donnell's gaze moved to where the Irish force waited.

On the plain a quarter of a mile before them flowed the Callan River. The banks at its narrowest point gleamed with yellow clay. It was here the English would ford the river.

Beyond the river to the right of the road grew long lines of hedgerows. In front of these deep trenches had been dug, and behind them Red Hugh O'Donnell's pikemen and musketeers lay in wait. On the left, concealed by the hedgerows, lay a bog, hiding Maguire's troops of foot and horse.

Huge potholes had been dug in the road itself, to overturn wagons and cannon as well as disrupt the marching men.

Behind Rory and O'Neill fifteen hundred pikemen stood at the ready. When Bagenal marched his army into the jaws of death spewed by the musketeers on his flanks, these pikemen would surge forward in squares into the splintered regiments, decimating them.

SIR HENRY BAGENAL RODE tall and proud at the head of his soldiers and directly behind his lumbering cannon. Ten miles beyond the Yellow Ford crossing of the Callan River he expected to engage and annihilate The O'Neill and his rebel hoard.

Two hundred yards beyond the river he got the first indication that he was fighting a new kind of Irish enemy, one who was trained as the English were.

Cannon veered in every direction when their wheels hit the gouged-out sections of the road. Then came the popping sound of muskets, and men began to fall around him.

"Close up! Close up the columns!" he cried.

But they couldn't. Horses and oxen were falling in their tracks. Wagons careened into confused companies of pikemen, and frightened drovers fled their charges for any cover they could find.

Behind him Sir Henry could see the gap between his vanguard and the main force already filling with Irishmen, cutting off all retreat.

Bagenal realized that the bulk of the musket fire was coming from beyond the hedgerows. It took several minutes, but he managed to muster enough of a force to charge.

Most of the English were cut down just as they left the road. The rest became musket fodder as they fell into the disguised trenches.

Sir Henry himself took a musket ball in the forehead from a member of his own Irish company, a mercenary who had decided to join the O'Neill forces.

COURIERS BEAT A CONSTANT PATH back and forth between O'Neill and the main arena of battle.

"Our musketeers fire at will into their powder kegs, m'lord!"

"Their cannoneers fall before they can load and fire!"

"The Irish companies under Bagenal desert to a man, m'lord! They turn on the English all along the line!"

O'Neill gave the order for Rory to move his cavalry and pikemen down the road. They would cut like a scythe through the center of what was left of the vanguard, and then engage the main body.

For the next hour Rory fought his way down the Armagh road like a madman. He cared not how close pike, lance or sword came to his body, even after his fur-lined mantle hung in shreds.

It was as if Death had extended his black hand through the burned powder that lay like a fog over the land, and Rory O'Donnell hurried forward to grasp it. His mind and heart soared, nearly bursting with pride and courage, knowing that he and his Ireland were rushing headlong into destiny.

At last he broke through the English ranks, joining his forces with those of his brother, Red Hugh. Combined with Maguire they decimated the main body and put the fourth and fifth regiments to flight toward the village of Armagh.

"M'lord, what English are left barricade themselves at Armagh, in the Cathedral of Saint Patrick."

"I would see for myself!"

O'Neill rode at the head of his underchiefs down the Armagh road. All along the way lay the English dead and wounded. On the hillocks beside the road Irishmen cheered, some of them waving captured banners of the English regiments. Others were confiscating the muskets of the fallen enemy, and Irishmen from Bagenal's company were joining their compatriots and swelling O'Neill's ranks.

At the foot of the hill leading up to the cathedral O'Neill halted. The O'Donnells and Maguire stopped behind him.

"'Tis the burial place of Brian Boru," Red Hugh croaked.

"Aye," O'Neill nodded. The English knew they were in safe harbor, at least for the time being. No Irishman would risk any harm coming to the crypt of Ireland's most legendary king. "'Tis no matter. Their lives will bring a good ransom from Dublin."

"Bagenal was a fool," Rory muttered, casting his glazed eyes down the carnage on the Armagh road. "Those who come after will not make the same mistakes."

WHITEHALL WAS IN CHAOS, and at the eye of the storm was Sir Robert Cecil. As if the English defeat at Blackwater weren't enough, his aging and infirm father, William Cecil, Lord Burghley, had finally gasped his last.

The Queen, who had fed her aging counselor gruel with her own hand as he lay dying, was beside herself with grief one moment and thundering her anger at the Irish the next.

Five hundred nobles accompanied the old gentleman's hearse through the streets of London to Westminster Abbey.

The shock of his father's passing affected Sir Robert far less than it did the Queen, for he had known the extent of the old man's infirmities for some time. Nevertheless, it was difficult for him to leave immediately after the funeral and return to the gloom of Whitehall.

The full report of the Blackwater debacle had reached the Queen's council and needed immediate attention.

It was worse than expected.

Twenty-five hundred soldiers had met death in battle. Another thousand or more had deserted, fleeing to Flanders or to France, and the remainder had been sent packing with nothing but their doublets and hose.

All artillery, small arms, and other equipment and victuals had fallen into O'Neill's hands.

It was estimated that O'Neill's army had swollen to thirty thousand, while the English forces had been decimated. Munster and Leinster in the south had taken their cue from Ulster, and were now in full revolt.

Red Hugh and Rory O'Donnell were marching through Sligo, and unless they were stopped it was expected that Connaught would fall in the winter campaigns. And it was rumored that O'Neill himself marched south toward Munster at the head of three thousand men.

The seriousness of the situation was not lost on the council members as they rose one at a time to address the Queen's first secretary, Robert Cecil.

"Two years of coin spent in the plantationing of Munster, and all is lost in a fortnight!"

"Methinks, Sir Robert, that this rebellion was too well planned. The tyrant O'Neill has made a mockery out of crown and country, and must be brought to heel!"

"Aye! Next they'll be to Dublin and we'll have no seat of government in Ireland at all!"

"M'lords, all of Ireland is open to O'Neill now. He is King of Ireland in all but name. Because of this disaster, rumors run rampant in the streets of London—rumors that Spain will invade England, that plotters conspire to assassinate Her Majesty, that Europe celebrates O'Neill's genius." Sir Robert spoke slowly and quietly, the picture of calm as he continued.

"M'lords, it is said that the Pope has commissioned a gold crown to commemorate O'Neill's coronation as King of Ireland, and that Philip of Spain, hailing O'Neill as ruler of Erin, readies troops even now for Ireland's shores."

This last was met by a gasp, and several members bolted to their feet, only to be seated again when Sir Robert held up his hands. "M'lords...we have just been struck with the greatest disaster of our gracious Queen's reign...."

Table thumping and loud angry agreement.

"'Tis a crisis, I fear, even worse than the Armada...."

More loud agreement.

"M'lords, methinks we are not on the verge of losing Ireland. Methinks we have already lost it."

This was met with stunned silence.

"And, m'lords, it will require England's most gallant warrior, at the head of the largest army ever to leave her shores, to get Ireland back."

Sir Robert Cecil sat down as voices rose all around the table. Already one man's name was on everyone's lips.

So, m'Lord Essex, Sir Robert thought, *now you have your war.*

CAPTAIN JAMES BLAKE had been clever enough to remove himself from Bagenal's command before the march to Armagh. He hadn't been clever enough to foresee that all of Ireland would erupt in rebellion and that Whitehall would be so slow to retaliate.

Not even those close to him, and they were few, knew that it was not the war or his current lack of position in it that made Captain Blake move like a dead man through the halls and rooms of Dublin Castle.

Indeed, only Blake himself knew the reasons for what others had begun to call his "madness." For mad he had come to appear, sleeping only during the day and moving about at night, his one eye flashing venom at all he met. He was heard to mumble constantly to himself in a form of gibberish none but he could understand.

James Blake had achieved one-half of his dream. He had gained great wealth, and had invested it in Munster land. He was certain that this wealth would overcome all else in Elizabeth Hatton's eyes. She was as ambitious as he; Blake could sense it.

And the marriage agreement he would offer her would be more than adequate compensation for the title she would bring him.

That was the other half of his dream; through the Lady Hatton's good influences at court he would gain a title.

And the whole dream had been washed away in a fortnight. For now James Blake was a pauper. His lands were scorched and worthless. He and Thomas Lee were still under suspicion by Cecil, and every letter Blake sent to the first secretary remained unanswered.

One sure way to get ahead at the royal court was through marriage. But now Blake had nothing left to barter for any widow's hand, much less a widow as highly placed as Lady Elizabeth Hatton.

How ironic it was. The lady would never know that he had even had designs upon her.

Well, no matter. He had greater things on his mind now than wealth or widows.

For now James Blake's all-consuming passion was revenge. He blamed much of his current status on Rory O'Donnell in particular, and the Irish aristocracy in general.

Cecil had not given Blake the writ he wanted to carry out his plans, but in the man's current state of mind he needed none.

One by one James Blake planned to assassinate the Irish chieftains, no matter the time or the cost.

"YOU'VE CHANGED, RORY O'DONNELL," Annie said. "And it makes me sad."

"Changed? How so?"

"You thirst, nay, lust, for battle. Your brother has even said that you fight as though you have a will to die."

Rory upended the tankard he held and drained it. Outside the wind blew against the walls of Donegal Castle. Now and then a stiff gust would rattle the shutters and force its way into the room, momentarily causing the peat in the hearth to glow brighter.

"I have no will, Annie," he whispered. "I have no will to live or die. I am but a soldier now, with tired eyes, seeing only the next battle when it begins."

"Mayhap...." She paused, biting her lip and moving closer to the fire.

"Speak, lass." He refilled the wooden tankard with *uisce beathadh* and drank noisily. "God, you start and stop your speech and do your beads until I would swear my Lady Deirdre didn't die but lives in you."

Annie's body became erect. She started to whirl on him and then thought better of it. "I only thought that...that perhaps a woman would do you good."

"Aye," Rory said, roaring with laughter. "A woman probably would do me good! But, damme, lass, I'm afeared I'm no longer a lusty Irish lad."

Annie went on as if she hadn't heard him. "I learned a great deal from the Lady Deirdre. She truly believed in happiness. And then, when she...when she did that, I realized how very deeply she loved."

"Aye," Rory nodded, his voice low and hoarse, "no woman has ever loved more."

"But had Shane O'Hara died in battle she would have gone on. She told me so. She would have loved another."

"And she was right, lass." She hadn't heard him rise and cross the room. Now his voice close to her ear, and his hands on her shoulders made her tense in surprise. "That is why you should be below in the great hall right now. There are a dozen hungry lads down there, each of them eager for your bed."

"And you, O'Donnell?"

"Me?"

"Are you off to find a wench?"

She turned suddenly and Rory found her in his arms, her huge almond eyes staring at him from her small face. He blinked, then shook his head in disbelief.

Gone now forever was the little Annie of old. There had always been maturity in those eyes, even when there was none in her body. But now the body, too, had blossomed. Her hips were womanly, and her breasts jutted from her bodice with an impudence he had never noticed before.

And her eyes. . . . Her eyes were filled with a look he knew only too well.

"No, lass. . . it could never be. You've had too much misery in your life to be heaped with more."

His boots scraped loudly as he turned and nearly bolted from the room.

Annie swayed slightly and grasped for the mantelpiece. At that moment Deirdre's words to her came back to echo in her mind: "There's no accounting for love, Annie. It can strike like lightning, and sometimes be as painful. I've wondered, as I wonder now, if a nunnery wouldn't have been a better choice. . . ."

CHAPTER THIRTY-EIGHT

ELIZABETH CLOSED HER EARS to all news from across the bitter Irish Sea. Only when alone in her chambers would she allow her mind to relax. Now and then during these times Rory's face would come back to haunt her, and she would feel the need to throw herself on the huge canopied bed and weep. During those nightmarish moments she felt that the very walls were closing in on her.

But the steel in her spine would not let her weep with self-pity. Instead she knew she must rise to the occasion and draft a plan for her future life.

She had taken to dismissing her maids and undressing herself in the evenings, for the telltale rise in her belly had begun. She had only a few weeks left before her position would become untenable. As much as the fact dismayed her, the choosing of a husband was now an absolute necessity.

But who should it be? The fluttery Bacon? The shy and wary Pembroke? The pompous Greville? Or the uncouth and domineering Coke?

None of them intrigued her after the passion and tempestuousness of a man like Rory O'Donnell.

But choose she must. So she willed her mind to return to the Elizabeth of old, the Elizabeth of years before who, as a young girl, had sat with her uncle in Wimbledon gardens and coldly calculated her future as the wife of Sir William Hatton.

"Love I have had. Now what *position* can a man bring me?"

Which of the four could she control, so that there would be little interruption of her own life-style? And how much would she have to barter away for that life-style?

Elizabeth knew her worth. Marrying widows was a profitable business in London, indeed, in all of England. She furrowed her brow and started pondering her situation.

Because women had no representation in Parliament, she reasoned, they neither made laws, consented to them, nor abrogated them. Since all women, unless they be born queens, were either married or about to be married, they had little influence over the lawmakers, their husbands or husbands-about-to-be.

"Hmm, 'tis odd," she said aloud, "that a man should have complete control over his wife but none over his mistress." She patted her belly. "But 'tis a mistress I've been and a wife I must be."

She took a pen in hand and wrote, "Sir Edward Coke."

"A good and wise choice," she mused aloud to herself, "for I think of him as rude, abrupt, and the epitome of arrogance—all good reasons to deny him my bed. And besides, I'm sure that no matter who he wives he will still be married to the law."

Elizabeth pushed aside the piece of paper bearing Coke's name and replaced it with a fresh sheet from her desk drawer.

My dearest uncle,

Before you frown, nay, even chide me for what you are about to read, let me say that I do sincerely believe that wedlock is a high and blessed order, ordained by God in paradise. It is a relationship wherein a man and a woman are coupled together in one flesh in the fear and love of God.

Marriages must be of minds rather than of bodies, since that is the way to increase unto Christ. And that, dear uncle, is what I would have, a marriage of minds. Knowing you will act completely on my behalf, dear uncle, I hereby do commission you to bring about a contract of marriage between myself and Sir Edward Coke.

I know, dear uncle, that this will please you greatly.

Now, whereof I spoke. I would have the grounds of this contract conveyed to the said gentleman thusly....

And as Elizabeth worried paper with pen, she couldn't, no matter how much she tried, hold back her tears. Nor could she erase the thought from the back of her mind that one day there would come a message, and she would fly to her hideaway cottage at Holdenby and the arms of Rory O'Donnell.

SIR ROBERT MADE A STEEPLE of his fingers and over them watched Sir Edward Coke as he read.

Elizabeth's choice had been excellent; Sir Robert would like the match to happen. He himself didn't care for Sir Edward personally. He found the man totally without guile or humor, and he could at times be almost boorish. But he was a ready and powerful ally, one that Sir Robert had used in the past and could use even more in the future.

At last Sir Edward looked up, his eyes saucerlike beneath the heavy brows that progressed in an unbroken line across his forehead.

"Sir Edward...."

"Sir Robert...." Then came the explosion. "Damme, man, what is the woman thinking of?"

"I daresay, Sir Edward, I have long ago given up trying to fathom the workings of my niece's mind."

"But, good God, man, how can she even ask, nay, *think*, such things?"

Cecil shrugged and barely suppressed a smile as he watched the flush creep up from the man's ruff to redden his face. He wondered if Elizabeth sitting directly above them could hear Coke's squeals. "I assure you, 'tis the very letter I received from the lady, and 'tis in her hand, for I know it."

"I don't doubt that," Coke practically roared, "for I've heard the woman is independent and obstinate! But this...*this*...."

He sputtered, unable to find words as a hooked finger jabbed at the paper in his hand. Cecil leaned forward and grasped a decanter on the table between them.

"Some wine, Sir Edward?"

"Nay, brandy. A glass!" Coke thundered, leaping from his chair and waving the letter as he paced up and

down. "I am a master of the law. Damme, man, I'm
the attorney general of England!"

"I know that, Sir Edward. I myself had you appointed. Your brandy."

Coke took the proffered glass without breaking
stride. "Then, sir, how in God's name can you ask me
to break the law?"

"'Tis not me who asks, Sir Edward. 'Tis the Lady
Elizabeth."

"Look! Look you here!" Coke raged, thrusting the
paper forward and again jabbing it with a finger. "She
would have me flout ecclesiastical law. She would have
us married without the procurement of special license
and without the publishing of banns. She would have
the wedding take place in a private house, *her* house,
whereas the law states that all marriages must take
place in a public church. No marriages are to be secret
before the court. But she would have ours performed at
night, and with only two witnesses...witnesses of *her*
choosing!"

In his state of agitation, Sir Edward splashed some
brandy from the glass in his hand. Cecil grabbed his
arm to steady him. "I have read the letter, Sir Edward."

"Well then, damme, man, what would you have me
do?"

"I would," Sir Robert said, opening his arms wide,
"have you follow the dictates of your heart."

"My *heart*? My heart be damned! Affairs of the
heart are for schoolchildren and the idle rich!"

"And rich she is," Cecil muttered, too low for the
room's other occupant to hear. "But, I fear, far from
idle."

"Begging your pardon, Sir Robert, but this woman,
this niece of yours, this infamous widow, is the most

stubborn, the most obstinate, the most unorthodox female I have ever come in contact with!"

"I know," Sir Robert sighed.

"Next to sanctity and holiness, the infallible marks of a good woman are modesty, bashfulness, silence, abstinence and sobriety. Such virtues, I say, are fundamental, because the wife's duties are meant to begin at the lower tasks and progress to the higher!"

"All admirable traits attributable, I'm sure, to your recently departed Bridget."

"Aye, bless her sainted soul," Coke said, his voice lowering only slightly at the mention of his first wife. "A woman among women she was."

Cecil nodded, adding his own thoughts to Coke's words. *And one who gave you a child practically every year of your marriage. Ten children, all under fifteen, at the poor woman's death!*

"A blessed and ideal woman, I'm sure, Sir Edward."

"That she was. A woman who knew to give way in all things, to show the inferiority of the wife in regard to her husband!"

At this Sir Robert groaned aloud. "I fear, Sir Edward, that my niece will be inferior to no man, much less admit it or make a show of it."

"Ay, 'tis a pall and a great sadness that will bring our country to ruin, this freedom of women," Coke intoned, letting his voice fall into the resonant baritone of the accomplished barrister. "Only ruin can follow where a woman would affect mastership, where she would seek to rule and overrule her husband. Such forwardness is on the rise, and every woman must learn to know her place and her part!"

"I think," Cecil said, rising wearily and moving to a huge carved-oak desk, "that m'Lady Hatton knows only too well her place, and plays her part in it better than most.''

The sheaf of papers Cecil took from a drawer of the desk was so thick that it had to be carried with both hands as he returned and seated himself opposite Coke.

''As you know, my half brother Thomas—m'Lady Hatton's father—and myself have assumed many duties as well as vast properties since m'Lord Burghley's passing.''

''Aye, Burghley House in Northamptonshire, Theobalds in Herefordshire...and this.'' Coke waved his arm to indicate the room in which they sat; one of forty-two in the Exeter townhouse.

''To name a few,'' Cecil replied, laying paper after paper on the table between them for Coke's perusal. ''I think you also know that I have been aiding my niece with her business affairs. This file is hers.''

Sir Edward Coke's ambitious eyes all too quickly read the documents before him, and just as quickly assessed the lady's value.

Lady Hatton, with or without Cecil's help, had amassed a fortune. Through her loans and mortgages on properties, half the men in Parliament were in some way in her debt.

Coke's trained eye fell on a particular document. The lady held a high mortgage on Stoke Poges, a property owned by the Earl of Huntington. Coke had long coveted the estate. It was perfectly located, four miles north of Windsor and just twenty-two miles from London.

Perfect for a summer retreat.

Coke went through the entire file and then sat back with a sigh. He was about to say something when Sir Robert spoke first. ''The hour is late, Sir Edward. Let us both think on this and return to our conversation on the morrow.''

Coke would have preferred to continue their discussion immediately, but Cecil deftly fended him off and provided him with an escort back to his own house in Holborn.

Wearily, his mind aching with all the details it contained, Sir Robert climbed the wide stair to Exeter's vast second floor.

A lesser man, perhaps one without Cecil's diminutive, malformed body, wouldn't have had the stamina and drive to shoulder the problems of state as well as those of family that he faced daily.

His own dear wife had died in childbirth. Sir Robert had barely recovered from that shock when his father had succumbed. Though he loved his brother Thomas dearly, the man had no head for business, be it state or personal. This had forced Sir Robert to shoulder the family fortunes and oversee their administration.

He handled all this in conjunction with counseling a dying Queen, who valiantly refused to give up but who daily became more trying with her demands.

And the problems facing England appeared to be insoluble.

Philip had died in Spain, but his son, Philip III, appeared to be not a whit different from his father. Like his predecessor he envisioned a totally Catholic world, and he looked upon England as the one stumbling block in his way.

And the situation in Ireland grew worse by the hour. The Pale was in flames nearly to the walls of Dublin Town, and O'Neill grew stronger with each day that England waited.

Yet with all these cares, Sir Robert smiled wryly as he

approached the room in which Elizabeth awaited and from whence came the soothing sound of a virginal.

He smiled because he saw the humor in his latest difficulty. Getting his niece, the Lady Hatton, married was a problem that made all the others pale in comparison.

He paused just inside the door, watching Elizabeth's fingers glide over the virginal's keys. She played well, just as she did everything she attempted—with a preciseness and a flair.

He thought, at that moment, that he had never seen her more beautiful. The fine angles of her face were enhanced by the light from the candles atop the virginal. The soft blue taffeta of her overdress, heavily laced at throat and sleeve, was costly and of the latest style.

She had probably paid more for the one dress she now wore than Sir Robert's late wife had paid for half her wardrobe. But then that was Elizabeth, he thought, feeling more pride than he would ever admit to.

The music stopped. Elizabeth seemed to sense his presence and turned "Oh, uncle, I didn't hear you enter."

"I was enjoying the music," he said, stepping forward and closing the door behind him. "You haven't lost your gift."

She glanced at the virginal and shrugged. "'Tis but one of the boring pastimes a woman must learn in order to amuse herself. Come, let us sit by the fire."

She took his arm and guided him to a chair. When he was seated she slid to the floor herself, letting the dress flow like a billowing blue sea around her.

"Well, what says our attorney general?"

"'Tis hard to say," Cecil replied, studying this picture of beautiful innocence sitting at his feet.

"Oh?"

"Aye. 'Tis hard to find the words, since he roars, rants and raves like a wounded bull."

The long column of her slender throat gleamed in the firelight as she lifted her chin and laughed heartily. Then her eyes met his, dancing with merriment. She was playing the coquette, as she had so many times in the past, and it brought a bubbling laugh to Cecil's lips.

"I think, my sweet niece, that you saddle me with this duty as revenge."

"Why, uncle, we have settled our differences, have we not? And have I not made a good choice? One that will strengthen the Cecil family's position at court?"

Sir Robert didn't miss the cutting edge in her tone or in her words. It was there frequently now, in almost everything she said. In some ways it was sad that his beautiful niece had crawled into such a hard shell. But he knew that in the times to come she would survive better with it than without it.

"I think, Elizabeth, that you have become a vixen as much as a woman."

"Why, uncle, are not the two interchangeable? Now, let's to it. What says Sir Edward to my proposals, beyond his usual railing?"

Cecil began by reiterating, as best he could by memory, Coke's opinions on women. By the time he had finished Elizabeth was holding her sides, and the room rocked with her laughter.

"You realize, of course, that all of London society will be shocked and then amused by this marriage.

"I *too* am amused!" Elizabeth replied "But how shocked?"

"Well, let me put it this way. I think they will wonder why this exceptionally beautiful woman of high birth, remarkable wit, and great riches should choose such a man for her husband over so many suitors obviously more to her taste."

"My taste, uncle, remains my own business."

"Aye, as it always has been," he sighed. "But still they will wonder, because many think of Coke as dull, very narrow-minded, slightly unimaginative—"

"Which he is," Elizabeth interrupted, smiling slightly. "And he is selfish, arrogant, ignorant of everything other than the law, and a bore in company."

Sir Robert nodded in agreement, his brow furrowing between his eyes. "That is precisely why I wonder at all this."

Now the smile faded from Elizabeth's face, and her emerald eyes glinted like cold stone.

"I would wed Sir Edward for precisely what he is, uncle—a man uninterested in everything except his own personal ambitions and finances. In short, Sir Edward Coke is greedy. And because he is he will marry me on my terms. And by the by, uncle, I have more terms beyond those already mentioned in the letter."

"My God, woman, *more*? What do you expect?"

"Everything, and I will have it. I mean to make my independence known before the wedding. For instance, I will not stand beside him during the ceremony."

"Elizabeth—"

"And furthermore, I plan on retaining my name. I'll not be known as Lady Coke. I'll remain Lady Elizabeth Hatton."

"Od's blood, you flaunt every convention in England!"

"Yes, I do, don't I?"

Sir Robert lurched from his chair and shook his head as he moved to the window. "Impossible," he groaned.

"Think you so?" came Elizabeth's determined voice from behind him.

"Aye. For the greatest lawyer of his time, yea, the attorney general of England, to disobey one law might be forgivable. But a multitude? Never!"

"Then you may inform the greatest lawyer in England that he should go back to trying his cases, and that he should refrain from trying my patience any longer, for there will be no wedding. And, uncle...."

"Yes?"

"Pray you, do it with speed, for it is of the essence."

Deeper became the furrow between Sir Robert's eyebrows as he gazed across the Strand and beyond, to where the River Thames was lost in the swirling fog. Only one tiny light could be seen from Whitehall Palace to his right.

And as he stared longer and longer at that light, it seemed to grow and expand, until it exploded like a revelation in his brain. He whirled around.

"Elizabeth."

"Uncle."

"You are with child."

"Aye, I am," she replied calmly. "Quite."

CHAPTER THIRTY-NINE

TRUE TO ELIZABETH HATTON'S OWN PREDICTION, London society attributed the choice she had made in a new husband to her famous obstinacy and ambition. A few courtiers, those closest to her, even ventured to dissuade her from her decision. They were rebuffed by her equally famous violent temper.

No one other than Sir Robert Cecil attributed her choice to shrewdness. But then only Sir Robert and Elizabeth herself knew that she already had a belly full of child. And only Sir Robert knew that his niece had no intention of living with the attorney general after the wedding.

Her reason?

"Surely, uncle, you know that the man does not control the woman's goods unless that woman has followed her husband and lives with him."

Sir Robert digested these words and this new wrinkle in his niece's life plan with his usual stoic aplomb. But privately he felt a slight tinge of pity for Sir Edward. The man had no conception of how tumultuous his future would be as the husband of Lady Elizabeth Hatton.

The wedding time and place remained a secret, known only to those who were going to attend. Elizabeth wouldn't budge from her decision as to the location, the great hall of Hatton House, or the date, the evening of the eighth of November.

During the two weeks prior to the wedding she made careful and elaborate plans. She would retire to Holdenby for her lying-in, and Honor would serve as midwife. A certain sum of monies had already been distributed among the officials at the local rectory, where the birth would be recorded when the time came.

Elizabeth was not so naive as to think there wouldn't be finger-counting and wagging tongues, but by taking these precautions she would keep gossip to a minimum.

As the day of her wedding crept closer and closer, the memory of Rory O'Donnell became like a specter hovering over her shoulder. Once, while being fitted for the gown she would wear at the wedding, she felt his presence so strongly that she burst into tears and sent the dressmaker away.

At another fitting, when the dress was nearly completed, she saw his image beside her in the mirror; tall, bearded, his face brooding darkly, his eyes glowering at her accusingly.

Forgetting everything, she burst into tears and screamed at the mirror, "No, no! 'Twas all your fault! Did you not desert me? Did you not flee like a whipped dog with your tail bent timidly between your legs?"

Then the image began to laugh at her, until she screamed hysterically and fell into a swoon.

Honor, who had been summoned from Holdenby, hustled everyone out of the room and lifted Elizabeth in her strong arms. Carefully she put her mistress to bed and held her until she was calm again.

It was then that Elizabeth told her everything, pouring out her heart and her soul to the girl.

Honor understood and absorbed it all. Calmly and quietly she talked with her mistress until Elizabeth was once again herself.

That outburst and her subsequent confession proved to be the catharsis Elizabeth needed. Even though thoughts of O'Donnell still lingered in her mind, she no longer felt his presence at her side nor imagined his image in her mirror.

At last the dress was finished. It was a green to match her eyes, with emeralds of a deeper green adorning the bodice and gold lace in abundance at her waist to disguise her pregnancy.

"What do you think, Honor?"

"I think you show not a whit, m'lady," Honor giggled. "At three months, if you remember, I was like a cow. You are tiny."

Elizabeth smiled. "Let us hope I remain so for three more days!"

The day before the wedding saw a feverish burst of activity at Hatton House. Servants were set to cleaning every inch of the seventy-two feet long and forty feet wide great hall.

And a monumental undertaking it was. First the furniture was removed from the hall, and the servants scrubbed and waxed the parquet floor to a mirrorlike shine. Then protective linens were stretched across the floor so that workmen could erect scaffolds and clean the ceiling, which towered thirty feet above them. Next came the paneling, of new oak and with stiles and rails painted a rich red. The panels themselves were decorated with designs in deep green and burnt umber.

Tapestries fresh from the loom combined with the existing stained glass, needlework, and silk hangings to form a luxurious combination of decorative color.

Elizabeth had chosen the best furniture in Hatton House to be placed in the great hall. Along the elaborate wainscot were ranged cabinets of the finest English and foreign workmanship. Most were made of walnut, rosewood and ebony; some were mounted in silver.

Decorative buffets displayed her finest treasures; majolica, china, bronzes, and other exquisite rarities she had collected or been given during her marriage to Sir William. The buffets themselves were elaborately inlaid with checkerboard marquetry of light woods and ebony, representing the highest quality of English craftsmanship.

As a final touch, to serve as a focal point for the ceremony, she placed a magnificent table of carved oak at one end of the great hall. It was inlaid with ivory and silver, and had figures intricately formed from tortoiseshell and precious stones adorning the sides.

When the last candlestick had been set out Elizabeth stood at the entrance to the great hall and admired the total effect of opulence and grandeur. Well, she thought with grim satisfaction, no one could mistake her for a pauper.

Now she had one more task to perform. Suppressing her distaste as she thought about the wedding night, Elizabeth had the servants prepare her bedchamber.

The giant carved-oak four-poster was stripped, and the bedclothes taken outside for airing, while the two casement windows with their diamond leaded panes were polished and the window seat cushions were washed.

Then the oak-paneled wall needed to be waxed, and its tapestry whisked clean of every trace of dust. Elizabeth allowed herself a slight chuckle as she looked at the legend depicted on the colorful tapestry. It was of Adonis, garbed in padded breeches and a jerkin, as he lay dying before Venus's temple. The goddess of beauty as well as three Graces—dressed in ruffs and farthingales—were weeping over him.

The carved oak table on which stood her mirror, cosmetics and candlestick of silver was next put under the polishing cloth. Then, after a final sweep of the floor, the down comforters were brought back in from their airing and were spread luxuriously over fresh satin sheets, and all was in readiness.

Elizabeth sighed as she looked at the bed. No matter how many ecclesiastical laws she broke, there was one law she had no intention of breaking, for Coke must be given no reason for breaking his bond.

The marriage had to be consummated.

ON THE DAY OF THE WEDDING Sir Edward Coke remained at Westminster working. He was readying a case of treason against Edward Squire, one of the Queen's former stableboys who had confessed attempting to assassinate Her Majesty by rubbing poison on the pommel of her saddle.

Coke did find time in the late morning to send a sealed note to Lady Hatton:

My dearest intended bride,

Once again I would like to appeal to a common sense I am sure you have. This method of matrimony you insist upon could lead to the ruin of my career. And I am sure, dear lady, that you understand the illegality of what you propose. For this reason I urge, nay, implore you to call off this sham and let us publish legal banns to insure our wedded bliss.

Respectfully,
E. Coke

Elizabeth took pen in hand and replied:

My dearest intended husband,

You have my terms. You may take them or leave them.

Respectfully,
Lady E. Hatton

In the late afternoon, he tried again:

My dear woman,

Need I warn you how you threaten your own future on earth and in heaven with your obstinacy? Would you ruin your own good name, which I understand you plan on keeping, as well as mine with this foolishness?

E. Coke

Again she took pen in hand:

My good sir,
    I can, I would, I will!

                                    E. Hatton

Coke implored her father, the new Lord Burghley, to step into the fray. He did so immediately with a letter of his own:

My dearest daughter,
    Would you make us the shame of all London with your stubbornness? I command you forthwith to end this charade before you become the death of your loving parents.

Elizabeth had a ready reply:

Lord Burghley,
    Do I take your missive to mean you do not plan to attend? A pity, for I've had cook prepare your favorite dishes for the wedding supper.
                            Your loving daughter,
                                    Elizabeth

She received one note that afternoon from Sir Robert:

Elizabeth,
    Ah, dear niece, I must beg off from this, your happiest of days, for thankfully I must to Wales and aid in the preparation of Essex's armies for the coming war in Ireland. I daresay, though, that I shall return in time to follow the next chapter in your war against mankind.
                                Your loving uncle,
                                        R. Cecil

As DARKNESS FELL OVER HATTON HOUSE, Lady Elizabeth remained in her upper chambers. Outside there was a brisk November chill, and rain threatened.

Behind Hatton House, in the darkness above Holborn, the groom and the guests arrived, one at a time, at the garden gate. A somber Charles, Honor's husband, escorted them to the great hall.

At precisely eight of the clock, Elizabeth descended the wide staircase and floated into the great hall, looking radiant and almost virginal in her green gown.

Her father, Thomas, was there, his complexion almost matching the shade of his daughter's gown. Sir Edward Coke was stoic; his dress as usual was darkly impeccable. Henry Bathwell, rector of Okeover, was there to perform the ceremony, but the unfortunate man looked ashen and was quaking with fear at the deed he was about to do.

"Gentlemen," Elizabeth said, taking her place, "shall we begin?"

The marriage took place in hushed tones, their voices barely audible over the crackling sound of the huge logs in the fireplace. The sputtering flames made the shadows in the room dance as the couple repeated their vows.

Only once did Sir Edward let his eyes linger on the woman who was becoming his wife. And when he did he almost gasped. Even as stodgy and conservative as he was, Sir Edward Coke realized how breathtakingly beautiful this woman appeared.

The light from the fire joined that of the candles to dance over the fine features of her face and the full swells of her white breasts. He noticed that her hands, where they rested in long white gloves on the cinch of her waist, were steady. And then he looked up to the thin hard line of her compressed lips and to the icy coldness in her emerald eyes and he shuddered.

In less than twenty minutes it was over. The only servants present, Honor and Charles, rushed up to congratulate the bride and then served supper.

The Reverend Bathwell pleaded an upset stomach and quickly departed. Elizabeth's father choked down a few mouthfuls and pleaded fatigue.

When he was gone, Elizabeth turned to Sir Edward. "Well, sir, we are man and wife."

"It would seem so."

"How strange, this look in your eye, Sir Edward, on such a happy occasion as this."

"Happy, m'lady? You call this travesty of justice happy?"

Her bubbling laugh unnerved him. "My dear sir, I think, as you can plainly see from the last hour, that I call *all* justice in marriage a travesty. But, no matter; I'll retire now. When I am ready to bed, Charles will show you up."

Coke, normally a temperate man, filled a glass with brandy and watched her glide up the wide stairs.

My God, he thought, *what have I done?*

And then he raised his eyes to the ceiling and thought of Stoke Poges. He thought of the Lady Hatton's loans, and how they reached even into the Queen's council. And being a man, he thought, too, of the round firmness of her breasts, which expanded so deliciously with each breath she took.

"The lady awaits, sir."

"Aye, aye," Coke said and climbed the stairs.

She was in a thin chemise, standing at the foot of the bed, when he entered the chamber.

Her beauty again struck him, but he pushed his desire away, preferring to match his demeanor to hers.

"You would keep your name."

"Aye, I would."

"I will oversee your estates and titles."

"That's to be seen."

"I think, m'lady, that you are more wench than woman."

"If that be true, then let's be on with it and see how it is you've fathered such a brood."

Sir Edward's face flushed, and he forced his eyes away from the outline of her body, which through the thin gown gleamed in the candlelight.

He didn't move, and Elizabeth shut her eyes tightly as fortification against her thoughts.

But it did no good.

On the inner part of her eyelids she saw Rory O'Donnell's smiling face, his flashing dark eyes, his soft lips that could capture hers with the true essence of desire and love.

Your rogue of the night, m'lady, who from this night on does your bidding.

Biting her lip, Elizabeth fumbled at the chemise with quivering fingers. A slight shrug let the garment slip down her body to puddle at her feet.

She opened her eyes. Sir Edward was staring at her, both awe and chagrin written on his face. "'Tis wanton," he uttered.

"Nay, Sir Edward, 'tis wifely. Now to bed with you. Let us consummate this affair and be done with it!"

THE FOLLOWING MORNING Sir Edward left her bed satiated and happy, but not without plans of his own.

He was at his desk promptly at seven-thirty, but doing much more than planning his prosecution of the ex-stable boy.

By late afternoon the exultation Elizabeth felt at proving her power over the most powerful barrister in England began to turn sour.

Through intricate legal maneuvers Coke proceeded to take over her entire estate. Within hours he foreclosed on mortgages that Elizabeth had been holding for months. In Star Chamber and among Parliament members he exercised the new power her wealth gave him.

His maneuvering, as well as the underlying reasoning that went along with it, wasn't lost on Elizabeth. She quickly realized that, although she would be able to live in her own houses, soon those houses and their revenues would be controlled by Coke. Her monies she could spend, but only with Coke's approval.

If Elizabeth had underestimated the brilliance and cunning of Coke's mind, he had equally underestimated the magnitude of her wrath.

He discovered it late that evening when he returned to Hatton House, and found the door barred to him.

"Madam!" he bellowed from the garden courtyard. 'You will open this door at once!"

Elizabeth appeared at an open window and threw down the meager collection of belongings Coke had brought with him the previous evening.

"And why, sir, should I open *my* door?"

"Because, madam, I am your lawful husband!"

"Lawful, sir? How so, lawful? Can you show the license, or where the banns have been posted?"

"Elizabeth, would you have this, the first full day of our marriage, marred by your petty bickering?"

"Petty? *Petty?* There is nothing petty about how you've spent your day ravishing my accounts, maneuvering my estates and shifting my interests to become yours so that without your gifts I would be penniless!"

"Madam, I am a man...."

"You are a pompous arse!"

"You will allow me entrance to my own house."

"Sir, across Holborn is Castleyard, near Cursitor Street. On that site, I believe, is the home of Sir Edward Coke. These many years Sir Edward has resided in that house, and, by God, that is where he will continue to reside!"

With that she slammed the shutters, and Sir Edward, cowed but not defeated, blustered his way back to his own house.

The ensuing battle between the attorney general and his beautiful wife provided more gossip in the following week than London wags had enjoyed in a year. Almost hourly, news flew from salon to salon across London, relaying each new reprisal by the pair.

It was inevitable that word of the scandal should reach the Queen, and worse, the Archbishop of Canterbury. The archbishop had of late been nurturing his own private war, trying to stamp out secret marriages in order to insure that there would be no Catholic ceremonies performed in England.

When word reached him that two such highly placed personages in London society had been part of such an illegal act, all Lambeth Palace shook from his anger.

Being a plodder, Coke moved too slowly to head off the Church. Lady Hatton, on the other hand, was much quicker about it, and she laid the full blame for the wedding at Coke's doorstep.

When the couple was summoned before the archbishop at Lambeth, it was Coke who suffered the greater ire from the Church's head.

"Such willful disregard of life's sacred ceremonies cannot be condoned, sir!"

Coke could only nod humbly and appear to agree, but inside he was boiling. He pleaded overwork as his excuse, and the fact that he was ignorant of the law.

The archbishop was dumbfounded. The most knowledgeable barrister in England, ignorant of the law? The prelate threw up his hands in disgust.

But wisely he knew that a trial and its attendant scandal would only make matters worse He levied a fine and instructed them to be properly married forthwith.

In the carriage returning to Hatton House Elizabeth laid down her terms. For the time being, Coke had no choice but to accept them.

But in his mind he told himself that the battle had just begun.

"Madam, you will be the death of me."

"Nay, I think not, Sir Edward. But I plan on making sure that you will not be the death of me."

CHAPTER FORTY

SIR ROBERT HAD NEVER SEEN such tension between the Queen and her now-not-so-favorite courtier, the Earl of Essex.

For weeks Essex had badgered the council with his recommendations for the position of lord lieutenant of Ireland, the man who would bring Tyrone to his knees. All to no avail.

And now he had invaded the privy chamber to harangue the Queen. It was a foolish move on Essex's part, and it played directly into Cecil's hands.

At the moment Essex was extolling in much too loud a voice the many virtues of Sir George Carew for the post. Cecil sat silently on the Queen's right, studying the man, as he always did, as if it were the first time he had ever seen him. Cecil thought that his rival's appearance was much like that of a fine horse, for the earl was handsome indeed, with a magnificent physique. He was tall, as well, with a fine nose, full sensual lips, and eyes that seemed to hide nothing.

His bearing, even in the Queen's presence, was aristocratic. And perhaps that was what would cause his downfall. Robert Devereux was much more of a man than he was a diplomat, and even though he had become Cecil's avowed enemy, the first secretary often wished it weren't so. For many of the man's qualities—the ability to attract followers, his magnetic presence, his fearlessness in battle—would be worthwhile assets had they been accompanied by a degree of rational judgment.

But, alas, they were not. And it was for that reason Cecil had to be ever watchful of Essex's power, always cognizant of his sway over the Queen.

That power and sway had diminished of late, Sir Robert realized thankfully, and even now the fool was lessening it further by trying to use Carew as an Irish offering.

Now and again Cecil slid his eyes to the Queen's face. He was sure Her Majesty was not being deluded by Essex's rhetoric.

Carew was a close friend of Cecil's and an archenemy of Essex's. Who was better suited, then, as far as the earl was concerned, to go to Ireland and fight the Irish plague, the ague, the rains and a superior army?

It wasn't long before the Queen's expression told Cecil that she had seen the transparency of Essex's motives.

"Nay, m'lord, I think Carew unable to muster the men needed for such an enterprise," she said, waving her hand in dismissal.

But Essex, unable to accept her response, foolishly renewed the attack. "Methinks Your Majesty errs, forgive me," he said, "as any woman must err when confronted with decisions of war."

Cecil's head spun toward his Queen. Sure enough, wrath filled her face like a dark cloud covering the sun. He almost groaned aloud, for Essex, as usual, had committed one of the ultimate blunders. Any talk of her death or her successor needled Gloriana to the point of fury. Only one other topic could arouse her ire as much—the fact that she was a woman and had to depend on men to do her fighting.

"Think you, m'Lord Essex," Queen Elizabeth asked coldly, "that your genius in the field has reaped riches and lands upon this realm in the past?"

"Aye, I do."

'Then you delude yourself as much as you try to delude us."

Devereux's face reddened to match the spike of his beard as he thrust it forward in defiance. "I think Your Majesty should remember that 'tis I, and not Your Majesty, who has been bloodied in battle."

"Od's blood, how can I forget when you remind me of it hourly!"

"A fig on this truculence, Madame—"

"And a fig on you forecasting yourself as a statesman, sir, for all battles are not on the battlefield won!"

"Those that matter are!" Essex roared.

It had gone too far. Cecil stood up as if to calm the troubled waters, but he was too late.

Essex again jutted his beard forward, mumbled an unintelligible oath and committed the gravest error of all, that of showing contempt for the Queen.

He turned his back on her.

Elizabeth lurched from her chair and swung her arm in a wide arc. As small as her palm was, the box it inflicted on Essex's ear sounded like a thunderclap in the room.

Essex whirled around, shouting, "Madame, never would I endure such an insult from any man, much less from a woman!"

As if that weren't enough, his hand crossed his body and fell on the hilt of his sword.

"Devereux, you fool," Cecil gasped, stepping between them.

"Aside, pygmy, or I'll brush you like the gnat you are!"

"Silence!" Cecil hissed, forced to look practically straight up at the taller man. "How bloody stupid can you be, man. She is the Queen!"

Only then, with the twin coals of Cecil's eyes challenging him, did Essex grasp the full reality of his rash act. But so large was his pride that even then he couldn't swallow it.

With another furious look at his Queen he turned and stalked from the chamber.

Cecil turned around. Queen Elizabeth was shaking, her face chalk white and her eyes blazing with a greater fury than he had ever seen.

"What think you, Sir Robert, of one who cares so little for his head?"

Cecil took several breaths to calm himself before replying, "I think, Your Majesty, that if m'Lord Essex considers so lightly your recommendations, you should take him at his word."

Elizabeth turned slowly to face him, her eyes boring into his. "How so?"

"If m'Lord Essex knows what is best for our realm in Ireland, then I suggest that he should go himself."

There was a moment of hesitation, of doubt in the Queen's eyes, and then she nodded.

"So be it!"

IT WAS A GRAY GLOOMY DAY with none of the freshness of spring as the Earl of Essex led the captains of his command down the Strand in the direction of Chester.

Crowds always cheered him when he left Essex House, but today, even with rain threatening, there were literally throngs of yelling, smiling faces. For today Essex was taking his true place as the savior of England's honor in Ireland. He was riding off to meet the destiny that all of England knew was rightfully his.

And true to character, Essex didn't smile or wave at the cheering multitudes. Leave that to Southampton and the rest.

Instead Essex brooded. His lips were curled in a pout, and his face was dour with the melancholy the people loved in their heroes.

But beneath the hooded brows, Essex's eyes didn't register the upturned smiling faces any more than his ears heard the crowd's acclaim. For his mind was turned inward, and his ears still rang with Bacon's words when news of his appointment had reached them.

"I would to Ireland, Francis. 'Tis the Queen's warrant. What think you?"

Bacon had read the warrant, and the warranting signature under the Queen's, Sir Robert Cecil.

"I think, m'lord, that—that you have been outfoxed."

As if it were an omen, the sky darkened even more as the regiments left London. They were barely into the countryside when the heavens opened in a downpour that lasted throughout the entire trip to Chester and the subsequent crossing of the Irish Sea.

As THE OLDEST HAND of the English force in Ireland, it fell to Captain James Blake to brief the earl upon his arrival.

Essex was shocked when the man appeared before him. Blake looked more like a heathen Irish rebel, filthy and ragged and straight from the mountains, than an English gentleman and an officer in Her Majesty's service. His dull gray hair was long and wild, and it was cut in the style of the Irish glib so that it covered much of his face. Even his voice had begun to take on a Gaelic lilt that Essex found difficult to understand.

Southampton sniffed, covered his nose with a scented handkerchief and left them.

Blake only smiled his lopsided grin and moved closer to where Essex sat unfolding a roll of charts and maps.

"Your arrival, m'lord, has been long anticipated, I assure you."

Good God, Essex thought, again taking in the man's manner and his appearance, *he's become a native. As such, can he be trusted?*

And there was something else about the fellow that Essex could only wonder at. The earl couldn't precisely place the feeling he got when he looked into the ebony coldness of Blake's single eye, but in a way it reminded him of the eyes he had seen staring from the cells of Bedlam.

"So you see, m'lord," Blake said pointing to a chart, 'the bastard O'Neill controls the north only by holding these three strategic routes. Here, the route north from Connaught through Ballylee and Ballyshannon at the western end of Lough Erne. Own that and you own Donegal. And here, the Armagh road through Blackwater. Own that and you own Tyrone. Once that is done, we can attack at Derry, at the neck of Lough Foyle. That's the chief pass between Donegal and

Tyrone, so if we command it the northern clans can't reinforce each other. Believe me, m'lord, split your force of sixteen thousand in half, and in a month's time the Irishwomen will be keening over their dead chieftains.''

The man's basic military strategy was logical and astute, but Essex had heard very little of it. Instead his eyes remained on the chart where Blake had pointed out the Yellow Ford crossing of the Callan.

Words of the message they had received in London months before came ringing back to him.

"...all the leaders and two thousand dead at Blackwater in a matter of hours. Sir Henry Bagenal's name will go down in infamy for such a debacle.''

FROM HIS OBSERVATION POST on Dungannon's great tower O'Neill watched as, far below him, Rory O'Donnell vaulted from his lathered horse. Then the chieftain moved down the narrow steps, turned, and entered the great chamber. His underchiefs already sat at the long oaken tables, waiting for him.

O'Neill took the high-backed chair at the end of the hall just as Rory burst into the room.

"So it has come," he stated quietly.

"Aye," Rory replied, "it has. Essex has landed about sixteen thousand men in the Pale, with enough arms and victuals to last them for a year.''

O'Neill sighed and leaned back in the chair. He raised his eyes to the beams of the arched ceiling high above him.

For years now they had skirmished successfully against small companies of the Queen's ragtag army in Ireland. For the most part they had won those skirmishes. And then Blackwater and a rout.

But this was different; this was an army of sixteen

thousand trained men, with a popular leader who had seen countless battles before.

The Queen had made her move.

"Damme," O'Neill muttered under his breath, "if only the woman would die."

No matter how strong his own force had grown, O'Neill was a realist. He still needed men and arms from Spain, and their arrival was imminent. That, or the death of the Queen, would give Ireland total victory. He was sure of it.

Elizabeth's death would serve his purpose best. In the confusion of the succession there would be little time at Whitehall to worry about Ireland.

"What think you of Essex?" O'Neill asked, his gaze still on the ceiling.

"I think the earl is more enamored with the fruits of victory than the picking of them," Rory replied.

"Your brother must be informed, and Maguire summoned again. I think we're about to journey to Blackwater and the Armagh road once more."

"Nay, m'lord," Rory said, "I think not."

O'Neill lowered his eyes to see Rory's bearded face split with a wide grin. "How so?"

"For reasons I cannot fathom, Essex is not marching north. At this very moment he marches south to Cork."

AND WHILE THE EARL OF ESSEX debated his fate in Cork, and O'Neill contemplated victory at Dungannon, and Rory O'Donnell drank more and more *uisce beathadh* while hungering for his next battle, Lady Elizabeth Hatton gave birth to a daughter in her Holdenby cottage.

" 'Twas an easy birth, m'lady," Honor smiled. "As I told you, you have the bones for babies."

Elizabeth could only nod. She was weary, first from months of fighting with her husband over her estates, and now from the hours of labor.

"She would suckle, m'lady."

Again Elizabeth nodded, and allowed the girl to open her chemise and free one of her achingly swollen breasts.

And then, as the child nourished herself for the first time, energy flowed back into the mother's body. The infant already had a wealth of coal black hair, and her eyes, as they gazed up to Elizabeth's face, were as black as her hair and seemed to dance with an impishness the mother remembered well.

The very sight of the child, and how much she looked like Rory, brought tears to Elizabeth's face.

Honor accepted them as tears of joy.

"What name, m'lady, for such a bonny little lass?"

Elizabeth closed her eyes, remembering a moment long ago, and hugged the child even closer to her breast.

"Brenna. Her name will be Brenna."

CHAPTER FORTY-ONE

FOR MONTHS Essex moved his vast army back and forth in the south. He engaged in minor skirmishes with the O'Tooles, the O'Byrnes and septs of other smaller clans.

His display of men and arms was formidable, and he acquitted himself magnificently, appearing poised and triumphant at the head of his army.

But he was triumphant over very little.

O'Neill had sent instructions to the southern clans to

observe and harrass Essex, to skirmish on his flanks, and to give full battle only when opportunity was on the Irish side.

This they did with very little loss of men. And while Essex didn't lose many of his own soldiers in battle, he lost them to disease, to the rain, and to desertion.

Slowly, in bits and pieces, news of the campaign seeped back to London. The privy council was made uneasy by accounts of their hero's unaggressive behavior in the south of Ireland while the Earl of Tyrone grew stronger in Ulster to the north.

The council, and the Queen herself, urged him continually throughout the summer months to turn and engage the real threat, O'Neill and the O'Donnells.

For the most part Robert Cecil stayed out of the fray. But when the full story of England's depleted army came to London from Essex himself, in the form of a request for huge reinforcements, it fell to the little humpbacked statesman to bring the problem before the Queen.

"Od's blood," she ranted, striking one bony fist on the scantly padded arm of her chair.

It was the only chair in the room, so Sir Robert was forced to stand before her, shifting nervously from one foot to the other. As if Essex's news weren't bad enough, word had also reached him that O'Neill was parleying by messengers with James of Scotland.

Sir Robert had been obliged to inform the Queen of this fact as well. The combined information was now feeding the usually banked fires of the royal anger.

"Od's blood, from what manner of popinjays do we make generals? Would I raise m'Lord Essex to the heights only to have him use my crown as a stool?"

"Your Majesty, I think the time has come to inform

the people of the true nature of m'Lord Essex's behavior," Cecil suggested.

Their eyes met, and the blaze of anger in the Queen's face turned to alarm.

Essex was the people's hero, the Queen's right arm. In the eyes of the ordinary citizen Essex and men like him were the male support of a female monarch; a monarch who could command men into battle but not lead them.

And what of Gloriana herself? Her erstwhile favorite made her laugh and feel young again—a balm for the soul of a lonely queen.

Cecil could read all these things in the woman's eyes before she suddenly looked away. Restlessly she stood up from her chair, and her booted feet made a hollow muted sound on the floor as she paced, kicking strewn rushes before her. Unregal were her shoulders now as they slumped and rounded.

"Your Majesty—"

"Sit!"

"Your Majesty?"

"Sit, sit, sit there!"

There was only one chair. Sir Robert sat down in it.

"How feels it, my little pygmy? How lonely is the island of that one chair in this chairless room?"

Cecil didn't speak. Her pacing slowed, her face emerged from behind her fingers. The brow, already wrinkled, furrowed deeper in concentration beneath the red periwig.

"Were that your chair, Sir Robert, think you that you could abide another ruler by your side of the same relation? And if not, think you that you might soon be lonely enough to need at least a stool, there...or there...anywhere to break the barrenness of isolation around you?"

Cecil swept his eyes around the spacious room and sighed. He knew his Queen's meaning too well. His only surprise was at her frankness in revealing the gnawing ache in her soul.

"Your Majesty," he ventured, "I fear m'Lord Essex would move from the stool to the chair if he sensed any further sign of weakness in its rightful occupant."

Cecil held his breath. Never had he or anyone else dared to expose Essex's ambition openly to the Queen. Any suggestion that at times she was ruled as much by emotion as by common sense, was usually met with a wrath that could melt stone.

"Think you there is such seed of ambition in m'Lord Essex?" she asked in calm measured tones.

Sir Robert exhaled a sigh of relief. "Verily, your Majesty," he replied, confidence now in his voice. "And I think the Irishman, O'Neill, will sense and feed upon it."

The Queen squared her shoulders and brought her lips together in a taut line. "Then, Sir Robert, 'tis time we prod our proud stallion with the spur of our royal reality. Your pen!"

Hastily Cecil spread board and paper on his lap and dipped his pen into the inkwell on the small table beside him.

Her voice began low, with the syrup of irony dripping from her words. But as she dictated it rose to a crashing crescendo of vindictive command:

My Lord Essex,

Have you begun to favor yourself so much that mayhap you no longer need our favor? Have your eyes been so misted by Irish gloom that they have lost the ray of English hope?

These months you war with the elements, yet

fail to kill or capture a single Irish rebel. With such force as you possess, along with cannon and cavalry, is it too much to ask that you engage the nobility of Irish rogues rather than their rabble?

I remind you, sir, of your own outspoken genius on the battlefield, and for that reason I do not pretend as a woman to tell you how to run your war. But as your Queen, sir, I tell you—nay, command you—to do some damnable battle.

Move north, sir, or move to hell!

Elizabeth R

RELUCTANTLY ESSEX MOVED NORTH. But by the time he did his force had dwindled to less than six thousand, and O'Neill more than matched his might.

Early September found Essex and his decimated army camped at the hill of Louth, near the Varney River. From the rise he could see O'Neill's army on the opposite bank.

The earl knew without being told that to engage O'Neill now would be futile. All he would accomplish by it would be to join the name Devereux in infamy with Bagenal.

"Send this word to the rebel," he said to an aide, and dictated a message to O'Neill.

It was delivered half an hour later under a white flag, and O'Neill read it aloud:

"If The O'Neill hath the courage of his cause and convictions, and if he hath any virtue that is not pure vanity, then I, Essex, will meet him in the field. He to be advanced alone, ahead of his kern, and I separated from my troops. Thus we will parley in the best fashion of soldiers, with swords to the death."

O'Neill crumpled the paper and guffawed, his eyes filling with tears of laughter.

At his side Rory O'Donnell muttered, "My God, what manner of fool is the man?"

"Methinks," O'Neill replied, wiping the tears from his eyes, "that our Earl of Essex fancies himself a Norman knight of old!"

He turned to the red-faced captain who had delivered the epistle. "Tell your master, lad, that I admire his bravado if not his courage, seeing he is a man of thirty-two and I approach fifty-five. Thusly, I must decline...but with grace. But do tell m'Lord Essex this. On the morrow, in the mists of early morn, I will meet him with truce talk at the ford of Bellaclynth, midstream of the River Lagan."

For three full hours Essex ranted about the lack of spine in Irish princes. But at dawn the following day the earl, followed by Southampton, Blake, and four other retainers, topped a hill overlooking the River Lagan. On the opposite bank they saw fifty Irish kern, and midstream O'Neill was calmly waiting, the water lapping at his horse's belly.

Essex put on the most dour face he could muster and guided his mount down the bank and into the river.

"M'Lord Essex, 'tis a pleasure."

"I can't say the same, sir. 'Twas you who requested this parley; let's be on with it."

"As you wish," O'Neill said, shrugging his fur mantled shoulders. "As you know, m'lord, my cause is a godly one, for I would have my people live by the true religion—"

"Pray you, O'Neill," Essex interrupted, "don't harangue me with your claptrap of beads and holy relics, for I know you care for religion as much as does my horse."

O'Neill smiled broadly. "I am truly glad, m'lord, that your eye has not been totally clogged by our Irish mists. Very well, then, I'll be on with it. But I would tell you first that there are but two of us here for good reason."

"Aye, that I can see," Essex replied, curious now at the gleam in the old warrior's eyes.

"The Queen, bless her, has but little time left on this earth, do you agree?"

"Would you have me speak treason that could be used against me on another day?"

"Damme, man," O'Neill hissed. "I would have you speak truth, for we talk of crowns and kingdoms here!"

Essex hesitated and then nodded. "Aye, Her Majesty seems to fade almost daily."

"And who but James of Scotland would be her successor? No one. I have treatied with James. When he comes to the throne he will not want the unpleasantness of constant Irish wars. I think, were the withdrawal suitable, he will not want Ireland at all."

"Mayhap it would be possible," Essex mused. "But that is then and this is now."

"Exactly. Time. As always, I need time. Given enough of it, I can gain the strength I'll need to negotiate for all of Ireland with James."

"And then?"

"And then I would plead for a separate kingdom."

"No English king would agree to that . . . for it would become a Spanish kingdom."

"Not if this separate Irish Kingdom were to have another Englishman on its throne."

Essex's eyes grew wide and he sat bolt upright in the saddle as the full import of O'Neill's words struck him. "You're daft!" he exclaimed.

"Am I, m'lord? Does not the Devereux name have a link to the Tudor line?"

"Aye, but—"

"I care not to be king of Ireland. I would rule Tyrone under Brehan law, as would O'Donnell rule Donegal, Burke rule Connaught, and O'Hara Ballylee."

"O'Hara is dead."

"Nay, he lives in his Rory, as we all live in our sons and always will. Think, m'Lord Essex, think of the lineage of your sons. Think of the Devereux line of Irish kings!"

Essex thought, and saw history span before him.

"And in the meantime, O'Neill, what would you have me do?"

JAMES BLAKE STOOD APART from the group around Essex and listened with disgust to the results of the parley.

The Irish were to retain possession of everything they now held. The English had agreed not to build any new forts or garrisons, and the existing army would headquarter in the Pale until they could be disbanded to the size of the former policing force. The truce would be extended every six weeks, until both sides could come to a full peace agreement.

Blake shook his head in wonder at the earl's naiveté and stupidity. It would take very few of those six-week intervals before Ireland's shores would be swarming with Spanish troops.

When Essex gave his captains the order to move in the morning for the Pale, Blake guessed the man's purpose. And he knew he was correct in his assumptions when the earl gathered his private group around him and ordered his stewards to ready their mounts.

That was when Blake slipped away from the camp headquarters and found his own horse.

Essex, he knew, planned to hasten to England and inform the Queen of his side of the story, before any other voice tried to pull apart his version of the events just past.

A way at last, Blake thought, as he drove his mount harder and harder toward Dublin. A way at last to secure his position with Cecil and the Queen once and for all.

He would have his title yet, and the heads of both O'Donnell and O'Neill as well.

" 'TIS TRULY A BEAUTIFUL CHILD, Elizabeth."

"And grows as quickly as the roses in my garden," she replied, rocking the sleeping child in her arms. "But Brenna is not the reason I asked you to Hatton House this night, uncle."

"I'm sure it isn't," Cecil said, his wan smile reflecting the tiredness in his eyes and the fatigue in his body.

"You must aid me in these matters, uncle. The man is like a beast, possessed as he is with his dealings. I fear he may impoverish the both of us."

"I think not, Elizabeth. I know Sir Edward as a shrewd and wise man."

"Shrewd, yes," she replied, her voice rising with her anger. "But wise, I am not so sure. Now, if you would—"

"Elizabeth," Sir Robert said, wearily interrupting her, "dear niece, if only you would agree to live with the man."

"Nay, not until he agrees to my terms!"

Cecil shook his head. "Did you really tell him that when next he visits with you he must use the back door?"

"I did, and I told him he's not to come unless he's invited."

"You are a shrew."

Her smile was sweet, almost demure. "Only to those inferior to me who would have me inferior to them, dear uncle."

"Pardon, m'lady!" It was a white-faced Honor curtsying in the entry way, "But there is a wild gentleman to see Sir Robert—"

"Pardon, Sir Robert. . .m'lady. . ." a voice boomed from the door.

Cecil got to his feet. Elizabeth nearly let the child slip from her arms in shock as the apparition burst past Honor and into the room.

"Blake! What in God's name—"

"Your steward told me where you were, Sir Robert. I have news, dire news!"

Cecil stayed outwardly calm as Blake told him the tale of the river meeting between The O'Neill and Essex, and of Essex's subsequent orders. Elizabeth could only stare in amazement, a feeling that was tempered with a degree of revulsion at Blake's appearance.

"And I fear, Sir Robert, that all Ireland will be lost if Essex succeeds in convincing the Queen to accept this treaty!"

"Aye, I'm inclined to agree," Cecil replied, thoughtfully stroking his beard. "And you say Essex is bound for England?"

"Aye, methinks he is close behind me."

"The court is currently at Nonsuch Palace. We must ride at once. I'll see to the horses." Cecil moved toward the door and paused. "But, od's pity, man, you can't appear before the Queen looking like that. Elizabeth, get someone to cut his hair, and try to find him some clothes that more resemble the garb of civilized people!''

Cecil disappeared, and Blake turned to Elizabeth, his eye falling on the sleeping child.

''My congratulations on your recent marriage and the birth, m'lady.''

Elizabeth shivered as the man's one eye leered at her. His grin was ugly, and it, too, unnerved her. It was hard to imagine that at one time, years before, this man's presence had had almost the same effect upon her as Rory O'Donnell's. Then she had welcomed his biting wit, his charm and his rakish, dangerous reputation. Now James Blake frightened her. In him she sensed pure evil.

''The child's name, m'lady?''

''It is Brenna.''

''Brenna? 'Tis odd.''

''Why so, sir?'' Elizabeth felt a flush creeping up her neck.

'' 'Tis a Gaelic name. I believe it means. . .raven.''

ESSEX THUNDERED THROUGH NORTH WALES with the four riders behind him, without even a pause at his Chartley estates. He wasn't positive that Captain Blake's defection had taken him to England, but in his belly he had a gnawing feeling of fear that it had.

Essex had committed a grave act in leaving his Irish command against the Queen's specific orders, and an even graver one in making a treaty with The O'Neill. But he was sure—positive, in fact—that if he reached the Queen with his version before she heard it from another such as Cecil, Her Majesty could be convinced that he had made the wisest move.

Down from the northern Cotswolds they rode, the lather from their horses' flanks spraying behind them and reflecting blue in the moonlight.

"Damme, men, faster! Spur your mounts!" Essex roared to his aides, although the horses' hooves were already barely touching the ground between their powerful straining strides. "We must hie like the wind, or all will be lost!"

He spurred his stallion to greater effort, his cape flying majestically behind him, and the five riders thundered on into the night.

And then they were through Westminster and boarding the Lambeth ferry.

"Ten miles to Nonsuch, m'lords!" Essex cried. "Pray God the little hunchback remains at Whitehall!"

"How DARE YOU, sir! Think you this is the bedchamber of some wench?"

"Nay, Your Majesty, but your ear I must have at once," the Earl of Essex replied from his position on one knee before the Queen.

Again his impulsive rashness had gotten the better of his judgment. He had stormed through the presence chamber, shoved the Queen's guards aside, and had bolted directly into the privy chamber and the royal monarch's bedroom.

Barely arisen and not yet bewigged or dressed, Queen Elizabeth was a sight. But not any more than the mud-caked weary figure kneeling before her, with his clothes torn and soaked with sweat from the long ride.

At first the Queen was afraid. Had the fool brought his army with him? Was this a rebellion? Did he plan on murdering her?

Then, as he spewed out the story of what had occurred in Ireland and his reasons for leaving, she was shocked.

As usual, Essex was certain that his words were golden to the Queen's ears, and that his mere presence, even with his appearance crumpled as it was, would be enough to convince her of the correctness of his deed.

And, as usual, he was wrong.

She thought him a blundering fool and his acts treasonous, and as her shock turned to anger she told him so. "My lord, I leave your fate to the privy council. Now be off!"

"Your Majesty—".

"Nay, m'lord, I fear you've ridden too far, too fast, this time."

Behind him a door was flung open and Essex whirled around. Cecil and Blake were in the doorway, and beside them stood the Queen's guards, their pikes at the ready.

CHAPTER FORTY-TWO

THE JUBILATION THAT THE IRISH LEADERS FELT over Essex's failure to fight O'Neill, and the further possibility of the powerful earl shifting to the Irish side, was short-lived.

For several months Essex was kept under house arrest in the care of the Lord Keeper Egerton of York House. Robert Devereux's dreams of wearing an Irish crown, indeed, his hopes of even retaining his status as an English subject in a court that no longer admitted him, grew dimmer each day.

And, as if fate had played a cruel trick on O'Neill by allowing him to outwit Essex, the Queen replaced her former favorite with the one man who could defeat Tyrone.

Charles Blount, Lord Mountjoy, was a quiet diffident man, but he was efficient as a soldier, and his bravery was unmatched in the field.

Unlike the arrogant headstrong Essex, Lord Mountjoy listened to James Blake. And while he sensed the same madness in the man that Essex had seen, he also saw the brilliance of Blake's strategy.

"And while you campaign in the field, m'lord," Blake told him, "I will continue my quiet war of sowing unrest among the lesser Irish factions."

Robert Cecil had informed Mountjoy before leaving England of the man's uncanny talent for deviousness, as well as Blake's thirst for the prestige of a title. Wisely, the new lord lieutenant dangled a promise of the latter in return for good performances of the former.

In a matter of weeks Blake proved his worth to his new commander. He convinced many of the small sept leaders under O'Neill and O'Donnell to shift their allegiance to the English side. Among these were Dermet O'Conner, and O'Neill's own cousin, Neill Garve.

Their defection was a stunning blow. This, along with the famine caused by Mountjoy's rampaging troops as they stormed the countryside burning crops and killing cattle, brought more and more of the starving underchiefs into the English camp.

Mountjoy himself built up the morale of the existing army left by Essex with smaller actions designed to harass the enemy, just as the Irish had formerly harassed the English. Slowly but surely he pressed into Derry, the breach that separated O'Donnell in Donegal from O'Neill in Tyrone.

So successful was he that by winter of 1600 he could write to Cecil:

Dear Master Secretary,

We move northward almost hourly. The subversive tactics used by Captain Blake work in conjunction with my troops' scorching of the land. The rebels have not been able to sow nor reap, for what corn they do sow we cut before it is ripe. It becomes a war of attrition. We starve them into yielding, and as long as reinforcements of victuals and men continue to arrive for our side from England, starve they will.

Also, by waging winter warfare we drive them from their lodgings into the cold.

I do believe, sir, that unless there is some intervention by a foreign power, the war will be ours by summer. . . .

Cecil firmly hoped so, for the exchequer was being strained almost beyond its limits to provide for the war.

And the conflict in Ireland was but one of the hundred things that demanded Sir Robert's time and energy. The Queen, despite her failing health, still refused to name an heir to the throne. Consequently Cecil had secretly started negotiations with James VI of Scotland. In this way he hoped to arrange a peaceful succession as well as stop any possible bartering between James in Scotland and O'Neill in Ireland.

The Queen had also told him in strictest confidence that if anything unforeseen should happen before the resolution in Ireland, Cecil should take it upon himself to insure that the only terms given O'Neill would be unconditional surrender. She wanted no more Irish treaties to blot her reign

It wasn't just war, and attempting to find some way to make peace with Spain and France, that taxed Cecil. Domestic problems, too, plagued him.

Attorney General Coke, now his in-law, fought daily with his wife, Cecil's niece. The scheming between the pair, and the constant appeals made by Elizabeth to her uncle for justice, left Robert weary of the entire affair.

And as if that weren't enough, it fell to Cecil to settle the problem of his old enemy, Essex.

Upon his release from York House, the fool had mounted a haphazard rebellion and had stormed through the streets of London to Whitehall.

Stupid and childish it had been, but it was the final act of treason that had forced the Queen to a resolution concerning the courtier she had held above all others.

And on this Ash Wednesday morning Cecil stood, as he had so many mornings, in the window of his Whitehall sanctuary, gazing across at the windows of the Queen's privy chamber.

Most likely Gloriana was already weeping with grief, for Cecil himself had witnessed the pain in the old woman's face while signing the warrant. And he had heard the plaintive cry in her voice when she instructed him; "...and pray you, sir, let there be two executioners. For I would not have him suffer should there be dallying. Should one faint, let the other stand by and perform the deed posthaste."

And Cecil had so ordered.

His gaze moved beyond Whitehall to the Thames, and down the river to the high wall of the Tower. There, at this very moment, the blade was probably removing Robert Devereux's handsome head from his marvelously athletic body, and Cecil would be rid of his last powerful enemy.

But the little man felt no elation. Indeed, his eyes watered with tears. For Essex, the cares of his personal ambition would soon be over. But for Cecil, the cares of state had barely begun.

There came a dull thudding knock on the heavy oaken door. Without turning he called out for the messenger to enter. "Well?"

" 'Tis done, Sir Robert, with three blows of the ax."

Cecil nodded, the lids over his large eyes sloped with fatigue as his gaze shifted from the Tower to the roofs of London.

"Hath the Queen been informed?"

"Aye."

"And the writ been read from St. Paul's to the people?"

"Aye."

Again he nodded. Sir Robert Cecil was now the most powerful man in England. But that power was lodged in a tired and haggard body.

Part V
Winter 1601

CHAPTER FORTY-THREE

"WE FIGHT," O'Neill sighed, "with the blessings of all Catholic Europe. We fight with the blessings of the Pope. We fight with the blessings of our starving people...who can no more eat blessings than we can."

"But we fight," replied Rory O'Donnell.

"Aye, we fight," O'Neill nodded. "As we have for four hundred years. We've a rebellion, and there's naught but to see it through."

So saying, the three of them—Rory and Red Hugh O'Donnell, and Hugh O'Neill, the Earl of Tyrone—spurred their horses toward their separate armies, to begin the last battle—the one battle they must not lose.

Below them on the plains of Kinsale lay Mountjoy's army. It had only half the Irish numbers, but those soldiers it did have were well-armed, well-fed and well-trained. Beyond them in the tiny walled city of Kinsale were the decimated Spanish troops of Don Juan del Aguila. Aguila had landed a force forty-five hundred strong a month before, and since then had lost half his men under Mountjoy's seige before O'Neill could reach the south.

But the Irish forces were in the south now, and on this freezing cold morning, still dark as pitch, they were preparing the last assault of a long and bloody rebellion.

"M'LORD, THEY DRAW INTO THE FIELD here, beyond this bog," Blake said, sweeping a finger across the chart between himself and Mountjoy.

Lord Mountjoy furrowed his high forehead and looked up at his captain. "All in the open?"

'Aye, m'lord.'

'And the Spaniards?"

'The fight is gone from them, m'lord."

Mountjoy rose, reaching for his sword. "It can only be a rout."

All three prongs of the Irish attack were met with the full force of Lord Mountjoy's cavalry before dawn. The Scottish gallowglass mercenaries fought well but fruitlessly in the forefront.

Without this edge to slow the English down, the Irish pikemen and swordsmen were no match for the organized onslaught of the British soldiers.

Back and then farther back they retreated, toward the safety of Dunboy Castle. But there they found no sanctuary, for Dunboy had fallen under siege.

Stoically the three rebel leaders faced each other among their vanquished and retreating troops.

"Mark ye well," O'Neill said, his eyes filled with tears, "we have rebelled and we have failed. Now I fear—nay, I know—that all Ireland will pay a terrible price for that failure."

"Then we must for the north!" Red Hugh cried. "For at least we'll hold Ulster!"

"Aye. Now we must fight for survival and self-preservation until such time as the Queen dies and we are able to gain terms from King James."

"I'll to Ballylee," Rory replied. "For that's where they would strike first to reach the north."

O'Neill could only nod his graying head and try to shake the weariness from his body. "Fight on, for 'tis all we know or can do. But I fear, lads, that today was the battle that lost a nation.''

JAMES BLAKE'S CRIMSON DOUBLET was freshly pressed and his hose gleamed whitely as he stood before Cecil. The man's appearance was greatly changed, but as he gleefully reiterated each gory detail of the bloody battle of Kinsale, down to the execution of prisoners in its aftermath, Cecil knew that the man still retained a spark of near madness in his brain.

''Enough, Captain Blake, enough of severed heads and bloody derring-do. I would know what the rebels do now. The Queen doth scream for their surrender, if not their heads.''

Even with the nerves in the side of his mouth and face shattered Blake managed a tight-lipped grimace. He started to speak, and then shuffled his feet instead.

''Sit, sit!'' Cecil said, waving toward a chair. ''And have some wine if you wish.'' He sighed and rubbed the throb in his forehead with long white fingers. ''Forgive me, captain. I see less and less of the light of day even though the days grow longer. I would to Bath for a month, but I can't even lie abed for more than a few hours. But enough of this. Feed my ears, Blake. What of O'Neill?''

''He has reached the north, but in the process his troops deserted, melting away daily to their homes or to the septs giving us allegiance. He lies now in the forests of Glenconkein, where he sues m'Lord Mountjoy for peace.''

''But he would have conditions?''

''Aye,'' Blake replied. ''Modest conditions, he calls them.''

''He always does,'' Cecil sighed. ''But the Queen will

have none of it. She would have total surrender and his pledge of fealty or else his head."

"I think, Sir Robert, that the Queen is wise. 'Tis the only way."

"Is it? God, it seems so, but Her Majesty would prefer a less bloody peace and would let the Irish put their own houses in order, now that the island is again ours. What of The O'Donnell, Red Hugh?"

"To Spain. I believe 'tis on the orders of O'Neill, who wants to convince Philip to send yet another army to his aid. The earl hopes that this time they will be wiser than del Aguila and land in the north."

The accusation, despite its seriousness, brought a smile to Cecil's lips. "The man is truly an enigma. He will do all to win, and then in defeat will do all to gain terms in his favor. Such a man would make a brilliant king."

"The O'Donnell's brother, Rory, is now under siege at Ballylee. I would have that command."

Cecil waved his hand. "It matters not," he said, "if 'tis to m'Lord Mountjoy's liking."

Here Blake leaned forward, his eye piercing to the point of making Cecil look away. "But before taking it, Sir Robert, I would to Spain."

"Spain?"

"Aye, on the Queen's business. For there is always the chance that The O'Donnell, Red Hugh, might be successful with the popish Philip."

Cecil stood up and examined the contorted contours of the man's face to make sure he read them correctly. Then he moved to his thinking spot by the window.

Assassination.

The subject was before him again. He knew Blake was right. It was a logical thing that should be done. And it wasn't as if it hadn't been condoned before. But could such a measure be condoned forever? How long could he let such things go on without finding other solutions?

The Queen would never agree to it.

"There are certain men in Madrid who could pave your way," Cecil finally said. "But know you, James Blake, that you're not on the Queen's business."

"It makes no matter, Sir Robert. I gladly take on the task as personal business of my own."

Cecil could not repress a slight shudder at the joy evident in the man's voice. "And when you return to Ireland and Ballylee, I would have the younger brother, Rory, spared upon capture. I'll not murder the whole clan."

"Of course, Sir Robert."

The tone in Blake's voice made Cecil whirl around. "I mean it, Blake. Rory O'Donnell goes to the Tower with his head intact, or I'll have yours!"

Not surprisingly, Blake rose out of his chair showing anger of his own. "Then, Sir Robert, I would trade his life and my service for what I deserve. The title you stripped me of I would have back. I would again be *Sir* James Blake!"

"The Queen is reluctant—"

"Nay, I care not for Her Majesty's constant reluctance. I would have *your* word, Sir Robert!"

Cecil eyed him stonily, carefully weighing his response. And in the pause a change came over Blake. The gleaming eye softened and the shoulders slumped as he came forward a few paces.

"Please. I beg this of you above all things, Sir Robert. 'Tis the one thing I must have."

Cecil could hardly believe it. Never in all the years he had known Blake had he ever heard the man utter the word, "please." Nor had he ever seen those shoulders slump, or that hand held out in supplication as now.

Suddenly James Blake was as pitiful as he was terrifying, as pathetic as he was unscrupulous, as human in character as his actions were devoid of humanity.

"My word on it, James, as soon as you return."

CHAPTER FORTY-FOUR

IT WAS OVER NOW, all over, and Rory O'Donnell had no doubt of it. O'Neill himself was running like a rabbit from one forest warren to another. The English had besieged Dungannon until he had been forced to flee through the countryside, what there was left of it. The scorched-earth tactics of the earlier Desmond wars had once again been used to bring proud Ulster to her knees, and to famine.

Rory had received word that his brother, Red Hugh, had been poisoned in Spain. Downhearted though Rory was by this tragedy, he reluctantly accepted the clan mantle out of reverence for the O'Donnells before him, declaring himself The O'Donnell.

But now what use was it, he thought, staring upward from the bailey at Ballylee. Like all of Ulster, the castle was in ruins. Its battlements, its towers, its proud parapets were rubble. They had crumbled like paper when at last the English had brought up their powerful new siege cannons.

And the walls themselves would be next. Already gaping holes were growing wider, until they would soon be large enough for the enemy to flow through en masse.

"M'lord."

At first Rory didn't answer. "M'lord" was unfamiliar to him. And then he realized.

"Aye?"

"'Tis only a matter of time, m'lord. It must be soon."

Rory nodded. "Are they ready?"

"Aye, the lass, the child, and The O'Hara."

Rory smiled. Little Rory was indeed The O'Hara now. Like himself, the boy bore a meaningless title. But he had to be saved.

"I urge you, m'lord, to be gone. For soon the time for surrender will be past and annihilation will follow."

Rory knew only too well the man's meaning. Terms had been offered. If they were accepted before the walls fell, there was a chance that the remaining kern inside Ballylee would be spared

A chance.

To a man, none of The O'Hara's faithful followers wanted to take that chance with Shane and Deirdre's children.

"May God, if there be one, have mercy on you," Rory said.

"Ahh, m'lord, I must believe there is one, and that He's Irish...else why do we fight these miserable wars?"

Rory clapped the man on the shoulder and hurried across the bailey. Once inside the great tower he charged up the stairs to the second ward.

All three of them were huddled at a window slit, looking down at the massing English army through the heavy pall of powder smoke that rose to blot out the sun.

Little Shanna was crying softly, as was Annie where she stood behind the child. Annie's face was black with powder, and her clothes were bloody from the men she'd tended. For like the fighter she was, she had been on the wall with the men these last forty-eight hours, nursing Irishmen when she wasn't firing a musket, killing Englishmen.

Nine-year-old Rory O'Hara's face was a mask of grim determination as he looked down at the vast waves of foreign soldiers.

"They come, don't they," the boy said.

"Aye. We must be through the passage and into the woods," O'Donnell replied.

"One day I will come back. I will return and rebuild the rubble they've made of our home, our Ballylee. And within its walls I'll properly bury my kin."

Other than the slight choking in his voice, O'Donnell could have sworn he heard the father's voice in the son's words.

They hid in the after-dungeon until false dawn. All sounds of battle had ceased hours before. It was then that O'Donnell removed the stone, and one by one lowered them into the moat.

"I'm afraid, I'm afraid!" moaned Shanna.

"Shh, hush, little princess," Annie urged. "Clasp your arms around my neck until you can ride The O'Donnell's back."

Rory dropped into the moat, and with Shanna astride his back, led the way around the remaining curtain wall and up the feeder channel. At last, chilled to the bone, they crawled up the grassy bank into the dense woods beyond the heathered meadows around Ballylee.

Behind them the castle was ablaze, and they could hear the raucous laughter of the carousing English troops as they celebrated their victory.

"Poor Ballylee," Shanna cried. "'Twas so beautiful."

"Shh," Annie said, wrapping the child in a dry cloak, which she had held above her head during the swim.

"Come, 'tis three miles to the booley and the horses—"

"Rory O'Donnell!" a voice surprised them.

Rory had been reaching for Shanna. Now he whirled around, the pistol from Annie's blanket dry in his hand.

"I am unarmed except for the blade in my belt," came the voice, and James Blake stepped from the trees into the eerie gray light. His hands were high above his head.

"Shoot him!" Annie hissed.

"If you do," Blake replied, "the sound will have a score of troops upon you within a minute."

"He speaks the truth," Rory muttered, but he lifted his pistol higher as Blake approached.

"Hold, O'Donnell," Blake said. "Your flight was betrayed. That is how I found you."

"Through torture?"

"Aye," Blake replied, "but hold. Only I know of this. It's why I'm here. I would have you all safely in England."

"Safely?" Rory asked in disbelief. And then his voice hissed through clenched teeth. "My kern...my officers, my people?"

"Dead," Blake said, "to a man."

"Slaughtered!" Rory growled.

"Aye, but that's why I allowed your escape from the castle proper. I have a few men at my allegiance. Believe me, O'Donnell, I would have you safe in London. 'Tis in my best interests."

"Nay, Blake, for I know you for the villain you are."

"You fool, I'm trying to save your damnable life!"

"I would rather it end here than on the Tower's block in London," Rory said.

"I swear, Cecil wants you safe... and warrants me to make it so."

"And them?" Rory inclined his head toward Annie and the children.

Blake's hesitation was enough to make up Rory's mind. He aimed the pistol.

"Nay, hold, I say!" Blake cried. "Od's blood, but you are a fool. I try, man, to give you your life. I would have you alive before Cecil!"

"Again I ask you, Blake... what of them?"

"I cannot say."

"Then you die," Rory hissed.

"Hold, you fool! Would you play the cur and shoot me as you did before, so long ago? Or would you meet me like the man you claim to be?"

"He didn't shoot you, you swine," Annie cried. "I did!"

Surprise registered on Blake's face, and then he bowed with some of his old rakishness. "Then, lass, 'tis your breast I should skewer!"

Rory handed the pistol to Annie. Shanna was wide-eyed with fear, and young Rory's lips trembled but he held his ground at O'Donnell's side.

"I would have your word, Blake—if there's an ounce of the man I once knew left in your body—I would have your word that if I should fall, they be got to France."

"You have it and I swear it. But before France, England."

"Why so?"

"Because I would have the woman's word that you forced me into this. I would have her swear before Cecil that I had no choice but to kill you."

If that much of what the fellow said were true, Rory thought, it would amount to a guarantee that Annie and the children would at least reach England safely.

" 'Tis an odd bargain, Blake, but you have it."

"Then so be it," Blake replied, almost sadly, Rory thought. "But know this. Though you do not believe me, O'Donnell, I would not kill you."

" 'Tis then an impasse, and one neither of us can break, Blake. Swear that you'll tell Cecil he was forced into this, Annie!"

"Nay, I'll swear nothing to the swine!"

"Damme, Annie, you must," Rory hissed. "Should the match be his, at least there is a chance for you and them."

"If you would have him die with honorable combat, I would not," she retorted in kind. "I would as leave shoot him and be done with it."

"Nay. For some reason I believe him in this."

"I do not!" She brought the pistol up again.

Suddenly the fingers of Rory's right hand were at her neck. "Swear, you wench, for I would have the three of you safe before all else."

"Swear, for God's sake, my Annie!" young Rory cried, his arms entwining her waist tightly, his fear and lack of understanding of this new situation more than he could cope with.

' Annie," O'Donnell said through gritted teeth, "swear by this God and Virgin you've newly found. And swear by the Lady Deirdre."

"Aye, then, I swear," Annie croaked. "I swear by my beloved God, by the Mother Virgin, and upon the memory of my Lady Deirdre!"

Rory nodded, released his grip on her, and turned to Blake.

"And do you swear, Blake? Not to God, but upon your black soul?"

"Aye, I swear," Blake replied, his blade leaving its sheath. "But I beg you one last time...listen to reason!"

"You, Blake? Beg?"

"Aye, does that not tell you something?"

"It tells me you are frightening in your willingness to die," O'Donnell replied, his own blade whistling in the air as it left its scabbard.

Steel rang as the two combatants tested each other's mettle.

Blake's skill had not abated with the years. With the rapier he was still the master.

The footing near the creek that fed the moat was soft with marshy dampness. This was to Rory's advantage, and Blake knew it. Like the expert he was, he turned O'Donnell around and drove him with rapid thrusts and lunges toward more solid ground.

"Your skill in battle has aided you in this gentlemen's sport as well, O'Donnell."

"Mayhap, but I think 'tis more a lack of fear that aids me," Rory grunted in reply as he danced around an awkward thrust and scored a slight hit on Blake's left forearm.

His opponent saved himself behind a tree and then was quickly back on the attack. "Is this a lack of fear of me or of death, O'Donnell?"

"Both," Rory said, feinting, then executing an octave and second that nearly scored another hit on Blake's left side.

It was then he realized the advantage, besides his superior strength, that he had over the other man.

Instead of balancing himself with his left arm arched over his head, Blake was holding his free arm outward, and partially bent in front of his face. He did this so that he could see his left hand with his right eye, and thereby gauge distances.

Rory began to work on the man's left side. His blind side.

Blake saw Rory's intent and became more reckless.

There were two more slight hits, and then Blake stumbled. Rory pressed in. No longer was the master's blade a blur before his eyes. Blake's parries were awkward and slow now, and he talked constantly, trying to unnerve and distract his opponent.

Once he nearly succeeded. "By the by, O'Donnell... I have seen your child."

"Child?"

"Aye. A girl child, by the Lady Hatton. Did you not know?"

Rory could hear Annie gasp from somewhere behind him, and he almost lost his grip on his sword. "You lie!" he exclaimed.

"Nay, for what reason would I lie? 'Tis true, I swear it." Then, trying to use his momentary advantage, he attempted a riposte after a parry that went wide.

Rory easily deflected the lethal point, stepped forward and thrust his sword home.

The blade went in nearly to the hilt. Rory withdrew it again as Blake dropped his own sword. The wounded man held his breast and stumbled against a tree as his rapier fell to the ground.

Rory set his feet for another thrust, then stopped. He could see blood running from between the man's fingers, and knew none was needed.

"Touché, monsieur. Ah, c'est donc ainsi."

'Riposte du mort!'' Rory nodded.

. "Aye, I do think you've killed me, O'Donnell. I congratulate you." From the corner of the fallen man's mouth came a stream of blood as he spoke.

Behind him Rory could hear Shanna crying and Annie praying aloud.

"Would the victor grant one last boon to the vanquished?" Blake choked, his face paling from the loss of blood.

"No boon will save you now, fool."

"Perhaps not from death, but that's not important any longer. You've taken the mantle of The O'Donnell?"

"Aye."

Blake nodded as if he were relieved. "Then you are a prince of Ireland, and as such I have a request to ask of thee. I would have you dub me."

"What?"

"Aye. For I would be a titled knight of Ireland, if not of England, before I die."

"Man, you are daft."

Blake managed a soft chuckle. "Perhaps. But I do beg this of you, O'Donnell. And I pray you soon, for the dawn fades to night before my eyes."

Rory felt foolish, but somehow he made himself step forward. He touched the bloody tip of his sword to Blake's left shoulder, and then to the right.

"I, Rory, The O'Donnell, do dub thee, Sir James Blake, knight of Ballylee, Donegal, and villainy."

Blake suddenly laughed, spitting out his life's blood as he slipped down the tree to a sitting position.

"How else, O'Donnell, could Christianity survive, were it not for villains like me?"

They were his dying words and as a last gesture Blake pulled a piece of paper from under his cloak. He dropped it to the ground as his head slumped to his chest.

Rory stepped forward, picked up the paper and read it. "He spoke the truth. 'Tis Cecil's order to see me and mine safely to London and the Tower. Come, we must move quickly."

As he gathered Annie and the children and moved into the forest, he took one last look at the slumped figure by the tree.

"I thank the heavens we'll not be meeting again. Farewell, Sir James Blake."

Five hours later they reached the booley house and the horses. But escape was impossible. The hills between Ballylee and Donegal swarmed with English soldiers. Within two days they were captured.

They would very probably have been slaughtered on the spot had it not been for Sir Robert Cecil's document.

O'DONNELL WAS BROUGHT SECRETLY into London and lodged at Lambeth Palace for a fortnight. And then, just as secretly, he was taken by barge down the Thames to the Tower.

"Am I never to see the light of day?" he asked the Lord Keeper Egerton, who had become his gaoler.

"Nay, 'tis not that, O'Donnell. But there are widows and mothers and fathers and brothers of those that have fallen in Ireland. The sight of you being moved by day would most surely cause a riot."

At Traitor's Gate Rory stepped from the barge and walked up the damp stairs. There was a rattle of chains, and the huge iron-toothed gate lifted.

Beyond it, at the top of the stairs, Sir Robert Cecil himself awaited the prisoner.

"O'Donnell."

"Sir Robert."

"It has been a long and costly war on both sides. Thank God it's nearly over."

"Nearly?" Rory said.

Cecil nodded. "There is but one left, The O'Neill himself, and his time of surrender nears."

Rory shook his head. "I doubt he will surrender, Sir Robert. Not until the Queen meets his terms, or dies."

"We shall see. Come along."

Cecil escorted him to the White Tower. Much to his surprise the accommodations had some degree of comfort.

"Daily I speak to the Queen. At this point she is angry, and I think she would have your head. But given time methinks I can save you."

"Save me, Sir Robert?" Rory said with a shrug. "What in God's name for?"

" 'Tis a promise I've made to someone."

Whether it was the way he said it or the smile that accompanied the words, Rory somehow knew.

"Elizabeth?"

"Aye. She was upon me the instant that news reached England of your capture. She has convinced me, easily I must say, that your death would do no good for England's cause."

Memories of times gone by flooded over O'Donnell. Her image swirled before his eyes, misting them. It had been so long since he had allowed himself a single thought of the woman he had loved, that remembering her now made him slump to a chair so that he wouldn't fall to the floor.

"How can she still care?" he said.

"That I know not," Cecil replied. "But then, there is very little in her beautiful head that I do understand these days."

"She is still beautiful?"

"Aye. Methinks, Rory, that our Elizabeth will always be beautiful."

Cecil shuffled a little awkwardly and then began pacing the room before he spoke again. "The woman who calls herself Annie Carey?"

"Aye."

"She is not important to the crown. I've issued a pardon under my own name."

"And the children?"

"Granted fosterage long ago, at the time of their father and mother's death. They are in the care of Lord Haskins, who has given me his word they will remain in England."

Rory could only nod. He was tired, and the rush of memories that had returned with the mention of Elizabeth's name had sapped his strength.

"I must go now, O'Donnell. I doubt that I shall see you again. But take heart, for I do think that in the end the Queen will grant amnesty."

Again Rory nodded, his mind elsewhere. "I care little...death or amnesty, it makes no difference." And then he remembered Blake's words. "Sir Robert...?"

"Aye?"

"I understand that Elizabeth has a child...a girl?" Cecil nodded, but said nothing. "Is the child mine, Sir Robert?"

Cecil started to speak, and then hesitated. "I know not, O'Donnell. Such a thing must be between the two of you, if for nothing else than the child's sake."

Rory's head fell to his chest, and wearily he closed his eyes. He heard the retreating sound of Cecil's boots on the stone floor, and then they stopped.

"The child's name—" Rory looked up "—her name is Brenna."

And Rory knew.

CHAPTER FORTY-FIVE

MARCH WINDS RATTLED THE WINDOWS of Richmond Palace, and the mood in the privy chamber was solemn. For weeks the Queen had been slipping more and more, until that morning the council had been summoned.

Now it was past midnight, and a light supper had been served. The men around the table ate sparingly, each absorbed in his own thoughts.

Many were fearful of the morrow, should it dawn without the Queen. For still no successor had been named.

Only Cecil, seated at the table's head, knew how well the way had been paved for James VI of Scotland to become James I of England. For a year and a half now the Queen's secretary had been in careful touch, through ciphered messages, with the monarch to the north.

He had urged James's silence and discretion, and he had gotten it. So much so that the government and the people of England were in daily fear of rebellion and civil war. But to the end Cecil had accommodated the Queen's reluctance, while readying the way for James.

Now, however, that silence must end; some proclamation would have to be made.

Only one thing was needed so that there would be no doubts or questions from pretenders—the word of Gloriana herself.

And time was running out for the Queen to speak at all. For days she had sat praying. She had worn her day clothes constantly, for she refused to undress and retire to bed.

"Your Majesty, you must to bed, for your own good," Cecil had told her.

"Sir," she had replied with just a spark of her old fire, "say you, 'must?' That is a word to be used *by* princes, not *to* them!"

But at last she had relented and allowed herself to be undressed and put to bed. She hadn't left it since.

A few hours earlier that evening she had seemed to rally. She had called for some hot broth, and for her ministers. But when they came she would neither eat nor speak, but only lay on her side, silent and brooding.

Now Cecil sat, listening to the comments of the other three men at the table.

"By her voice alone the great woman sounds weary of life."

"Aye, she doth sigh many times in what speech she utters."

"In truth, I've not heard her sigh but once before, and that when she signed the writ for the Scots' Queen Mary's execution."

"She would not hear me speak of any wish for her longer life, but only of her joy in the kingdom of heaven."

They were still talking solemnly when a quiet voice interrupted them. "M'lords...."

They turned as one.

"I believe it nearly time."

Queen Elizabeth, the last of the Welsh Tudors, is dying, Cecil thought. *And, may God will it, long live the King.*

The four of them filed into the bedchamber. The archbishop, Whitgift, fell to his knees at the head of the bed and took the Queen's hand. The lord admiral, Nottingham, took his place at her right, with Lord Keeper Egerton on her left.

Sir Robert Cecil stood at the foot of the bed, staring down at the woman whom he and his father before him had served for so long. The gray hair was gone in spots, and was thin where there was hair at all. Her cheeks without makeup were heavily lined and were sunken in hollows. And her eyes, as they flickered open, were without depth.

"Your Majesty would have words?"

"Who...?"

"Cec...Your Majesty's little pygmy," Cecil said.

He thought he saw the brief flicker of a smile cross the thin lips at the use of the name she had called him so often, the name she knew he hated even though she used it as an endearment.·

"What words would I say?" Her voice was weak, so they all had to lean slightly forward to hear her. "I would say that there is a burning in my breast and my throat is a desert of dryness. What else would you have me say?"

Three of them exchanged quick glances, while Archbishop Whitgift kept his head bowed in prayer. At last Nottingham summoned his courage.

"There is, Your Highness, the matter of the succession."

"I have often said before that my seat hath been the seat of kings. Therefore, who should succeed me but a king?"

"Pray you, Your Majesty," Cecil pressed, "but *what* king?"

As if the stubbornness in her mind and body would

not abate, even near death, she changed the subject. "What of Ireland? I would have that blight on my reign be over before the reign itself is over."

" 'Tis near done, Your Highness. Even now O'Neill travels to m'Lord Mountjoy's presence to surrender and plead Your Grace's amnesty."

"Amnesty? Amnesty, for that bush-kern, that would-be king?" There came a rattling sigh, and then the watery eyes fixed on Cecil. "Aye, amnesty it should be, for too much death there has been. Now, I pray you, trouble me no more."

"Your Majesty," Cecil said, an urgency in his voice, "should I inform your Scottish cousin—"

"She sleeps," Whitgift interjected.

"Sleeps?" Cecil asked.

The archbishop placed his fingers to the wrinkled temple and nodded. "As yet it is still the sleep of the living."

Nottingham and Egerton started to move away, but Cecil's voice stopped them.

"M'lords, 'tis a delicate thing I say, but it needs must be said. The Queen hath declared her seat the seat of a king, and only a king shall occupy it. That is enough said, perhaps, but there are pretenders who would call themselves kings. Do you agree?"

Heads nodded in assent.

"Therefore, I do believe I heard the Queen say, 'Who but our cousin, King James.' Did not all of you hear the same words?"

There was more shuffling, and fleeting glances passed among them all.

"Well?"

"Aye," Nottingham said at last. "I heard."

"Clearly," Egerton nodded.

"So be it," Cecil said, leading the way from the room.

Two hours later the Queen died in her sleep without saying another word.

At dawn the council rode to Whitehall and drafted a proclamation of the new reign. At midmorning Cecil read it on the palace green, across from the tiltyard where Essex had so delighted the Queen with his feats.

They moved down the Strand and entered the city at Ludgate. Twice more Cecil proclaimed James King of England, at St. Paul's, and at the Cheapside Cross.

An hour later he formally claimed entrance to the Tower in the name of James, King of England, and sighed with relief that it was done.

"M'LORD, THE MASTER REBEL, Hugh O'Neill, Baron of Dungannon, Earl of Tyrone."

The aide stepped aside, and Mountjoy watched the proud O'Neill step from the midst of his underchiefs and, flanked by them, drop to one knee.

Blount, Lord Mountjoy, sat behind a table piled high with documents, and stared down at the bowed graying head and the broad shoulders now sagging in the crimson mantle.

Sitting there silently, with his round chin, his full ruddy cheeks, and his amiable expression, Mountjoy looked anything but the conqueror of the most fearsome rebel in Ireland's history.

But conqueror he was, and conquered was O'Neill.

It showed in the man's body and it was evident in the deep lines of his seamed face. For over a year he had been hunted in the hills around Lough Neagh. Bravely he and what was left of his loyal septs had fought Englishmen and starvation.

But now he bowed in submission.

He had fought one day at a time, hoping for the Queen's death so that he could then surrender to James, with terms.

But now he could fight no more.

For a full hour Mountjoy kept O'Neill on his knees in silence before him. Then at last the commander of the victorious army stood up and spoke.

"Hugh O'Neill of Tyrone, do you surrender before this Irish council and Parliament?"

"I do, m'lord."

' Louder, sir, so there will be no doubt of your words!"

"I do, m lord."

"Do you renounce your claim, now and forever after, to the Irish title of The O'Neill, swearing by all that is holy on God's earth that you will never again take upon yourself that title that sets you aside from the English crown?"

"I do, m'lord."

"Do you swear to cease, as of now and forevermore, any negotiations or alliance with the King of Spain, or kings and rulers of any power foreign to the crown of England?"

"I do, m'lord."

"Do you, Hugh O'Neill, hereby renounce all power and authority over your kern, peasants, and urraghs, and all underchiefs of all clans and septs who have in the past given you fealty?"

There was a pause during which O'Neill raised his head and stared with tear-filled eyes at the chieftains kneeling around him. "I do, m'lord."

"And, O'Neill, do you hereby resign to the crown of England all titles, all lands, and all revenues which you possess, from now and henceforth forever, so help you God?"

The pause was even longer now, and the tears squeezed from the old eyes to roll down the weatherbeaten cheeks and into the grizzled graying beard.

"What say you, Hugh O'Neill!"

"I . . . I do, m'lord."

"So help you God!"

"So help me God."

"Then I, Charles Blount, Lord of Mountjoy, the crown of England's lord deputy in Ireland, do hereby accept your surrender in the King's name. God save the King!"

O'Neill's head snapped up and his eyes opened wide. "The *King*, m'lord?"

"You have been too long in the hills, O'Neill. Elizabeth, the Queen, died four days ago."

Part VI
The Defeated

SIR ROBERT CECIL stood at one of the high paned windows of his beloved Theobalds. With brooding eyes he watched the King and his huge retinue ride up the wide oak-lined avenue.

James sported a beaming grin and joked loudly with his current favorite, Master James Hay, and the other courtiers that fawned around them.

Cecil sighed. If the King's current mood meant anything, it had been a good hunt. And Sir Robert now knew that on the afternoon of a good hunt some small amount of state business could be done.

For nearly a week Cecil had entertained His Majesty at Theobalds with rivers of fine wines, goodly horses, fleet and deep-mouthed hounds, and innumerable hawks of swift wing.

In return the King had complimented Sir Robert on his hospitality and had hinted that it was perhaps unseemly for a subject—even one as loyal and powerful as Sir Robert—to own an estate as grand as Theobalds.

"But, Your Grace," Sir Robert had replied, "as monarch you have Hampton Court as well as palaces at Richmond, Greenwich, Nonsuch, Oatlands, Sheen and Windsor. And, in London, of course, Whitehall."

"Ah, yes," the King had quickly replied in his thick Scottish burr. "They are now all mine...and, to be sure, I will visit and hunt at them all. But none of them is so grand as this, this Theobalds. Don't you agree, little Cecil?"

Sir Robert had agreed. In the span of time since bringing James to England he had learned that agreeing went much further with the King than disagreeing.

Other than James's view of himself as God's chosen one, Sir Robert had learned only two other facts for sure about the man: that his first and only love was the hunt, and that he had a propensity for falling off his horse.

"Sir Robert?"

"Aye."

"The King would have audience with you in the great hall."

Cecil nodded to his secretary, gathered a huge bundle of papers from his desk, and wearily made his way through the sprawling house.

Audience me in my own house, he thought. *In my own great hall, with a hundred pairs of prying eyes and ears to see and hear it all. How differently the ship of state doth now rock along!*

"Ayee, my little Cecil!"

"Your Grace."

Cecil bowed and started to place his load on the table.

"Nay, nay, little Cecil. Come sit here by your King. Wine! Some wine for the man who hath made my kingdom secure. Sit! Sit! And drink!"

Cecil did as he was bidden, eyeing his King with a sidelong glance. The man's tongue, already too large for his mouth, was made thicker by drink. The huge round eyes rolled from side to side as he quipped with one courtier and then harangued another.

Cecil moved to a stool at the King's left, and with a sigh, waited for recognition.

Though he called Cecil "little," James himself was but an inch or two taller. Already corpulent, the King made himself more so by wearing only heavily padded doublets. He did this because of his constant fear of death by an assassin's stiletto.

At last James finished a brief theological discourse with an outpouring of profanity and turned to Sir Robert.

"So, my little Cecil, what boring matters do you bring me today?"

"There are several instruments which need your signature, Your Grace, and many matters pending your decision."

For the next half hour Cecil managed to keep James's attention long enough to settle some state business—this in the midst of the hundred or so reveling courtiers who ate and drank with gusto and chattered with ear-piercing loudness.

"And now to the matter of Ireland, Your Grace."

"Ayee, yes. . .the heathen land!"

James raised a full cup of wine to his thick lips. As he drank he appeared to be eating the cup, and a great deal of the burgundy liquid ran down from his chin to stain his doublet.

Cecil turned his eyes away.

"Tell me, Sir Robert, 'tis said that the Ulster lands are even more fertile than those of Munster in the south of Ireland."

"Aye, I've heard."

"And the ports for trading in the north could be more profitable."

"That is rumored," Sir Robert replied. "But to date, as you know, few revenues have flowed from Ireland."

James's eyes momentarily ceased their rolling to fix on Cecil.

"That's because we don't have good Scottish and English hands tilling the soil, and bright English traders running the ports!"

"We have some plantationing, Your Grace—"

"Ayee, but we should have more, much more, my little Cecil."

"But the Ulster earls under Queen Elizabeth's amnesty—"

"Damn the Ulster earls!" came the thick-tongued reply. "Be they not papists?"

"They are Catholic," Cecil replied. "And you did promise, Your Grace—"

"A promise, my good Cecil, is but one small part of God's prerogative and thusly a King's. Na, na, we will not need the papist earls now!"

"But, Your Grace, there is always the threat of another rebellion."

"Na, na," the King replied, roaring with laughter. "M'Lord Mountjoy has broken their backs, and m'Lord Chester will keep their heads bowed. More plantationing, Cecil, much more!"

"Your Grace—"

"Sir Robert, like England and Scotland, this Ireland is ours to do with as we will. See to it!"

And with an imperial wave Cecil was dismissed.

Gathering his papers, the little man backed from the royal presence and walked down the long room muttering to himself. "On England what have I wrought?"

Just outside the double oaken doors he was momentarily blocked by a tall rotund man with a square frowning face. Beside the man was a stoutly built lad of four or five, with narrow piercing eyes.

"Good day to you, Sir Robert."

Cecil bit his lip and strained his memory, but no name would come.

"Squire Hinchinbrook, from the north."

"Ah, yes, Hinchinbrook. Good day to you."

"I've brought the lad, my nephew, on his birthday to meet the King and pledge his allegiance to the crown. Introduce yourself to Sir Robert Cecil, lad."

"How do you do, sir," the boy said, bowing slightly. "My name is Cromwell. Master Oliver Cromwell."

TOGETHER O'NEILL AND RORY O'DONNELL STOOD on the flat plain of the hill of Tullaghogue. The wind whistled fiercely through the rocks around them and sent their hair flying and their long cloaks flapping.

About them the thunder roared, and the heavens sent more torrents of rain to beat against their faces.

They had ridden all night from Slane Castle on the River Boyne. Now they stood looking at the shattered throne and ancient stone of The O'Neills.

Lord Mountjoy's soldiers had used their hammers well. There was not a piece bigger than a pebble remaining intact, and the name was gone from the stone above where the carved chair had been.

"And so go the O'Neills. One by one we have been murdered or forced into the sea."

Rory could only nod at The O'Neill's words and shrug deeper into his mantle. His face remained impassive, but his heart ached with the reason for this visit to Tullaghogue.

"Oh, that I could die and thereby end the problems that plague us all," the old chieftain sighed.

Rory O'Donnell sounded a mirthless chuckle that was lost in the wind. "Nay, m'lord. Death, I fear, rarely solves problems, save for those who do the dying."

"Aye," O'Neill muttered. "We were beaten, and still they beat us. They would have us die, yet give us enough for half a life."

It had been many sad and sorry months since Rory's release from the Tower and his return to Ireland. For the first few of those months there had been hope—hope that was soon dashed. James in his rule of Ireland proved to be even more intractable than his predecessor. Worse yet, his court was more corrupt, and his fiscal ways that of a spendthrift.

"Think you our position truly lost?" O'Neill asked.

"Aye," O'Donnell nodded. "For the English are hungry when land is on the table for the asking. In Donegal I rarely see an Irish face upon the land. No better it is in your Tyrone. Now they wall Derry, and would call it... *Londonderry*." Rory turned his head and spat.

"And Dublin?"

"Lord Deputy Chichester has deaf ears to an Irish voice," Rory replied.

"Then," O'Neill nodded, "there is not even little hope."

To glean as much money from Ireland as possible, James, over Cecil's wishes, had installed as corrupt a government in Dublin Castle as was his own court in England. In the beginning they had left barely enough in Ireland for the Irish to survive, and of late they had begun plantationing again.

One by one the Irish—nobles and kern alike—were pushed from their lands to make way for English settlers. As if that weren't enough, the Irish leaders already abroad in Spain, France and the Netherlands were being systematically assassinated, to make sure they would never return and lay claim to their lands.

That done, the Dublin assassins were now turning their talents to those old clan leaders still in Ireland.

Worse yet, a sham plot had been conceived in Dublin, with false evidence that the earls were again arming for rebellion. Nothing could have been further from the truth, and if proof were needed, it was in the shabbiness of the clothing worn by these two warriors as they stood in the driving rain, mourning a shattered dream.

But proof, false as it was, the governors in Dublin were sure they had, and O'Neill and O'Donnell knew it. They also knew that total forfeiture of all their lands, for good and ever, would most likely be the result.

It was time to leave.

Even now negotiations had been completed for a ship from France, and messengers sent out to the clans.

Those who would lose their lands but keep their lives were invited to flee.

O'Neill turned to his old friend. "I would be alone for a moment here."

'I'll be off then," O'Donnell replied. "For Cecil would give me audience five days hence."

O'Neill nodded. "Think you he will agree?"

"I believe so," Rory said. "The presence of young Rory and Shanna since m'Lord Haskins's death places a burden on the state. And," he added dryly, "James would have what's left of Haskins's lands for his always empty purse."

"Go you then, with Godspeed, and we will meet again in one month's time on the banks of Lough Swilly."

O'Donnell walked to the path and paused to look back at O'Neill. It would be hard for he himself to leave Ireland's shores, never to see them again, but he knew it would be even harder for this old man whose dream still hovered atop the hill of Tullaghogue.

He watched as O'Neill slid to his knees and pulled a pouch from beneath his cloak. Reverently the old chieftain began filling the pouch with tiny white pebbles that had once been the mighty stone of O'Neill.

LADY HATTON moved like a floating swan across the room and embraced her uncle. Lightly she kissed him on both cheeks and then gaily pirouetted from his embrace.

"Months. . . it has been months since we talked!"

"Has it?" he replied. "I fear the hands of my clocks stand still."

"Come in, come in, sit! And how heavy does the great house of Cecil weigh on your shoulders this day, m'lord?"

Robert Cecil, Earl of Salisbury, laughed aloud as he kissed the Lady Hatton's hand and then took a high-backed chair near the fireplace. Though it was a pleasant fall day outside, the air was just crisp enough for a single log to be burning.

"Wine, m'lord?"

"Damme, Elizabeth, will you please call me Robert, or uncle? Sherry."

"I'll not. I now have the Earl of Exeter for my father and the Earl of Salisbury for my uncle, and I'll use the titles whether you be in or out of your miniver-and-velvet robes!"

Cecil smiled. He was pleased that at last he had reached the pinnacle—an earldom.

But he deserved it, and he was also not so proud that the coronet he held overruled his common sense. Indeed, his title seemed almost hollow, for unlike Queen Elizabeth, who had been so spare with her favors as to give them value, King James had begun to sell them like a vendor sells chestnuts in Cheapside.

"Here you are."

Cecil accepted the glass and watched her sink onto a settee across from him.

As usual his niece was attired in a costly and elegant frock. This one was of shimmering satin, with an open, high-standing ruff springing from a deep vee neckline that plunged nearly to her waist. Delicate floral pendants and perfect pearls decorated the lacy fringe that supported her breasts.

Cecil couldn't help but note that Elizabeth's breasts were still high and firm. But then the rest of her body was just as firm and youthful.

She amazed him. Her smile was open and wide, her teeth clear and white. It seemed that she had schemed somehow to keep her youth forever, and that realization somehow made him seem even older and even more weary.

Cecil shook his head. "Do you know, Elizabeth, that you are still the most beautiful woman in all of England?"

"Ha! I won't be for long, with the gray my knave of a husband puts in my hair!"

Here she launched into the latest episode of the constant marital duel between the Lady Elizabeth Hatton and her barrister husband, Sir Edward Coke.

Cecil knew it well, but he listened in silence.

Sir Edward had conspired to obtain a transference of an old debt owing to the crown by Elizabeth's first husband, Sir William Hatton, to himself. Then he had used the debt as a rather indirect means of foreclosing on Hatton House itself, trying to transfer his wife's rents to his own coffers.

The transaction was shady, but just legal enough to get away with...temporarily.

Elizabeth had hauled her own husband to court. Together they had faced the court, and had railed enough at each other in public that yet another year's worth of gossip had been provided for the London wags.

If it hadn't been so hard on Cecil playing peace-maker between them, he would have found it laugh-able.

"Lord, lord, Elizabeth, will it never end?"

"Nay!" she replied. "Not until he treats me as a woman, and one of means, instead of a wife he would have as a common churl!"

"I fear I weary of it," Cecil sighed.

"As do I, uncle. Do you know he has spent nearly thirty thousand pounds on his manor house at Stoke Poges. . . and would do *more*?"

"Mayhap he does it to make you live there with him."

"Nay," she scoffed, "he does it to force me into the sale of Holdenby, so he can *make* more."

"But Sir Edward has made your estate grow, Elizabeth."

"He has," she admitted. "But 'tis still a daily duel to force him to allow me the use of it. But enough of my month-in, month-out bickering with Coke. Tell me about the scandals at court!"

"I fear you know more of the court and of our King than I do, Elizabeth."

"How so?"

Cecil sighed and gazed into the fire as he sipped from his glass. When he spoke it was more to himself than to her. "Without rebellion or strife I placed a king upon the throne, and I am now weary of his government. He spends as if there were no bottom to his coffers, and prefers the hunt to the running of the state—"

"And the company of foppish men and boys to that of his wife."

Cecil chuckled. "I daresay we have no Henry, with a palace full of mistresses, on the throne. How goes James's wife, the Queen?"

"Anna? Patient, forbearing, and, just between you and me," Elizabeth said, leaning forward and lowering her voice, "slightly boring. But the lady is pleasant to me, and I am well received at court. Therefore...." She shrugged and stood up to pour them another glass.

"The King has a new favorite, you know."

"I know: Robert Carr. And already you have placed one of your spies at his side."

Here Sir Robert chuckled. "If one is to learn what the King thinks in this court, one must know what the favorite is thinking."

"I was with the Queen a few days ago when we met Robert Carr and your Thomas Overbury in the garden. Do you know what she said?"

"Pray tell me."

"'And good day to the King's keeper and to the keeper of the King's keeper!'" Suddenly her voice turned harsh. "Alas, uncle, what a sour tide has turned that you are forced to run a kingdom on the whim of foppish boys."

"I worry not," Robert sighed, "for I fear that one day soon my tenure will end. And, I must say, I bear no sadness for it."

"You sound weary."

"Aye, I am. But enough of my problems with the royal house of Stuart. How is it with my favorite niece? Are you happy?"

Elizabeth was about to turn with newly filled glasses, but paused. "I hawk, I hunt, I visit Corfe Castle and give fine parties. I... why do you ask?"

"Because you seem so...." His voice died away. "And I would know for sure."

"Uncle ..." She was standing near the window, the light from behind her highlighting her auburn curls and the fullness of her still-youthful figure in the deep green dress she wore. But he couldn't see her face.

"Yes?"

"There is something besides weariness in your voice."

"Aye, there is. Sit down."

She returned with his glass and sat down once again.

"Do you still follow the news in Ireland?"

A shadow passed over her eyes, but quickly disappeared. "Nay. There is no reason. They live in peace now, I understand, and left long enough alone they will probably revert to their savage ways—"

"Elizabeth," Cecil interrupted, "the King's government in Dublin has made it impossible for the earls or any of the old clan chiefs to remain on their home soil. 'Tis a sad thing, this negligence in the ruling of a proud people."

"Please, uncle, I would hear naught of it."

"O'Neill and O'Donnell, and most of the other clan leaders, have chosen to leave Ireland . . . for good. 'Tis a secret only I know of."

"To . . . to England?" she gasped.

"Nay. There would, I fear, be still no safety for them here. Rory O'Donnell has begged me to allow the O'Hara children to go with them."

"You've. . . ." She paused, stood up and returned to the window. "You've seen him?"

"Aye. He's in England at this moment, and he would have me—and you—grant him a second favor."

"Me?" she said with a nervous laugh, willing her fingers to stop twisting the kerchief she held in her hand. "What favor can I possibly do him? Or better yet, how dare he ask me?"

"The man still loves you, Elizabeth."

Her voice when she replied was curt, with a tone of steel on steel. "He negated that love long ago."

"Elizabeth, 'twas not him but me that made his decision that night at Corfe Castle."

"*You?*"

"I forced from him a promise that if I let him return to Ireland he would agree never to see you or to contact you again."

He watched as his niece's shoulders came up and her head bowed. He heard a slight choking sound, and then a tiny cry as her hands went to her face.

"Why? Oh, dear God, *why*?"

"Because I thought it best. . . and still do."

Suddenly she whirled around and almost flew across the room to stand over him. "So you would rule my life to the end, uncle! My God, will I never be done with it?"

"Elizabeth, you are the only relative I love. Only to you, all these years, have I been loyal. And you of all people should know that statesmen and servers of kings and queens cannot afford such luxuries as personal loyalties. In the beginning I pushed you together, both for my own purposes and because you were unhappy. I thought of him as just an idle adventurer for you to have an affair with, a passing thing. I didn't realize until it was too late how deeply you had grown to love each other."

"Oh, damn you, damn you, you would now bring it all back!"

"Aye, for him, I would. He's a broken man, Elizabeth—aged far beyond his years—with nothing left, not even his Ireland."

"If it hadn't been for you, he might have chosen me over his Ireland. Damn. . .*damn*!" The kerchief went to her eyes.

Now it was Cecil's turn to move, and he did, to the window with his shoulders hunched as if he were fighting a strong wind that threatened to blow him over

"I think not, Elizabeth, for in many ways we are unlucky to be born men, just as you have said so often how unlucky it is you were born a woman. We men are weak, sometimes, because we are expected to be strong."

"What is it you would have of me?"

"Not me. . . him."

"Very well, what is it he wants?"

"He would see, would talk briefly, with the child."

She whirled around, and the eyes that met his were full of fire and something Cecil felt was akin to hatred.

"Surely he jests. . . you both jest!"

"No," Cecil replied, slowly moving his head from side to side. " 'Tis something he dearly wants, and, I believe, needs above anything else."

"No!"

"He has given his word that he will say nothing to Brenna—nay, even hint to her—that he is anything but a stranger."

"No!"

"Elizabeth, listen to me. My ambitions, and the errors I have sometimes committed to achieve them, weigh heavily upon me at times. I beg you to grant this to O'Donnell, for when he asked me I saw such pleading in the man's eyes that I was indeed moved to tears."

The dam in Elizabeth's body broke. Her heart ached so much that she felt it would explode in her breast. She rushed to Cecil and fell on her knees before him. Like the little niece he remembered so many years before she clutched his waist and sobbed against him.

"Oh, uncle, is there no end to this living?"

"None but dying," he replied. "And that once done, it is better to say we lived for something."

O'DONNELL STEPPED DOWN from the carriage and spoke to Annie. "I'll be but a while."

Annie nodded. Shanna was asleep, with her head in the woman's lap. Young Rory was atop the coach, discussing with the driver the merits of English horses versus the smaller Irish breed.

O'Donnell walked the short distance to the familiar gate and gently pushed it open. The sight of the cottage, and most especially of the second-floor windows, brought a catch to his throat.

Quickly he turned away and searched the garden until he found her. She was in a white dress bedecked with silver lace, with blue ribbons over the shoulders and around the bodice. With her head buried in a book, she sat on a bench under a yew tree, among an abundance of roses that seemed to highlight the sheen of her dark hair.

She looked up just as his foot crunched on the gravel that was spread around the bench.

"Hello."

"Hello."

"My mother said a gentleman was coming to call on me."

"Did she now? And what did she say I was calling about?"

"She didn't say. She just told me...." Here the composure that had seemed so mature broke slightly and she giggled. "Mother just said that I've long had a secret admirer, and that I should wait today for him in the garden."

"Well, she's right. I have long been your secret admirer, and now I meet you at last. Do you mind if I sit beside you?"

"Not at all. Do sit! Mother said you were going on a long voyage."

"Oh, not so long. To France, actually. But ı have friends going all the way to Spain and to Rome."

"Oh, I would to France one day. But never to Spain nor Rome. They're still popish, you know!"

"Aye, aye, I know."

"Do you speak French?"

"Aye, I do."

"So do I, and a bit of Italian, and of course, Latin."

"Of course."

"Are you one of the King's Scots Guard?"

"Why do you ask that?"

"Because of your speech. You're not English."

"No, I'm . . . I'm not one of the King's guard."

How beautiful she is, he thought, *and how like Elizabeth she looks.* His arms ached to hold her, but he managed to keep them still.

"Who is that?"

O'Donnell looked up, his gaze following her pointing finger. "His name is O'Hara, Rory O'Hara."

She flashed her dark eyes up at him and smiled. "He's very handsome, isn't he?"

There was a movement, and young Rory bolted back to the carriage.

"Is he your son?"

"No . . . well, in a way. His father and mother died, so I've taken him to raise myself."

"I say, that's very nice of you. Would you like to see the gardens? They're very beautiful, and we may not have them next year."

"Oh?"

"No," she said, taking his hand and tugging him from the bench to follow her. "My father, you see, is a very greedy man. He wants to sell Holdenby so he can make more money with the capital . . . or so my mother says."

"You sound as though you don't approve of your father."

"Oh, I do. It's my mother who doesn't. She refuses to live with him. They rail at each other when they're together, anyway, so I think it's just as well. My name is Brenna Coke, but of course, since you're my secret admirer, you know that. Do you know what my name means?"

"I think so."

"Ah, I wager you don't. No one ever does!"

"Could it mean. . .raven?"

"How ever did you know?"

ELIZABETH SWALLOWED, choked slightly, and then involuntarily swallowed again. Here eyes misted and a line of dampness appeared on her lower lashes as she stared down into the garden through the partially shuttered windows.

"Rory, The O'Donnell. My O'Donnell," she whispered, blinking the mist of her eyes into tears that gently rolled down her cheeks.

But they were tears of joy as much as of sadness. They looked so right, so perfect together, walking the graveled paths, with Brenna's tiny hand enveloped in Rory's gentle clutch.

Now and then he would bend from his great height and cock his ear to his daughter's upturned face. Brenna would confide yet another pearl from her storehouse of childish wisdom, and he would smile and nod, or even break into a roaring laugh.

Her uncle had been right. Elizabeth was glad now that she had allowed this meeting, for she could see how happy it was making him.

And her uncle had also been right that he looked sad and worn down until he was not the same wild Rory that she'd known. Now and then she could see vestiges of the carefree manner and a wisp of the rakish smile she knew so well. But he was no longer the dashing rogue of the night, with black flashing eyes and shining raven hair, who had stolen a kiss in a carriage and then later made of her the woman she knew herself to be.

Now the hair was graying, and there was a slope to the shoulders that had never been there before. His walk was steady, but there was a slight shuffle, a dragging motion to his left leg. From a wound, she guessed, for Cecil had told her that he had suffered many.

She closed her eyes to the man in the garden, and saw the man she remembered. His strong naked body took shape in her mind as he stood over her bed, gazing down at her with loving tender eyes. She saw him, darkly handsome in the windswept rain, standing on the parapet of Corfe Castle. Her heart thudded as again she heard him whisper, "Elizabeth, my love, my only love."

No, she thought, closing the shutters and moving back into the darkest part of the room to rest and think a bit.

No, she would have him always as he was. She would remember the wonderful moments she had had with the man she had loved, and who had loved her.

"Goodbye, and perhaps one day we'll meet again."

"Goodbye, Brenna, I...I hope so. That would be very nice."

He watched the small smiling face surrounded by raven curls until she was out of sight.

He waited until the carriage was far from Holdenby and rocking on the Chester Road before he opened the miniature she had given him.

"My mother told me I was to give you this, as a parting gift."

Now he looked at the tiny portrait of the mother so fair and the daughter so dark, and gasped involuntarily. Only then, seeing them together, did he realize how much she looked like himself.

"Who was that girl?" Rory asked from a corner of the carriage.

"Her name is Brenna. Brenna Coke."

"She's a very pretty child," the boy said.

"Yes," O'Donnell said, "she is."

THE FIRE ROARED as it rushed through the roof and leaped skyward. One wall had already fallen in, and the roof was about to go.

Elizabeth stood watching her beloved Holdenby cottage burn with a tearful smile on her face. Beside her, Brenna clutched her skirts and whimpered.

"Oh, I'm so sorry, mother."

"Sorry?"

"It is your private place, your place to be alone... and you look so sad."

"Sad? Do I, darling? Yes, I suppose I do, but 'twill only last a little while. That is one of the things you will learn. Often there is sadness, but just as often there is much happiness that goes before it."

She looked up and met Honor's and Charles's gaze where they stood a few yards away. Faithful still they were, with not a question asked when she had ordered Charles to burn the cottage.

Then she looked back at her daughter's beautiful upturned face, and felt all the love in the world swell in her bosom.

"Come along with you now, little darling, for this is but one house, and it is gone. But no matter, for we're rich and I have many houses, and one day you shall be chatelaine to all of them."

"And I'll grow up to be as beautiful as you, and marry a prince?"

"At least a lord," Elizabeth laughed.

"Are we to London, mother?" she cried, running along the path to keep up.

"Aye, we're to London and the court, little one," Elizabeth said. "Damme, we must find you a prince, mustn't we?"

"Or at least an earl!" Brenna giggled. "Damme, were I but a man so I could do the choosing!"

Elizabeth stopped and scooped the girl into her arms.

"You will do the choosing, little one. On that, I'll promise you! And don't ever say you want to be a man, for the things they must do to be men are sometimes terrible. Now, come along. It's on to London and tomorrow for us!"

THE SWISH OF THE OARS and the slap of the sail as it filled were the only sounds as the ship slipped from the harbor mouth and found the sea.

"What think you, O'Neill?"

"What else but sadness," the old man replied, as they watched the shoreline of Ireland fade. "For we were defeated by ourselves, which makes it even sadder."

"Aye, I think of McTeague and all the others who went over to keep what they had. . .and now they have nothing."

"Aye. Nothing."

Behind them a balladeer sang a mournful song, as if he were putting music to their thoughts.

Ever when a chieftain rallied,
Shunned him half his selfish peers;
Ever when high truth was spoken,
Prudent traitors stopped their ears.

"There was no way," O'Donnell sighed, as much to himself as to the stooped figure beside him. "For as men we were not born to be at the mercy of a foreign crown. We were not meant to live in the hope of grants and favors from a court, but on the revenues of our own estates."

O'Neill did not reply. O'Donnell's words needed no answer.

So they stood silently, side by side. Across the gray-topped waves and through the vapory mists they watched the windswept, rocky outline of their land of misery slowly recede.

"Oh, my Ireland," O'Neill whispered, his voice barely a croak, "tonight you are a desolate island. If there is a God, let him keep faith with you and one day bring back your sons. And, pray, let not all we leave turn to dust or be so changed by the tooth of time that it matters not to our sons what we have tried to do."

There were no more tears, for neither had any left to shed.

Rory could take no more. He turned from the rail and left the old man to his thoughts and lost dreams. On the deck around him stood almost all the nobles of Ireland, watching what was gone in the mists.

Among them he saw fair Annie's bowed head. Her fingers worked at the beads in her lap as her lips moved in silent prayer. He could slit his eyes and almost see the cowl and collar she would be wearing soon, and the image brought a wry grin to his lips.

For dear Annie had found the religion that he had lost.

There was a movement at his shoulder and Rory looked up. His eyes met those of The O'Neill's young nephew, Owen Roe. For a moment Rory saw the flash of rebellion in the lad's eyes, the same flash that he knew had once been in his. He looked away.

Unlike O'Neill, Rory didn't want to search each youthful face for a new savior of Ireland.

Slowly he made his way through the crouching bodies aft, for perhaps one last sight.

A breeze from the land brought a last fragrant scent of heather and clover, before it was swallowed by the salty smell of the sea.

"Farewell," he breathed to the land that had been his home, now disappeared into the mists. "Farewell."

O'Donnell was about to turn away when he heard young Rory's voice from the rail.

"I say, Shanna, you mustn't cry. Remember you are an O'Hara, and one day I will take you back to Bally-lee! Now, sit you down there and I will tell you a story. Nay, 'tis not a sad story, but one of love."

"What story?" came the girl's tiny voice.

"'Tis the beautiful tale of Deirdre of the Sorrows."

The
Survivors
MARY CANON

France, 1616

OUTSIDE IT HAD BEGUN to rain. Through partially opened shutters water could be heard rolling down over the stones of the old abbey walls. Inside the tension was as heavy as the silence between the room's three occupants.

Shanna de Chinon, once known as O'Hara, sat stiffly at a table still wearing her dark blue velvet riding costume. Her eyes stared nervously but intently at her brother across the table.

The O'Donnell sat silently by the fire, wrapped in his mantle. Now and then his eyes flickered up to appraise one or both of his godchildren.

"How long have you had these?" Rory O'Hara said, gathering the papers in his huge hands and shuffling them in O'Donnell's direction.

"Years," O'Donnell sighed.

"And you never mentioned them?"

"There was no need...until now."

"Evidently my mind is thick," Rory said at last. "Why would Cecil, before his death, draw up documents that would one day restore to me my grandfather's lands in England and my father's lands in Ireland?"

O'Donnell smiled wryly. "Enough to say that Cecil felt he had done us all—myself, you and Shanna—a grave wrong. When the Haskins lands and Ballylee in Ireland went to the Crown, and in turn were given to King James's favorite, Robert Carr, Cecil must have seen a way to right some of his wrongs to us. Thus, those documents."

Rory's frown turned into a look of puzzlement. He perused the papers a second time and moved to stand with his back to the fire. "I fear I still don't understand. This is a right of forfeiture from the Crown to me should the lands of Haskins and the barony of Ballylee ever be lost to Carr?"

"Exactly," O'Donnell replied. "And Robert Carr and his countess were convicted of murder by a jury of their peers a fortnight ago. They were spared death by the King's grace, but all their lands save one manor were stripped from them."

Shanna gasped and leaped to her feet. "That means by the King's own hand the lands are ours again!"

"I think not, sister, for James is a greedy and spendthrift king," Rory warned.

O'Donnell lurched to his feet, his bones aching from so long in the chair. "James will want the *Haskins* lands, lad, don't you see?" he growled, the strain in his voice mirrored in his face. "But *not* Ballylee."

The silence was awkward as the two men stared straight at each other. Rory's face was troubled, while the exiled O'Donnell's was full of light, his eyes radiating a look of pleading mixed with joy.

Shanna broke the silence. She moved to her brother and threw her arms around him, then looked up into his face with tears in her eyes. "Rory, oh, Rory, don't you see? It's come at last. We can go home to Ballylee."

Rory's stony gaze never left Shanna's eyes. "Methinks, dear sister, that for all your time at the French king's court you still have been too long in a convent to truly see the ways of the world. Even if King James were to give me the barony of Ballylee, to attain it I would have to pledge the oath of supremacy to claim," he finished calmly.

A tiny, painful gasp escaped Shanna's lips. "Oh, no," she said, whirling on O'Donnell. " 'Tis not true!"

The older, almost broken man nodded sadly. "I fear 'tis true, lass. Rory would have to renounce the religion of our fathers and adopt the English Church of Ireland."

"And what does my arch Catholic, convent-raised sister say to that?" Rory challenged.

The pain on Shanna's face faded to an expression of tight-lipped resolution. Neither man was prepared for her reply.

"I think of myself as a Catholic by baptism, French by cultural background—but by desire and birth I am Irish! One man insists his religion is the only religion; another of a different faith says the same. I say be done with them all. Let us all be Christians and I would be a Christian. . . in Ireland."

Rory whirled and stomped to the window. "I've not learned to plead nor speechify," he said, his voice controlled. "I am but a soldier and understand damn little beyond my sword. 'Tis all I know, and all I want to know."

O'Donnell tried a different tack. "Rory, lad, 'tis for yourself I'm thinking. Some of the Irish chiefs have received regrants from the Crown. You could take your place among them. . . ."

"Aye," came Rory's thundering reply, "but you'll wait till the Pope marries before I do! Where are the O'Haras of Ballyhara, my distant cousins? Are they proud landowners on the plains of Antrim? Nay, they are wretches struggling between the Presbyterian Scots and the Protestant English for survival!"

"But, damme, they struggle," O'Donnell roared back, stung to wrath. "Would you have James turn all of Ulster into a playground for his fellow Scots, with not a strong Irishman to say them nay?"

"Aye, that I would, and they can use Ballylee for their sewer for all I care!"

With a speed that surprised both brother and sister, O'Donnell stepped forward. The flat of his hand against Rory's cheek was like a thunder clap in the room. The younger man's head snapped around as his big body crashed against the window casement.

Shanna stood silently, tears streaming down her cheeks. Anger burned on Rory's face as he eased himself to his feet, then stomped to the door and flung it open. But before he could exit, his godfather's strong voice stopped him.

"There was a time, lad, when we Gaels were famous meat eaters. A time when we stood on our own castle keeps and fed from our own land. . . a land that grew proud men and comely women."

"Aye," Rory replied, his voice flat and toneless. "Even now every village in Ireland has its castle and keep. . . and they're all in ruins." He partially turned, fixing the twin coals of his eyes on O'Donnell. "I'll not to Ireland and I'll not to England. I'll be for Paris with dawn's first light."

And then he was gone.

"By God's blood," Shanna rasped, "were I only a man!"